THE SCIENCE OF PHYSICAL EDUCATION

FOR HANDICAPPED CHILDREN

THE SCIENCE OF PHYSICAL EDUCATION FOR HANDICAPPED CHILDREN

Donald K. Mathews
Professor and Coordinator of Research
Department of Physical Education
The Ohio State University

Robert Kruse
Director, School of Physical Therapy, Cleveland Clinic

Virginia Shaw
Professor of Physical Education, Washington State University

Illustrations by Lou Allison Close

HARPER & BROTHERS
Publishers, New York

CONTENTS

ILLUSTRATIONS

PREFACE

BOTH adaptive and developmental physical education deal with programs designed specifically for children who have a physical handicap or who are considerably below par in terms of the professional objectives of physical education. Working with these children carries with it a responsibility far greater than that required for those who teach physical education to the so-called "normal" child. This is true for a number of reasons.

First of all, activity programs must be established within the confines of medical safety for each individual child. It is therefore necessary that the physical educator have a good working knowledge of the diseases which he will find most prevalent in the school situation.

Second, the physical educator should be extremely competent in designing exercise programs. In many instances he will have to assist the family doctor in formulating an exercise plan for a child recovering from polio or some other disabling disease in which the pathology has been arrested. Speaking and working with confidence in this area requires a knowledge of basic muscle physiology and the principles that govern the physiology, methodology, and techniques of conducting the exercise program.

Third, the physical educator must have an elementary knowledge of physical laws, especially those dealing with the forces, equilibrium, and motion fundamental to all movement. A knowledge of these laws is essential if he is to bring any background whatsoever to the construction of physical education programs for the handicapped child.

And finally, he must know and understand all the aspects of a child's growth and development, so that he can easily recognize obvious deviates from what is referred to as the "normal" growth pattern. An understanding of child growth and development enables him to evaluate in a qualitative manner the degree to which a particular child seems to deviate from the norm, and thus to observe the child's progress subjectively once a program of amelioration has been intiated.

With these primary factors in mind, the authors have compiled most of the available up-to-date material on physical education in order to assist physical educators, therapists, and physicians (particularly those in physical medicine) in designing adaptive and developmental programs for children who are desperately in need of their help.

D. K. M.
R. K.
V. S.

September, 1961

THE SCIENCE OF PHYSICAL EDUCATION
FOR HANDICAPPED CHILDREN

Chapter 1

DEVELOPMENTAL AND ADAPTIVE PHYSICAL EDUCATION: A CHALLENGE AND A PRIVILEGE

DEVELOPMENTAL[1] and adaptive physical education is the practice of physical education with handicapped children. Handicapped children are those youngsters who for some reason cannot take full advantage of the general physical education curriculum, or who need specialized attention in addition to the regular program. Among those youngsters whom the physical educator might find in this category are postpolio cases, the cerebral palsied, victims of heart disease, amputees, substrength cases, epileptics, postsurgical cases, as well as children suffering from obesity, malnutrition, poor motor coordination, postural difficulties, or emotional problems. Perhaps in no other area of educational services do we receive the gratification that comes from working with the handicapped child. In many instances these youngsters need the values inherent in physical education much more than do children without a physical handicap.

NEED FOR THE ADAPTIVE PROGRAM

It is estimated that there are approximately 4 million children in the United States who require special education because of a handicap. Of this number, more than 3.5 million receive regular classroom instruction, whereas the remaining pupils attend special

---

[1]*Developmental,* as used throughout this book, applies to a program designed to increase such attributes as muscular strength, flexibility, coordination, and cardirespiratory and muscular endurance.

1

schools. Not counted in this large population are those children whom the physical educator might consider to be handicapped according to the objectives of his profession. That is, the child with such problems as poor motor coordination, substrength, obesity, and impaired body mechanics might fall short of certain physical education standards. Indeed, the number of youngsters who would greatly benefit from an individualized as well as adaptive physical education program is staggering.

PREPARATION FOR WORKING WITH THE HANDICAPPED

Working with disabled children requires intensive education and sacrifice on the part of the teacher. Not only must the physical educator adapt a program of activity so that it is within the margins of medical safety for children suffering from a variety of pathological states, but he must also show a great deal of patience and compassion and be extremely able in establishing rapport between these children and himself. Even though he may need more education and, in order to acquire the necessary skills, have to work harder than a physical educator not working with handicapped children, the goal is well worth the effort.

The physical educator who is planning to work with the handicapped will have to concentrate in the areas of the basic sciences. Clarke and Elkins (1) suggest a four-year undergraduate physical education program which includes such fundamental courses as anatomy, kinesiology, physiology of exercise, psychology, correctives, and measurement and evaluation. In addition, to become a specialist in the field of developmental physical education, he should have postgraduate study at a school especially prepared for providing such advanced education. Graduate courses in anatomy, kinesiology, physiology, and psychology should be studied, as well as the relationships of these sciences to pathological conditions. Finally, he should be offered an opportunity for extensive supervised clinical and field experiences. We might comment that this education would prepare a physical educator to do a fine job in helping not only the handicapped child, but the normal child as well.

As we mentioned earlier, the goal is well worth the effort. Seeing a little handicapped boy or girl who, for the first time in his or her life, is able to bat the ball like other kids because of your interest is a reward worth working for.

WHAT THIS BOOK IS ABOUT

The fundamental objective of this book is to assist the student to do a better job of working with disabled children in the field of physical education. In order to accomplish such an assignment, the student will have to master a fundamental body of knowledge dictated by the needs of the handicapped child. What kind of knowledge must he have? And with what particular fields of science must he become especially conversant if he is to educate these children most effectively? In this book we will try to answer these questions, and the answers will serve as an orientation to a physical education program designed for the handicapped child.

For example, the next chapter deals with children's physical and motor development. Each one of us must be well informed about the developmental aspects of the child. Observing physical-growth patterns and knowing how much we should expect in the way of motor performance enables us to bring much insight to bear regarding proper program construction. Also, we must not overlook the fact that a child's normal growth patterns, when thoroughly understood, serve as a standard in evaluating pupil status and progress.

Neglecting the handicapped youngster's social development is disastrous, for it is this aspect of the child's adaptation which can be most significantly modified by a good physical education program. The feeling of successful accomplishment among his own group does wonders for the disabled youngster's personality. Therefore, if we are familiar with the personality problems of these children, we will be able to do a much more effective job. Chapter 3 reveals some of the most recent research findings dealing with adjustment problems of the handicapped.

We must not think that a list of activities can be written out for each type of handicap. The fact that a youngster is a hemiplegic does not necessarily infer that his participation must be limited to a particular group of activities. For example, a child with one leg amputated might have difficulty in learning how to walk on crutches; this would be especially true of children who may be overweight, as well as of those youngsters who have a background of limited activity experiences. Another child may have no problem with crutches but may experience difficulty in adjusting to his prosthesis. Some amputees of lower extremity have become extremely proficient in skiing, a most arduous activity requiring advanced motor coordination even for those who have no disability. These illustrations are given to make us aware that, like the so-called "normal" child, these disabled youngsters are individuals, and as such come to us with varying degrees of pathological complications, motor abilities, and motivation. What is good for one youngster may not be justified for another. Recognizing the child's abilities, rather than his disabilities, is a wise principle from which to start when adapting his program.

We, as physical educators, are the most proficient professionals there are when it comes to physical activities. By thoroughly understanding the principles of adapting sports to the handicapped child, we should be able to draw from a vast array of activities and select the variety most suitable to the needs of the *individual* child. Chapter 4, "Principles of Sports Adaptation for the Handicapped Child," was written for this purpose.

Man moves by means of his muscles. Running, jumping, playing, talking, singing, and following academic pursuits all require muscles. To a certain extent, the stronger the muscle, the more effective will be its performance regardless of the activity. Understanding the muscle and knowing how we can modify its function are fundamental requisites to the construction of an individual program. What is the most rapid way to hyertrophy a muscle? How does a muscle respond to exercise? What physiological principles must we understand to design an exercise program effectively and scientifically? These are only a few pertinent questions, to which answers are essential if we are to do our best in serving the needs of the handicapped child. Chapter 5 "Strength," contains such answers, along with other interesting and readily applicable information.

Our work, as we have mentioned before, involves carefully studying and evaluating the way in which children move. The following example will illustrate how truly important it is for us to know our mechanics. Little Johnny comes to us wearing leg braces. He is a postpolio child with both legs almost completely paralyzed. Do our hearts go out to him only in pity? Or is there something specific our profession might contribute toward Johnny's progress? Surely, we feel, in our vast array of activity knowledge there is something that can help him. There *is* something, for mechanical laws governing movement permit us to better understand body motion, and this information can be effectively applied in teaching Johnny how to manipulate his braces better and how to perform activities more efficiently. By being thoroughly aware of these mechanical principles, we will be able to develop more scientific programs for the hundreds of Johnnys whom we shall have the privilege to serve. Chapter 6 deals with very fundamental information concerning the mechanical principles of movement. Extra effort spent in mastering problems of forces will provide rich dividends in all aspects of the physical education program.

What specific attributes result from a well-constructed exercise program? How do we exercise for strength, endurance, flexibility, and coordination? A physical educator who cannot answer these questions and who isn't well versed in exercise programs is poorly prepared. He should be completely familiar with the most recent research findings in his field, and be able to put them into practice. Chapter 7 deals not only with the specific attributes of the exercise program, but with the principles governing the construction and development of such a program. In that chapter, we will see how the most recent research in exercise is applied to the activity program.

Chapter 8 deals with the mechanics of the spine. We must understand the spine and how it functions before we can acquire a good understanding of the total body movement patterns. Furthermore, an important objective of the physical educator is to gain the ability to appraise qualitatively the mechanical symmetry of growing bodies. Chapter 8 was written as an aid in serving this need.

Chapter 9 demonstrates the application of the mechanical principles discussed in Chapter 6. Activities most commonly performed by everyone throughout the day include sitting, standing, walking, climbing, descending stairs, stooping, and lifting; and being able to perform these daily living activities is almost a minimal requirement if the handicapped person is to learn to care for his individual needs and gain a feeling of independence.

We must be fully aware that many children, even though they

have no physical handicap per se, require good instruction in daily living activities if they are to perform at maximum, or near maximum, efficiency. For valid evidence of this statement we can observe the way in which many girls walk in high heels, or watch how inefficiently many men lift heavy objects. From the aesthetic as well as from the functional standpoint, efficiency in daily living activities is a valuable concomitant of the physical education program. The materials in Chapter 9 should help toward this end.

Measuring a child's status and demonstrating his progression require the use of both qualitative and quantitative measuring instruments. Chapter 10 lists a variety of instruments that can be used to quantitate his status objectively. Once status is objectively defined in regard to a specified factor, proper programming will be much more obvious. Following the child's progress, a prime motivator, requires continuous evaluation.

The remaining chapters in this book deal with a variety of the diseases most prevalent among school-age children. To understand the child and his handicap, to establish a program within the confines of medical safety, and to be able to converse intelligently with the medical authority in charge of the pupil's rehabilitation require a degree of scientific competency regarding these pathological states, particularly as they apply to the child's activity needs. The titles of each of these later chapters are sufficiently self-explanatory in regard to the need for their incorporation into the repertoire of the professional person who will teach physical education to the handicapped child.

ORGANIZING AND ADMINISTERING
THE HANDICAPPED CHILDREN'S PROGRAM

Initiating a developmental and adaptive physical education program is not easy. However, once the *modus operandi* is established in accordance with sound administrative principles, the satisfactions realized more than pay for the effort (2). The directions which must be adhered to in establishing the program are dictated by the objectives of that program. Thus, it becomes necessary for us to spend a moment to briefly review our objectives.

PHYSICAL EDUCATION OBJECTIVES

As was mentioned earlier, the adaptive program is simply the modification of the regular physical education curriculum in order to meet the needs of handicapped children; therefore, the objectives we have already studied in other professional courses in physical education apply in this instance as well. Most briefly stated, these objectives include a degree of competency in the following areas (3):

1. *Recreation.* The necessary skill to participate in a variety of activities sufficiently well to enjoy ourselves.
2. *Social Efficiency.* Sufficient social abilities to get along with one another in a group.
3. *Physical Fitness.* Most frequently this term implies total fitness including the following four components:
   a. Psychological fitness:
      (1) The emotional stability necessary to meet the everyday problems characteristic of one's environment, and
      (2) Sufficient psychological reserve to handle a sudden emotional trauma.
   b. Health or normal physiological function.
   c. Body mechanics, or efficient performance in skills of movement, from the common everyday skills of standing, walking, and sitting to the most complex, such as that manifested by a football player executing a perfect block, or the performance of an intricate pattern of movement by a dancer, or, for the handicapped, skillful use of crutches and prostheses.
   d. Physical anthropometry, a type of fitness perhaps reflected in body contour as a result of good muscular tones as well as proper body weight.

From this review of objectives we are aware of the complexities involved, particularly of the fitness objective, in constructing the adaptive program. Certainly we must include, in addition to the physically disabled, those children who significantly deviate from the average in regard to the stated objectives—for example, children suffering from obesity, substrength, postural problems, emotional disturbances, lack of coordination in motor movements, and nutritional disorders—conditions for which the physical educator is mostly responsible, as indicated by the professional objectives of physical education. As we become more fully oriented to this fact, the numerous ramifications of the complete adaptive and developmental program gradually begin to take form.

First and foremost, we must realize that the handicapped child is not the physical educator's sole responsibility. On the contrary, all specialists whose background is conducive to the understanding of the child's problems must work as a coordinated team toward better service to that child. Therefore, in addition to the actual planning and initiation of the adaptive curriculum, the physical educator must enlist the services of a number of other specialists. Consequently, instead of having a single specialist work alone, there is a group approach to the child's problem. This approach has outstanding merit, for information gained from the other specialists is pooled and a more complete and elaborate history of the child is revealed than could ever be possible for one person to compile. A most effective and efficient way in which to get specialists together is to form a health or fitness council.

HEALTH COUNCIL

The health council's purpose is twofold: (1) it assists in advising the physical educator in regard to the individualized physical education program and (2) it recommends or provides proper medical care when necessary. In most instances it would be desirable to involve in such a group the following specialists: school nurse, physician, physical educator, guidance director, and dietition, as well as homeroom teacher, principal, and parents.

The guidance director, or counselor, is a key person when dealing with the handicapped youngster's program. He will have in his files pertinent data on the pupils that have come through his own testing program, as well as those which have been collected by such school personnel as the principal, nurse, and classroom teacher. This material would include such information as medical examination results, academic index, anecdotal records, and personality-test scores. Actually the guidance office might be compared to a Central Intelligence Agency, since it functions as a center where all available information concerning the pupil may be found.

In most instances, the guidance director gathers useful information about the child, but does not necessarily council or guide each child. The actual guidance is left to the individual teachers; and because of their unique position, the physical educator and the guidance director can effectively join forces in "seeing through Johnny, and seeing Johnny through."

The school nurse is also important in this measurement scheme, for she is the liaison between the school, the physician, and the parent. In addition to rendering follow-up services, she is vital in serving as a medical consultant to the physical educator.

The dietician or home economics teacher can contribute information about diets and other nutritional problems that may be the fundamental cause of low fitness among some children. Too frequently this specialist's valuable services are overlooked in the total physical education program.

Because the classroom teacher is with the pupils for as many as six hours a day, she has an oportunity to become most familiar with a child's behavior characteristics and home background. As a result, she is a valuable source in gaining more insight into a particular child's problems. The physical educator should confer with this person regularly as an aid in evaluating the total progress of the handicapped as he learns to live, work, and play within the confines of his disability.

The physician will be of value in determining the level of restriction which should be imposed on the child so that the activity program can be designed within the limits of medical safety.

A parent should be on the council to represent the interests of all the mothers and fathers. He or she can contribute in terms of parental reaction to the program and help in disseminating information about the purposes and actions of the council to such agencies as the Parent-Teacher Association.

The school administrator or principal has as his chief concern the cooperative efforts of his entire staff in accomplishing the aims of education. Therefore, he is in a position to aid in coordinating the entire program of the council.

PHYSICAL MEDICINE

In larger communities will be found additional medical specialists in the field of physical medicine who will be extremely interested in all aspects of the physical education program. This group deals

mostly with diseases primarily affecting the neuromuscular and musculoskeletal systems. Heat, massage, and exercise are important aspects of physical medicine.

A key person among this group is the *physiatrist,* a medical doctor
who has specialized in the diseases primarily affecting the muscular
and skeletal systems; he would therefore be an excellent advisor to
the developmental and adaptive physical education program.

The *physical therapist* is another important member of physical
medicine. He administers medically prescribed treatment by the use
of such physical agents as light, heat, water, electricity, massage, and
therapeutic exercise. The therapists also perform tests to determine
muscle, nerve, and skin conditions or reactions. The physical therapist must be a graduate of a school of physical therapy approved by
the American Medical Association. His fine background in anatomy
and kinesiology makes him an outstanding person in the field of
therapeutic exercise and, as a result, he can contribute a good deal
to the handicapped child's physical education program.

COMMITTEE ON ADAPTED PHYSICAL EDUCATION

To further define the unique contribution of the adaptive physical education program, the Committee on Adapted Physical Education of the American Association for Health, Physical Education,
and Recreation (4) has set forth the following guiding principles:

1. *There is need for common understanding regarding the nature of
   adapted physical education.* Adapted physical education is a diversified
   program of developmental activities, games, sports, and rhythms, suited
   to the interests, capacities, and limitations of students with disabilities
   who may not safely or successfully engage in unrestricted participation
   in the vigorous activities of the general physical education program.
2. *There is need for adapted physical education in schools and colleges.*
   According to the best estimates available there are about 4 million children of school age in the United States with physical handicaps. Only 11
   percent of this group requiring special educational services are receiving
   them through special schools and classes. The vast majority of exceptional children are attending regular schools. The major disabling conditions, each affecting thousands of children, are cerebral palsy,
   poliomyelitis, epilepsy, tuberculosis, traumatic injuries, neurological
   problems, and heart disease. Further evidence indicates that at the

college level there is a significant percentage of students requiring special consideration for either temporary or permanent disabilities.

3. *Adapted physical education has much to offer the individual who faces the combined problem of seeking an education and living most effectively with a handicap.* Through adapted physical education, the individual can:

   a. Be observed and referred when the need for medical or other services are suspected.

   b. Be guided in avoidance of situations which would aggravate the condition or subject him to unnecessary risks of injury.

   c. Improve neuromuscular skills, general strength and endurance following convalescence from acute illness or injury.

   d. Be provided with opportunities for improved psychological adjustment and social development.

4. *The direct and related services essential for the proper conduct of adapted physical education should be available to our schools.* These services should include:

   a. Adequate and periodic health examination.

   b. Classification for physical education based on the health examination and other pertinent tests and observations.

   c. Guidance of individuals needing special consideration with respect to physical activity, general health practices, recreational pursuits, vocational planning, psychological adjustment, and social development.

   d. Arrangement of appropriate adapted physical education programs.

   e. Evaluation and recording of progress through observations, appropriate measurements, and consultations.

   f. Integrated relationships with other school personnel, medical and its auxiliary services, and the family to assure continuous guidance and supervisory services.

   g. Cumulative records for each individual, which should be transferred from school to school.

5. *It is essential that adequate medical guidance be available for teachers of adapted physical education.* The possibility of serious pathology requires that programs of adapted physical education should not be attempted without the diagnosis, written recommendation, and supervision of a physician. The planned program of activities must be predicated on medical findings and accomplished by competent teachers working with medical supervision and guidance. There should be an effective referral service among physicians, physical educators, and parents aimed at proper safeguards and maximum student benefits. School administra-

tors, alert to the special needs of handicapped children, should make every effort to provide adequate staff and facilities necessary for a program of adapted physical education.

6. *Teachers of adapted physical education have a great responsibility as well as an unusual opportunity.* Physical educators engaged in teaching adapted physical education should:
   a. Have adequate professional education to implement the recommendations provided by medical personnel.
   b. Be motivated by the highest ideals with respect to the importance of total student development and satisfactory human relationships.
   c. Develop the ability to establish rapport with students who may exhibit social maladjustment as a result of a disability.
   d. Be aware of a student's attitude toward his disability.
   e. Be objective in relationships with students.
   f. Be prepared to give the time and effort necessary to help a student overcome a difficulty.
   g. Consider as strictly confidential information related to personal problems of the student.
   h. Stress similarities rather than deviations, and abilities instead of disabilities.

7. *Adapted physical education is necessary at all school levels.* The student with a disability faces the dual problem of overcoming a handicap and acquiring an education which will enable him to take his place in society as a respected citizen. Failure to assist a student with his problems may retard the growth and development process. Offering adapted physical education in the elementary grades, and continuing through the secondary school and college, will assist the individual to improve function and make adequate psychological and social adjustments. It will be a factor in his attaining maximum growth and development within the limits of the disability. It will minimize attitudes of defeat and fears of insecurity. It will help him face the future with confidence.

SUMMARY

First, and most important, we must recognize the need of the handicapped child for a good physical education program. The disabled youngster, perhaps even to a greater extent than the non-disabled, requires for complete growth and adjustment success in the objectives to which our profession subscribes.

Second, in order for us to adequately adapt a program of activity within the margins of medical safety we need special preparation. Familiarity with pathology, mechanical principles of movement, physiology of the muscle, emotional problems commonly associated with the handicapped, and characteristics of growth and development are among the important areas of study in which we must become quite capable.

Finally, the initiation of the developmental and remedial curriculum will require careful planning. As there are few of these programs in our schools, a real effort to orient all of the people concerned must be started by the physical educator; the size of the community will determine the extent of organization necessary. Once installed, the developmental and remedial program will become one of the most important aspects of the entire physical education department. However, much time, patience, and effort will be required before a truly satisfactory program can be established.

REFERENCES

1. Clarke, H. Harrison, and Elkins, Earl C., "Relationships in Developmental and Remedial and Corrective Therapy," *The Journal of the Asscociation for Physical and Mental Rehabilitation,* May-June, 1959, 75-78.
2. Mathews, Donald K., Shaw, Virginia, and Risser, Philip, "The Moses Lake Project: A Field Study in Physical Education," *Journal of Health, Physical Education, and Recreation,* April, 1958, 18-19.
3. Mathews, Donald K., *Measurement in Physical Education,* Saunders, Philadelphia, 1958, pp. 4-5.
4. Prepared by the Committee on Adapted Physical Education, Washington, D.C., American Association for Health, Physical Education, and Recreation.

Chapter 2

PHYSICAL AND MOTOR DEVELOPMENT OF CHILDREN

THE professional worker who is dealing with children, particularly with those classified as subfit and those who show characteristics of the emotionally maladjusted, must recognize factors influencing growth and development of children, as well as be familiar with the normal growth pattern. This is essential if the instructor is to serve the needs of the child completely.

Before progressing into a more thorough study of growth and development, it will perhaps be better to briefly illustrate how knowledge of certain growth and developmental factors will help to prepare the professional physical educator. For instance, one of the least valid measures of biological progress is chronological age, even though this criterion is often used with careless abandon as an objective indicator. Consider that a 12-year-old boy may be as much as 4 years older than his chronological age from the standpoint of biological maturation; so, too, a 16-year-old youngster may be retarded in terms of biological development by as much as four years. Krogman (10), in studying the 1957 Little League players who were invited to participate in the World Series, found they had an average chronological age of 12 years and a biological age of 14 years!

It is a documented fact that today's children are taller, heavier, and more mentally advanced, and possess physical skills unequaled by earlier children of the same age. For example, some of the findings among Little League baseball players indicate they are as tall and heavy as average 16- and 17-year-olds of 25 years ago.

To the physical educator it should be of extreme interest that those children who excell in sports are usually at least one to two years advanced in biological maturity than the same age group was a generation ago—and sometimes they may be as much as three or four years in advance. The average 14-year-old boy has increased 5 inches in height and added 24 pounds to his weight in the last 75 years. In the same time interval, the average 10-year-old girl has grown 4 inches and added 14 pounds to her weight. In fact, many anthropologists believe that someday man may grow to tremendous dimensions.

Of considerable concern to the physician and educator alike is the maturation rate. The greatest change in children is to be found at the age of pubescence or just prior to it. This advancement in maturation rate must be correlated with academic status, for early physical maturation is closely associated with good scholarship; the contrary is also true.

Sports Prowess among Teen-Agers

Dramatic evidence of early physical maturation is demonstrated by increased performance abilities among high school athletes. Hale (8), measuring a large number of Little Leaguers, has demonstrated that 11- and 12-year-old boys run as fast as average 15- and 16-year-olds; Little League pitchers equal speed of college pitchers in throwing ability. Record times in track and field and swimming events are rapidly falling to teen-age prowess. For example, of the twelve world records in track during the reign of the famous Jim Thorpe, nine have been surpassed by teen-agers.

Today, the rise of the teen-ager in the ranks of topflight competitive swimming has been phenomenal. The only 220-yard free-styler ever to break 2 minutes was Dave Lyons, a high school boy from Winnetka, Illinois, in 1:59.7 minutes; both the 100-yard breast stroke and the 100-yard free-style American records belong to high school youngsters! One more example of the teen-ager's prowess comes from Steve Clark of Santa Clara, California, who recently won the NAAU 100-yard free-style with a 46.8 second swim, bettering the existing record by 1.4 seconds. To be sure, good swimming programs and improved training methods have made their contributions toward such fantastic performances, but it is without question that credit must also be given to increased maturation levels of these high school boys.

Puberty, or the period of growth at which time either sex becomes functionally capable of reproduction, is the standard reference used by the scientist to describe the child's stage of growth. Prepubescence and postpubescence refer respectfully to the years immediately before and after the period of pubescence. As the child exhibits behavior characteristics closely allied to his biological development, it behooves the professional person to become aware of the more valid criteria which can be used to reflect the youngster's stage of growth in terms of puberty.

Children experience growth spurts, at which time more than the usual amount of food intake is employed for new cellular growth. Overindulgence in prolonged activity and excessive fatigue among the children during their periods of rapid growth *should be guarded against.*

An outstanding characteristic of growth is its irregularity from child to child. Realizing this, and understanding the characteristics of the "early" and "late" maturers, is to better understand the child —and therefore do a more effective professional job in assisting him in his development. Height, weight, and growth of body segments are important factors constituting physical growth. Understanding the pattern of this aspect of growth should be almost second nature to the physical educator, for such information has application to individual curriculum construction. As an illustration, we must be able to differentiate between normal and abnormal weight gains in order to understand and apply principles of weight control.

Bone and muscle development are the single most important elements underlying the structural growth of the child. In order to appraise mechanical symmetry, evaluate muscular performance, and plan exercise programs, it is necessary to be informed regarding physiological characteristics of bone and muscle development. It should be further recognized that strength is closely related to pubescence. The rapid development of strength can actually be used as an indication of premature puberty.

The objectives of physical education are accomplished predominantly through the use of motor skills. During the period of adolescence, motor competence is a primary factor in the child's level of social acceptance.

Briefly, then, these are several of the more important developmental characteristics with some implications for the physical educator as he plans programs for the handicapped as well as the so-called normal child. The more we know about growing boys and girls, the better we can serve them.

CRITERIA OF PUBERTY

As was mentioned earlier, complex changes, both physical and physiological take place during the stages of puberty. We might ask ourselves: Is it necessary to recognize the status of the youngster's development and, if so, how best can this be accomplished? It has been noted that chronological age and physiological age may differ by as much as six years. Certainly a child's needs in terms of our professional objectives are dictated more by his maturation than by his chronological age. As an illustration, the world's champion Little League baseballers, a highly select group, like the cream on the milk, rose to the top because of their demonstrated superiority. These boys' physical development surpassed that of the "average" 12-year old. Therefore, we should know that the child's biological development is more valid index of his growth status than is his chronological age. Understanding this we will better understand the child, and be able to establish a program that is more suitable to his specific needs.

In studying physiological maturity as related to certain characteristics of boys and girls, we may use the following criteria: pubic hair, axillary hair, rapid growth in height and weight, appearance of second molars, enlargement and changes of appearance of breast, enlargement of pelvic breadth, development of larynx, and menstruation. The criteria commonly used to determine onset of puberty for boys are as follows: pubic hair, rapid growth in height and weight, appearance of second molars, enlargement of genitals, change of voice, appearance of beard, and seminal emissions.

One author (13), in studying the sexual growth of Negro and white boys, used a set of more simplified criteria consisting of age at first ejaculation, age at first appearance of pigmented pubic hair, and age at first recognition of voice changes.

There are several rather reliable criteria used singularly to determine the onset of puberty. Among the most valid are Crampton's pubic hair test, the menarche, and X rays of bones. Crampton, as early as 1908, suggested the type and amount of hair over the pubic bone as an index of puberty. At present, prepubescence is associated with lack of pubic hair (this excludes the fine hair which is present on other parts of the skin); youngsters are considered pubescent when there is pigmentation in the pubic hair (this is the time of most rapid growth of pubic hair); and postpubescence has occurred when the pubic hair is kinked.

Probably the menarche (first menstruation) is the best single criterion of sexual maturity for girls. Usually the menarche is considered as the midpoint of puberty. Menstruation is brought about as a result of the production of the gonodal hormone. This particular hormone must be produced in certain minimal amounts before menstruation begins. The discharge resulting from menstruation is made up of four constitutents: blood, mucous, minerals, and broken-down cell tissue. The blood, which is released from the capillaries imbedded in the uterus lining, totals about 2 ounces on the average for the entire period; the mucous makes up the larger portion. The menstrual period generally lasts from 3 to 5 days. Irregularity of menstruation is extremely common throughout the adolescent period; this has numerous causes, perhaps the more common of which are physical strain, emotional tension, and illness. Also, during the early stages of the menstrual flow, there is great variability between periods. Engle and Shelesnyak (5) report the time from the beginning of one period to the beginning of the next ranges from 17 to 45 days, and there are more long cycles during the summer months than in the winter. Irregularity decreases as a girl reaches maturity, and maturity exerts a stabilizing effect on the variability and length of the menstrual cycle.

During the first few menstrual periods, there is a wide variation from individual to individual in the length of the flow; for example, in the first one or two menstrual periods, the flow may last a day or even less; later, the duration may vary from 1 to 14 days. A mean variation of between 4.6 and 4.85 days is an acceptable range.

Today, taking X rays of bone development is probably the best single criterion of sexual maturity in both boys and girls. The "skeletal age" of an individual is a term indicating the percentage of his total wrist area that is ossified in relation to the mean values for various age groups. The area, of course, is determined by X-ray factors. Skeletal age is an extremely useful index of physiological maturity for a number of reasons. In the first place, it is closely related to growth and stature. During the pubescent period, maximum adult height can be predicted quite accurately from a person's skeletal age. The skeletal age is highly correlated with such criteria as sexual maturity, and can be used as an objective index of pubescent status. Studies reveal that genital growth of boys and girls always occurs at a specific time in the bone development of the individual. Maturation is determined by observing changes in the outline of the chest and hands and in the ossification of epiphysis. Some years before puberty, an X ray of the hand will actually distinguish children who will mature early from those whose maturation will be delayed.

The age of menarche is more closely related to prepubescent skeletal age than the height or weight or annual increments in height. We find that skeletal growth takes place over an interval of approximately 20 years. The rate of growth is marked by two spurts, each of which is succeeded by periods of very slow growth. The first spurt occurs in early infancy, and the second growth spurt begins one to two years before pubescence—at about age 11 to 12 in girls and 13 to 14 in boys.

CHARACTERISTICS OF PUBERTY

Puberty is generally expressed in three subdivisions: (1) prepubescence, which is the immature stage, and even though certain body changes have taken place and are taking place, in which the reproductive function is not yet developed; (2) the pubescent period, at which time sexual cells are beginning to be produced by the sex organs, but the bodily changes are not complete; and (3) postpubescence, or the state of maturity as characterized by fully functioning sex organs and by the appearance of sufficiently developed secondary sexual characteristics. The average age of pubescence is 13½ years for girls and 14½ years for boys. Studies show that 50 percent of girls mature between 12.5 and 14.5 years, while 50 percent of boys mature between 14 and 15.5 years. Sex differentation is particularly obvious during the ages from 12 to 14, at which time there are considerably more mature girls than mature boys. A number of factors influence the age of maturation. Among the more important are heredity, intelligence, health, and climate. Usually the period of puberty lasts from two to four years, and the period of postpubescence lasts from six months to two years. It is observed that the puberty period generally lasts twice as long as the prepuberty and postpuberty periods combined.

Early and Late Maturers

One of the most outstanding characteristics of growth is its irregularity from individual to individual, particularly when comparisons are made on the basis of chronological age. There are marked individual differences in the patterns of adolescent growth and development. For example, the faster-maturing individual usually has a greater spurt of rapid growth; and these youngsters attain adult proportions rapidly. On the other hand, individuals who mature slowly experience growth which is more gradual and less variable. It is of interest to note that the slow-maturing individuals usually develop into larger adults, as compared to those youngsters whose maturation takes place quickly.

There are specific characteristics associated with the maturation of boys and girls, as well as fundamental characteristics of "early maturers" as compared with "late maturers." On the whole, boys' maturity period is longer than girls', and every stage of puberty is longer than that experienced by girls. Three to three and one-half years is required for girls to mature, while between two and four years is required for boys. Early studies show that there is far less uniformity in boys' maturation than in girls'. Also, it has been found that boys whose maturity is delayed mature much more rapidly than the average once they get started. For example, boys who reach puberty at 13½ years usually remain pubescent for about 1.2 years; however, with those reaching puberty earlier or later, the pubescent state will last about 2.5 years. Early-maturing boys are generally large in late childhood, with feminine body types characterized by broad hips and short legs. Their maximum growth is attained early and over a short period of time. For girls, menarche comes sooner, accompanied by osseous development and secondary sex characteristics. Late maturers are usually small in late childhood, with masculine body types (broad shoulders and long legs). Growth is mostly slow and over a long period of time. Menarche and osseous development in presence of secondary sex characteristics are later than usual.

PHYSICAL GROWTH

HEIGHT

The height of an individual, when growth is completed, depends on numerous factors. Such things as exercise, prenatal and postnatal health and feeding, heredity, racial stock, amount of manual labor during growth years, frequency and seriousness of illness during period of rapid growth, and climate. Today the average height of the American male is 67 inches, and for the female 64 inches. Mills (12) compared today's college freshman with those of 30 years ago and found that girls are 1 inch taller today and boys are 2 inches taller. As was indicated earlier, age of maturation influences height for both boys and girls. Another study of college girls found that the girls who matured at or before 11 years were, on the average 1 inch shorter than those reaching puberty at 15 years.

Children pass through the adolescent phase of accelerated growth at widely different chronological ages, and this factor should be kept in mind when interpreting growth studies. Actually, there is far greater uniformity among children when chronological age is ignored and a more valid criterion of growth is used, such as age of either initial growth acceleration or maximum growth.

When considering average growth in height, the increase year by year continually diminishes from birth to maturity—except for the period of adolescent spurt. Simmons (14) reports that girls increase in height at an accelerated rate between the ages of 9 and 12. The accelerated rate of boys' height occurs between 11 and 14 years. Growth in height decelerates rapidly from the age of 13 in girls and 15 in boys. Growth increases cease in both sexes after about three years. According to Simmons' data, maximum increases occur at the age of 12 in girls and 14 in boys. For boys, the greatest increase in height comes in the year when they pass from pubescent to post-pubescent age regardless of their chronological age. The beginning spurt in height seems to come between 10.4 and 15.8 years, with an average at 12.9. It ends between 13.1 and 17.5 years, the average being 15.3 years. The most rapid period of growth in height comes between the ages of 11.9 and 16.7, with a mean of about 14 years.

WEIGHT

Following the initial infantile spurt of growth, deceleration in weight takes place more rapidly than height. Weight increase between the ages of 2 and 5 remains fairly constant. From 5 years to about 12, there is a steady increase in the weight increment for girls. The weight increase for boys comes at age 5 and steadily increases to age 14. At age 12 for girls and 14 for boys there is a rather abrupt decrease in the weight increment. There is a proportionally greater increase in weight during adolescence than height. Stuart (15) attributes a part of this increase to a tendency for the adolescent to accumulate larger quantities of fat in the subcutaneous tissue, this being more pronounced in girls than in boys. Furthermore, this increase in weight may also be accounted for by the broadening of the skeleton and the increased size of individual bones. The growth of muscles at this time, which is more marked in boys than in girls, may also account for a considerable part in the gain in weight.

In childhood, muscles contribute about 30 percent of the total body weight, whereas in maturity they make up about 40 percent. Growth in weight begins later than growth in height, perhaps because weight increase is closely associated with sexual maturation. During the stage of early adolescence, the individual is more apt to experience weight increase. Girls are usually heavier than boys between the ages of 10 and 15, because girls are further advanced than boys in sexual maturation. It is only after the age of 15 that boys become heavier than girls.

The greatest increase in weight for girls occurs during the year prior to puberty (an average of 14 pounds). A girl experiences two more large gains in weight: (1) two years before puberty (average 10 pounds), and (2) during the year following puberty (average 10 pounds). Thus, during those three years the average increase in weight for girls is 34 pounds.

The weight spurt for boys comes a year or two later than for girls. During the pubertal period, the gain in weight for boys is from 17.2 to 64.8 pounds, with an average of 39.9 pounds. This maximum growth in weight occurs during or after the maximum growth in height. About 50 percent of the boys might be considered fat during their early adolescence. As a matter of fact, it is quite common for both boys and girls to experience a fat period early in their sexual maturation. For boys, this period comes at or quite near the period of rapid growth in height. The fat period seems to last about two years, following which the body returns to normal proportions.

The fat period for girls comes at the onset of puberty. Obesity in female adolescence is quite frequently associated with the pre-menstrual growth spurt. During this time, food intake is usually above normal. If puberty continues, the obesity characteristics of the girl usually disappear. However, a girl quite often finds at this time that an increased appetite may cause exaggerated gains in weight. If this conflict is not properly recognized and steps taken to satisfy the condition, a weight problem may result. In every instance, researchers have found early-maturing individuals are heavier than those who mature late.

Recognition of proper weight development by the trained professional is necessary in order to understand application of weight-control principles and to differentiate between normal and abnormal obesity. One of the best current devices available for assessing the adequacy of growth in weight (according to the individual's own idiosyncratic growth pattern) is the Wetzel Grid technique, which rates maturity in terms of the percentage level reached with respect to ultimate level.

GROWTH OF BODY SEGMENTS

At the time of rapid growth there is noticeable change in body proportions. The reversal in the ratio of sitting to standing height, occurring in both sexes, is one of the most noticeable. As compared to the preadolescent years, the trunk begins to grow more rapidly than the legs until the ratio stabilizes as growth is completed. The relative growth of various organ systems may be compared in Scammon's (9) grouping of their growth trends under four general types: lymphoid, neural, general, and genital. Ausubel (1) makes reference to Maresh in stating that "Genital growth increases most spectacularly during adolescence, and there is a substantial but not as great an increase in general (skeleton, musculature, internal organs) growth. Neural growth tapers off, and lymphoid tissue actually decreases in weight. Growth of the respiratory and vascular organs tends to keep pace with growth in skeletal (bone and muscle) tissue, thereby obviating the possibility of physiological imbalance in meeting the enhanced nutritive needs of an enlarged body frame."

Changes in adolescent body proportions, are either sex-linked or related to "velocity of maturation"—in girls, widening of the hips; and in boys, a corresponding increase in breadth of shoulders. These differences, together with characteristic sex differences in muscular development and distribution of fat, constitute the basis for standards of male and female body build.

Late-maturing boys and girls tend to be relatively long-legged and to have shorter trunks than their more rapidly maturing contemporaries. Early-maturing boys tend to be relatively broad-hipped and narrow-shouldered in comparison to late-maturing boys.

The trunk grows rapidly between the ages of 6 and 7. It is twice as long and wide than it was at birth. From this period until early adolescence, trunk growth is slow. Rapid development in shoulder width is a characteristic for boys, as the development in hip width is characteristic for girls. The pubertal cycle and the gain in shoulder and hip width is closely related. Usually early-maturing boys have broader hips than late maturers. The masculine figure of slender hips and broad shoulders seems to be more common in the late-maturing boy. Also, the late-maturing girls, like the late-maturing boys, seem to have broad shoulders. At puberty, legs are four times as long as they are at birth, and at maturity five times as long. Among girls, the slowing down in height increase the year following puberty is due to a large extent to the cessation of growth in the long bones of the leg. Possibly the age of menarche affects the length of girls' legs and varies according to whether she is an early or late maturer. It seems that in late-maturing children, leg growth continues for a greater period of time; hence, at maturity the individual is long-legged. Legs of early-maturing children have a tendency toward being stocky, while those of the late-maturing person are generally slender. At birth, the upper part of the body, including the head and the trunk, is longer than the legs of the lower part; at puberty the upper and lower parts appear equal. This is attributed to the fact that the long bones' growth is much more rapid than that of the trunk. At puberty the sex hormone is introduced, which causes the epiphyseal union of the long bone ends. If, by chance, the sex hormone is produced too early, growth will cease before full length of the long bones has been achieved. Sometimes the sex hormone production is delayed, permitting growth to continue over an abnormal period of time. If this happens, the lower measurement will exceed the upper. It appears, then, the proportions of an individual (upper and lower) are indicative of the stage at which the sex hormone was effective. The arms are characterized by similar growth, for just prior to and immediately following puberty, the arms lengthen. The appearance of exceptionally long arms for a short period of time is caused by the delayed spurt in growth of the trunk. Individuals who mature early usually have short arms, for their growth ceases at the beginning of puberty. Hands and feet of boys and girls reach their full growth before the arms and legs. This factor is probably the reason why, at a particular period of growth, the hands and feet may appear exceptionally large.

GROWTH OF BONES AND MUSCLES

BONES

Greulich *et al.* (7) have reported that skeletal maturation parallels the external characteristics of sexual maturation. Bones, in addition to their change in size, change internally also; that is, during the early ages of development there is a preponderance of cartilage which makes the bones soft and spongy, and because of this factor they may become easily deformed. It is for this reason that during the early years children's body mechanics should be carefully watched. Perhaps you have observed children sitting in a circle with the inside of both knees and legs against the ground. Such position, if held for a long period of time, is apt to cause the knee joint to become weakened by stretching the medial ligaments. As the youngster continues to grow, the bones become larger, cartilage commences to ossify, and the bones become more solid. The conversion of cartilage to bone is a result of the thyroid hormone. Girl's bones, on the average, are close to maturity at age 14. At the age of 17 the bones should be almost completely ossified. In boys, skeletal maturation is not completed until age 19 or 20.

MUSCLES

Accompanying the skeletal growth is the development of the musculature of the body. The average youngster of 8 years possesses muscles which comprise about one-fourth of the body weight; and at maturity, the muscles contribute about 40 percent of an individual's weight. Girls between the ages of 12 and 15 and boys between 15 and 16 experience a pronounced increase in muscle tissue, which parallels sexual maturity. Androgenic substances dumped into the bloodstream stimulate the growth of muscle cells. In boys the abdominal muscles and muscles of the extremities follow maturation of the testes. Muscles of the male body are a part of secondary sexual characteristics; girls' muscles do not develop to the extent that boys' do, and as a result, girls have less strength than boys.

During pubescence, a marked increase in strength occurs. We know that muscle size is related to strength and that strength is important for good motor development; and growth in muscle size precedes development of strength. Regarding the growth and development of an individual, structure usually comes before the acquisition of function. There is a time lapse between the structural acquisition and function. For example, the vocal cords greatly increase in size during the forepart of pubescence. However, there is not a corresponding increase in the strength of the cords. When plotting grip strength against age for both boys and girls, a significant increase is seen during the years of pubescence. Data gathered by Dimock (4) forcefully illustrate changes in strength during pubescence. He found that from age 12 to 16 boys' strength doubled. It has been conclusively illustrated that such gains in strength are a direct function of pubescence rather than an operation of age. The average pubescent boy exceeds 97 percent of prepubescent boys in strength. One may use precocious development of strength as indicative of premature puberty for, as mentioned above, growth in strength parallels sexual maturity.

In girls, such development begins early and reaches a maximum much sooner than for boys. Strength development for girls begins to taper off between 13 and 14. By contrast, gains in strength for boys do not reach maximum until age 16, at which time the gains begin to taper off slowly. In addition to numerous anatomical and physiological factors, complete muscular development is certainly related to use; that is, sufficient exercise will aid in the development and growth of an individual's musculature.

MOTOR DEVELOPMENT

Boys, because of their greater height, weight, and muscular development, have an advantage in motor skills. In locomotor activities, boys are seemingly more favored because of increased strength and the more mechanically efficient angle the neck of the femur makes with the pelvis. Numerous researches have shown that the motor ability of an indivdual during the adolescent stage, as well as in earlier stages of development, constitutes a vital part of his feeling of competence in adjusting to his environment. In addition to the development of his own social well-being, proficiency in motor skills is an extremely important source of personal satisfaction and relaxation for leisure activities. During adolescence, motor competence is of primary importance in the matter of a child's status in the group. It has even been shown to figure prominently in his deliberations about choice of vocation. As regards boys' prestige and social esteem, athletic skills are a major source of individual status during the adolescent period. As a result of the increasing importance attached to the body during adolescence, noticeable physical incompetencies, as well as awkwardness, become acute sources of self-consciousness, of embarrassment, and of social ridicule. For this reason alone, motor handicaps may result in serious damage to the youngster's self-concept.

The age trend in motor ability obtained from scores in simple motor functions throughout the period of adolescence is continuous, and not marked with dramatic decreases or increases. There is no question that growth curves illustrate rapid increases in height and weight with certain variations is growth proportions. This could lead one to believe that during the periods of rapid growth there is an apparent awkwardness in motor skills. However, one must conclude that the question of an adolescent becoming awkward is *not* a result of lessened motor ability. The question of adolescent awkwardness might better be answered through psychiatric adjustment to social situations. Social poise must be developed as any other social trait, and during the adolescent period the youngster may find it difficult to make these adjustments. Certain motor ability tests have been administered to youngsters experiencing the adolescent stage; the results indicate that there is a gradual increase and leveling off of motor ability rather than a decrease. For example, reaction time, the time lapsing between the stimulus and the movement, seems to reach the maximum level at 13 or 14. Apparently there is little sex difference in reaction time. In spatial eye-hand coordination tests (inserting a stylus the size of a pencil in a hole only slightly larger) or temporal eye-hand coordination (as pressing a button when a rotating disk gets to a given point), better performance is obtained between 14 or 15, with boys showing superior performance. A test which involves speed in packing spools in a tray using both hands simultaneously showed no sex difference. In one test which involved fine manual precision and steadiness, the girls were better than the boys.

Ausable (2) states: "Retardation in motor competence is the beginning of a vicious cycle in social maladjustment that is difficult to break. Boys with poor physical ability tend to enjoy low prestige in the group. They have reason to shun both physical activities and group participation because both are associated with failure." Biddulph (3) found, in studying 461 high school boys, that significant differences in personal and social adjustment exist between the top 50 and bottom 50 pupils as measured by athletic achievement. He also found that scholastic achievement as measured by grade-point averages was significantly higher in favor of athletically superior students even though no significant difference exists between IQ scores.

As was indicated earlier, development of strength is fundamental to proficiency in motor ability. Tests of complex motor skills, such as running, jumping, and throwing, show that as age increases, boys' ability to run, jump, and throw also increases. Studies reveal that girls are inferior to boys in all efforts at all ages; and girls' best performances in these activities are at 13 years of age. As the age increases, the difference in the scores on these efforts also increases. Even though the ability of the girls in the broad jump, for instance, tends to decrease with increasing age, we may wonder if the poor showing of the older girls is a result of lessened physical ability or lessened desire. In other words, are such activities as running, throwing, and jumping as important to girls at 14 years and above as it is with boys? Kuhlen used data from material gathered by Lund which show the percentage of boys and girls in grades 7 through 12 who asked to be excused from gym for medical reasons. The average number of absences for boys was 7, with a range of 6 to 8. This may be contrasted with the girls, whose absences increased from 7 at grade 7 to 24 at grade 12. The author points out that the marked increase for medical excuses occurs during adolescence, which is a time when girls show strong social interests and when interest in physical activities is on the decline. It is a far-different picture with boys; for with them, physical prowess lends prestige, hence bringing about an entirely different motivation picture. Perhaps the decline in interest on the part of the girls does not necessarily imply that physical educators should consider physical education a lost cause for them. However, the physical educator must be alert to recognize the program may be only as successful as the degree to which feminine interests are considered.

Very few studies have been conducted to evaluate the patterns of motor development of children from the time they start school until the time they leave. One of the most commonly employed tests used in measuring motor ability is the one devised by Brace. This test has since been revised by McCloy and appears in measurement texts. It was first designed as a test of motor educability; that is, the ability of a person to learn new motor skills. The test consists of stunts which are performed by the individual. The items range from extremely simple ones to difficult tests of coordination and balance. An example of one of the more difficult tests is one which requires the subject to jump into the air, clap the feet together twice, and land with the feet spread apart. Dimock has measured motor ability for boys 12 through 16 years of age, using the Brace test. He concluded that during adolescence motor ability, as measured by this test, does not increase with age. For example, he found that the average score for the 12-year-old boy was 45, whereas the average score for the 16-year-old was 55. The increase in motor ability during the four years is reported as 22 per cent. He also measured physical strength for the four years and found an increase in 86 per cent from 12 to 16 years of age. Dimock started out to determine whether or not physical growth outruns neuromuscular control resulting in awkwardness and clumsiness. He found that the pubescent and post pubescent boys have a lower motor ability score than the prepubescent boys at every age level, with the exception of one postpubescent in the 12-year-old category. The study indicates that even though the differences are not large (with the one exception noted above), there may be a general slowing up in the development of motor control with the arrival of puberty. Further analysis of these data shows the average increase in motor ability for boys who reach puberty but not postpubescence within a year, is only about one-third as much as that of the boy who remains prepubescent, or the one who remains pubescent, for the same period. It seems that boys who change from prepubescence to postpubescence within the year increase more rapidly in motor ability following pubescence. The rapid improvement in motor coordination is during the two-year period when the boy passes from prepubescence to puberty or postpuberty. During the months just before and immediately after the advent of puberty, there appears to be a reduction in the rate of motor ability increase. It is important to remember that increase in motor ability does persist, but it is less than before or after puberty. Furthermore, this period of reduced improvement in motor ability precedes the most rapid growth in height and weight. To try to determine what effect accelerated growth in weight and height had on motor coordination, a comparison was made between the change in the motor ability scores of the boys who had grown the most in height and weight and those who had grown the least. It was observed that, by and large, the average boy who grows most rapidly in height and weight increases as much in motor ability as those youngsters who exhibit the least amount of growth. These results, of course, are interpreted from the scores obtained on the Brace test.

To summarize the results of this comparison, there seem to be five pertinent points:

1. As measured by the Brace test, motor ability increases throughout the adolescent years. There is, however, a slowing down of this increase when pubescence is reached.
2. The period of most rapid increase in height and weight has no relationship whatsoever to motor ability.
3. Ten percent more boys register loss in motor ability during the year in which they reach puberty than boys either in the prepubescent or postpubescent state.
4. As concerns growth in height and weight, it was found to be most rapid from pubescence to postpubescence during a one-year period.
5. Strength increases throughout the age period from 12 to 16; the most rapid increase is the period immediately following postpubescence.

Espenschade (6) has done extensive research on motor performance tests as applied periodically to a number of adolescent children at the Institute of Child Welfare, University of California. Six tests of motor performance were used to reveal coordination, strength, speed, and accuracy. Essentially, it was found that the average performance of the boys increased steadily up to 17 years of age. As regards girls, there was improvement up to age 14; thereafter no improvement followed, and in some instances there was a decline. There were definitely marked individual differences for all tests in both sexes. Because of the wide variations in performance of boys and girls at any one time, Espenschade points out that in physical education an unselected group may participate without inequality only in activities that might be carried on independently, such as gymnastic stunts and tumbling, walking, social dancing, or games of low organization. On the other hand, for team sports or activities requiring special skill, the youngsters should be classified. Obviously, this would result in more homogeneous groups, and thus allow the players to get more satisfaction from the experience.

Espenschade also shows that as age increases, boys' ability also increases; girls are inferior to boys in all events at every age; and compared to boys, girls perform best at age 13. As age increases, the differences between the sexes also increase. When comparing the top and bottom groups for both boys and girls in terms of motor ability, the adolescent girls who score one or more standard deviations above the average in the gross motor tests are average in height,weight, fine motor performances, and strength. They are of average age, mature at a normal time in terms of skeletal and physiological development; they have a tendency toward relatively short legs and narrow hips and are slender in build; on the average, they exhibit a healthy appearance and good posture; they appear to enjoy physical activity and spend a little more time than the ordinary girl in activity. Girls who score more than one standard deviation below the average on these motor tests have the same age as their classmates, but mature somewhat earlier physically and skeletally; these girls are taller than average and have a tendency to be overweight and they possess less strength and are less skillful in fine motor performance. Their posture is less than average, although it does show improvement with age. These girls experience a number of health difficulties which include sprains and dislocations of knee and shoulder. They participate very little in physical activity in comparison with the average girl.

As for boys, the one who excels in group motor performance is chronologically a little older; however, he matures at about the average age. He is somewhat below par in skeletal development. In terms of body build he is slightly below average in height and weight and is of medium build, with relatively short legs and narrow hips. In strength, he is unquestionably superior; and he is slightly above average in fine motor performance. His posture and health are good. He does express some interest in physical activity, participating regularly, but does not spend more time than the average boy in sports. The boy who is poor in physical activities is a little younger than the average. He does mature normally in terms of physiology, but is delayed in skeletal development. Although he is average in height, he does tend to be overweight. He is of stocky build, with relatively long legs and wide hips. In terms of strength and fine motor coordination, he is below average. His health is average; and although his posture is poor, it improves steadily as he becomes older.

SUMMARY

A striking characteristic of children, which should be recognized by all teachers, is the irregularity in their growth patterns. The physical educator must pay special attention to this if he is to meet the child's best interests. He should also be aware that there is much less uniformity among growth and development in boys than in girls.

The most used, but least valid, indicator of growth is chronological age; the most valid measure is the development of the carpal bones, which can be evaluated through X rays. Crampton's pubic hair test is a practical means of evaluating sexual maturation; menarchey is the best single criterion of sexual maturity for girls and may be considered to be the mid-point of puberty.

A great deal of research has shown that an adolescent's motor ability plays a vital part in his adjustment. In addition to developing his social well being, proficiency in motor skills is an important source of personal satisfaction and relaxation for his leisure activities. Because of the prestige and social esteem attributed to success in athletic skills, motor handicaps may seriously damage the child's self-concept. It is primarily for these reasons that the physical educator should spend considerable time in developing a physical education program for the handicapped child.

Few studies have been conducted to evaluate a child's patterns of motor development during the time he is in school. It is probable that the most rapid improvement in motor coordination occurs when a boy passes from prepubescence to puberty or postpuberty; furthermore, contrary to what some people believe, motor ability increases during the adolescent period, although there is a slowing down of improvement.

A girls' motor ability improves until she is about 14. Lack of further progress may be due more to cultural reasons than to any real lack of physical ability.

REFERENCES

1. Ausubel, David P., *Theory and Problems of Adolescent Development,* Grune & Stratton, New York, 1954, p. 117.
2. *Ibid,* p. 128.
3. Biddulph, Lowell G., "Athletic Achievement and Social Adjustment for High School Boys," *Research Quarterly,* March, 1954, **25** (1), 1-7.
4. Dimock, Hedley S., *Rediscovering the Adolescent,* Association Press, New York, 1941.
5. Engle, E. T., and Shelesnyak, M. C., "First Menstruation and Subsequent Menstrual Cycles of Pubertal Girls," *Human Biology,* 1934, **6,** 431-453.
6. Espenschade, Anna, *Motor Performance in Adolescence Including the Study of Relationships with Measures of Physical Growth and Maturity,* monographs of the Society for Research in Child Development, 1940, **5** (1).
7. Greulich, W. W., "The Rationale of Assessing the Developmental Status of Children from Roentgenogram of the Hand and Wrist," *Child Development,* 1950, **21,** 33-44.
8. Hale, Creighton J., "Changing Growth Patterns of the American Child," *Education,* April, 1958, **78** (8), 1-4.
9. Harris, T. A., *et al., The Measurement of Man,* University of Minnesota Press, Minneapolis, 1930.
10. Krogman, Wilton, "Maturation Age of Fifty-Five Boys in the Little League World Series, 1957," *Research Quarterly,* March, 1959, 54.
11. Kuhlen, Raymond G., *The Psychology of Adolescent Development,* Harper, New York, 1952, p. 49.
12. Mills, C. A., "Temperature Influence over Human Growth and Development," *Human Biology,* 1950, **22,** 71-74.
13. Ramsey, G. V., "Sexual Growth of Negro and White Boys," *Human Biology,* 1950, **22,** 146-149.
14. Simmons, K., *The Brush Foundation Study of Child Growth and Development,* monograph, *Social Research Child Development,* 1944, **9** (1).
15. Stuart, H. C., "Normal Growth and Development during Adolescence," *New England Medical Journal,* 1946, 234, 666.

Chapter 3

ADJUSTMENT PROBLEMS OF THE HANDICAPPED PUPIL

THE disabled child comes to school wanting to take part in the majority of activities with his contemporaries. The handicapped youngster, like any other child, wants desperately to achieve and maintain a social status. But his disability interferes with achievement of this goal. Permitting him to take part in the physical education program, through adapting activities when necessary, will help his adjustment.

It is difficult for the average child to seek and arrive at a satisfactory adjustment through enough group interaction; how much more difficult it is for one with a physical handicap! Suppose you were to run a race with a group of contemporaries of comparable ability, but were required to compete with one leg immobilized. It would be difficult enough to finish the race, to say nothing of crossing the tape with a socially acceptable score. To better understand the child with whom we deal, we will consider a few important aspects of personality which we must take into consideration when we are working with handicapped youngsters.

THE HANDICAPPED'S SOCIAL STATUS

For the handicapped child, the social and psychological effects of his disability may result in far greater problems than the actual physical impairment itself. Force (3) conducted a very interesting study to compare physically handicapped with normal children, all of whom were attending the same classes. The purpose was to ascertain the effect of a specific disability on the social position of the disabled child. There were 361 normal youngsters and 63 handicapped.

A sociometric instrument was administered to reveal choice behavior on three criteria—friends, playmates, and workmates—with a total of 42 comparisons to be made. The average number of choices received by the physically handicapped children was significantly lower than the mean number of choices received by the normal children. These findings reveal rather objectively that the handicapped child in elementary school is not enjoying a social status comparable to that of his normal classmates. Orthopedically handicapped pupils, those suffering visual defects, and cerebral palsied children received significantly fewer number of choices on all criteria than the nondisabled children. Children with hearing defects were chosen less as playmates than all other children with the exception of the cerebral palsied child. By contrast, youngsters with heart conditions and those with congenital anomalies were apparently most accepted as friends.

One characteristic usually associated with classes in school is cohesiveness; for these groups usually generate a feeling of unification, an *esprit de corps*. Force concluded from this study that there is a rather strong tendency for classes to increase in cohesiveness as the number of handicapped children in the class is reduced. We must also conclude from this study that status and acceptance, which are recognized as of vital importance for the adjustment of the handicapped adult, are also of significant concern for children as young as 6 years old.

Let us not forget how our society actually devaluates the handicapped through the cultural values placed on the normal physique. Our concepts of rugged American boy and healthy American girl are widespread, and constantly being fostered through contests based primarily on appearance—and even more by advertisements and commercials. These only aggravate the situation for those who are trying to help the disabled to achieve respectable social status.

PERSONALITY CHARACTERISTICS OF THE HANDICAPPED

What personality characteristic is most frequently associated with the physically handicapped? Levi and Michelson (8) are among the researchers who have examined this problem. A battery of psychometric tests were administred to ten adolescent boys with varying handicaps. The results revealed no specific emotional or intellectual pattern peculiar to physically disabled adolescents. However, they did conclude from this study that *the child's personality structure and ability to relate to people are the greatest factors contributing to success in a rehabilitation program.* They also concluded that the youngsters assumed their particular personality structures as a result of their developmental histories prior to their disabilities.

BODY IMAGE

The body image, sometimes referred to as the self-concept, is a person's conception of his own body. According to psychologists and psychiatrists, it plays a vital role when dealing with the handicapped. Garrett (4) points out that the self-image is conditioned by one's occupation, culture, and experience. A person may be overly concerned about his nose, ears, feet, or heart; yet certain cultures in Africa value a scar on the face as a distinguishing mark. Garrett states that physique is one of the raw ingredients of personality. A person's own body image modifies his personality as well as his interrelationships with those around him.

During the growing years the body plays an increasingly important part in our adjustment to and acceptance in the group. Physical educators, and especially any person on the rehabilitation team, should know how success in skills—or the lack of it—contributes to the acceptance of the child by his contemporaries. Baker, Wright, Garick (1) and Garrett (4) stress the problem of body image as it pertains to the adjustment problems of the handicapped. As these authors point out, rehabilitation workers (who certainly include the teacher) must remember that they are not treating a disease or a disabled body part, but rather the patient's body image of the affected limb, atrophied muscles, sightless eyes, or paralyzed body.

They are dealing with "the youngster's personality so far as his sense of worth, ambitions, fears, guilt, shame or injured pride are involved in the disabled part." For desirable adjustment to take place, this self-concept must be changed. These changes will only occur gradually. One important change required is in the area of dependency; the more severe his handicap, the greater is the child's need for dependency.

Wenar (13) studied 12 nonhandicapped, 12 moderately handicapped, and 12 handicapped children between the ages of 8 and 10. He was interested in problems arising as a result of disability among the three groups. He particularly studied the effect of the disability on the child's body image, the special complications of dependency needs, and the expression of hostile impulses, parental reactions of guilt, rejection or overprotection, and the peculiar social attitudes of the nonhandicapped toward physical disability. He found no difference between the groups in terms of overall adjustment, variety of interests, and concern over interpersonal relations. Also, there was no difference in the number of destructive fantasies. However, the handicapped children were significantly weaker in their ability to establish self-protection defenses and were more quickly or more chronically concerned with their destructive fantasies.

Cruickshank (2) found children with orthopedic, cardiac, and neurological handicaps as seeing themselves with more fears and more feelings of guilt than children of normal physical characteristics. Wenar (13) found the integrative ability, or the resourcefulness of a child in dealing with problems of daily living, to be significantly decreased in children with motor handicaps; in fact, there was a tendency for increased severity of handicap to result in a corresponding decrease in integrative ability. Manson and Devins (9) claim that the differences which are noted in rehabilitation activities are undoubtedly the products of personality structure and dynamics.

Mussen and Newman (10), in a review of literature dealing with personality problems characteristic of handicapped children, seem to feel the adjustment of these youngsters tends to be less mature; and the interpersonal relationships constitute major conflict areas for them. Also, they appear more concerned with maintaining their existing ego structures than with adjusting to new social situations. Finally, parental understanding and acceptance are important considerations in the child's psychological well-being and adjustment.

These authors, in studying 14 well-adjusted and 13 poorly-adjusted disabled children, as determined by teachers' ratings, found: (1) Realistic attitudes toward disability should be fostered at home and at school; the handicapped should learn that it is permissible and desirable to ask for help at times. (2) The children should be encouraged to aspire to goals which are attainable. (3) They should be rewarded for showing independence in work and thought. And (4) they should be taught to derive social satisfaction from a relatively small number of close friendships, rather than from extensive social contacts.

Here are some conclusions to be drawn from various investigations:

1. Physically disabled persons, more frequently than physically normal persons, exhibit behavior which is commonly termed maladjusted.
2. About 35 to 45 percent of disabled individuals are reported to be as well adjusted as or even better adjusted than nondisabled persons.
3. The kinds of maladjusted behavior exhibited by physically disabled people are not peculiar to them; they are similar to those shown by nondisabled people.
4. There is some evidence that withdrawing, timid, and self-conscious behavior are more frequent.
5. There is no evidence of a relationship between kind of physical disability and type of adjustment behavior; within a wide range of physical disabilities, the behavior results do not differ.
6. Emotional attitudes toward their disabilities are dynamic and can be altered.
7. It is probably true that persons with a long history of physical disability are more likely to exhibit behavior maladjustment than those with a short history of disability.
8. The physical effect of disability has social significance, for physique is one of the bases on which class and caste distinctions are

made. Also, as was stated earlier, physique is a raw ingredient of personality.

9. The physically disabled has been likened to a minority group in terms of obtaining social status.

LIVING WITH THE DISABILITY

In addition to facing and coping with the numerous problems the so-called normal child must solve, the handicapped youngster's problems of adjustment are complicated by his disability. The most fundamental principle in aiding the handicapped is *to help him to accept the disability and do something about it.* We should be aware of the disabled child's need for dependence. He is quite apt to be insecure in his dealings with his physical environment, and we must help him to develop his resources to the fullest possible extent. Garrett (4) points out that we must beware of our own ego needs which we might possibly try to realize through a "superior status" feeling. The child's feelings and opinion must be considered by constructing an atmosphere of self-respect and acceptance, which are indeed positive factors in helping him adjust to his disability.

Gider (6) says that one of the most important goals of the rehabilitation team is to help the child to a constructive personal philosophy. This is greatly assisted by a faith in something superior to man. Thus, religion has been found to be one of the strongest allies of the disabled in assisting him to construct a satisfactory philosophy. It can help him to accept his disability and develop his remaining resources.

THE AMPUTEE CHILD

The concept of body image is of special importance for the amputee. Ventur (12), in a study dealing with 16 amputee children, found dependency relationships to be a frequently encountered emotional conflict.

Siller (11), studying 24 child amputees, found feelings of inferiority and shame to be important components in the psychological functioning of more than one-third of the children, and most particularly among amputees of traumatic origin.

THE PROSTHESIS

According to Siller, the prosthetic replacement of the lost member should take place as early as possible. In the event of a congenital amputee, it should be done before the child is ready to enter school; and for those children who suffer limb loss through accident or disease, it should be done as soon as possible. Siller points out that early fitting is important for two reasons: It enables the child to incorporate the prosthesis into his self- and body image; and it minimizes the potential psychological trauma arising from an unusual physical appearance. But it is also important to avoid great physical change during the school year; for if a child has been accepted by his classmates as an armless person, and he suddenly and without forwarning appears among them wearing a prosthetic device, a re-evaluation of his status may be precipitated. Thus the curiosity of his peers, coupled with the awkwardness of the new user, might produce additional problems of adjustment.

As an example, Siller tells about a 10-year-old boy who, despite a well-fitting prosthesis, would not wear it because he felt he already had achieved acceptance in his group and that the artificial limb would serve to change his social status. In another case, a youngster aged 12 was dubbed "Captain Hook" when he appeared in school with his new arm.

INTRODUCING THE PROSTHESIS

Siller has done a fine job in outlining a plan that is based on parental cooperation in preparing both the handicapped child and the class for their first meeting. Most satisfactory results are achieved when the child and class have been previously prepared in a frank manner. Obviously there are numerous ways in which the introduction can be handled. However, based on a number of past experiences, Siller presents the following outline of an acceptable *modus operandi*:

1. Meeting between parent and teacher.
    a. The teacher may gain insight into the personality of the child.
    b. Familiarity between the teacher and child is achieved before the disabled youngster contacts an entire class of strange faces.

    c. The teacher has an opportunity to dissipate any strange feelings or reservations she may have in regard to the child.
2. Preparing the class.
    a. Inform the class of the impending arrival of the new classmate.
    b. Discuss matter-of-factly the condition or disability the youngster has sustained.
    c. Effectiveness might be enhanced by stressing the extent of functional restoration as a result of the prosthesis rather than emphasizing the remaining disability.
3. Presentation to the class.
    a. A demonstration by the child of how the prosthesis enables him to accomplish certain tasks will aid the children in more fully accepting the youngster.
    b. The disabled child must be prepared for rebuffs by the class; he must recognize that he is disabled and as a result the class may make damaging remarks.

Certainly the entire program to introduce the disabled child to a group must be carefully planned; for the more care that is taken, the easier it will be for all concerned, particularly the handicapped child—and after all, he has enough problems achieving social status without his peers complicating them.

DEGREE OF DISABILITY

The child with an amputation of the leg or distal end of the arm is usually capable of most of the physical activity required during the academic day. Generally the lower-extremity amputee has the lesser of two handicaps, for the functional restoration afforded by artificial legs is superior to the prosthesis devised for the arm. Furthermore, the arm amputee is in most cases more conspicuous.

SUMMARY

There is no simple prescription for dealing with the emotional factors arising from a disability, because no one personality characteristic can be associated with particular disabilities. But being aware of certain general principles can help in understanding better the problems of the handicapped. For example, to understand the psychological deviation that may be attributed to the disability, we should consider the personality as it was prior to the traumatic experience. Many workers in the field of rehabilitation believe the prepersonality patterns are of such importance that the impairment has served mainly to intensify the undesireable characteristics.

The attitudes exhibited by children are frequently reflections of adult attitudes. Thus, we must make considerable effort to aid the parent to better understand his handicapped child, as well as to help the normal parent to better comprehend the problems of the disabled child. There is obvious need for a strong educational program for our nondisabled population so that we can better serve the handicapped in his fight for emotional and social adjustment.

Lerner and Martin (7) have demonstrated that providing proper attention in the form of guidance and counseling is made available the handicapped youngster can succeed. A total of 59 cases were studied over a 10-year period to ascertain their success from a professional and academic standpoint. Of this number, 48 were considered to have proved themselves as succeeding—indeed, the prospect for graduation for these students is considered better than that for the average freshman.

REFERENCES

1. Baker, R. G., Wright, B., and Garick, M., *Adjustment to Physical Handicap and Illness,* Social Science Research Council, New York, 1946.
2. Cruickshank, William M., "The Relation of Physical Disability to Fear and Guilt Feelings," *Child Development,* December, 1951, **22** (4), 291.
3. Force, Dewey G., Jr., "Social Status of Physically Handicapped Children," *Exceptional Children,* December, 1956, 104.
4. Garrett, James F. (Editor), "Psychological Aspects of Physical Disability," Office of Vocational Rehabilitation, Rehabilitation Service Series No. 210, Superintendent of Documents, U.S. Government Printing Office, Washington, D.C.
5. Garrett, James F., "Psychological Aspects of Physical Disability," *Education,* (October, 1955), **76** (2), 119.
6. Gider, F., "An Descant of Mine Own Deformities," *Nervous Child,* 1949, **8** (2), 234-243.
7. Lerner, Ruth, and Martin, Marion, "What Happens to the College

Student with a Physical Handicap?" *The Personnel and Guidance Journal,* October, 1955, **34** (2), 80.

8. Levi, Joseph, and Michelson, Barbara, "Emotional Problems of Physically Handicapped Adolescents—A Study of Ten Adolescent Boys," *Exceptional Children,* April, 1952, 200.

9. Manson, R. Morse, and Devins, George V., "Some Psychological Findings in the Rehabilitation of Amputees," *Journal of Clinical Psychology,* January, 1953, **9** (1), 65.

10. Mussen, Paul H., and Newman, David K., "Acceptance of Handicap, Motivation, and Adjustment in Physically Disabled Children," *Exceptional Children,* February, 1958, 255.

11. Siller, James, and Peizer, Ed, "Some Problems of the Amputee Child in School," *Education,* November, 1957, **78** (3), 141.

12. Ventur, P. A., "Survey of 23 Upper Extremity Child Amputees at the Mary Free Bed Hospital, Grand Rapids, Michigan," New York University College of Engineering, Research Division, Prosthetic Devices Study, Report No. 115, 1955, 117.

13. Wenar, Charles, "The Effects of a Motor Handicap on Personality: I. The Effects on Integrative Ability," *Child Development,* December, 1954, **25** (4).

14. Wenar, Charles, "The Effects of a Motor Handicap on Personality: III. The Effects of Certain Fantasies and Adjustive Techniques," *Child Development,* March, 1956, **27** (1), 9.

Chapter 4

PRINCIPLES OF SPORTS ADAPTATION FOR THE HANDICAPPED CHILD

THE "Child's Bill of Rights," as stipulated some thirty years ago at a White House Conference, proclaims the right of every child to develop in a world which does not set him apart—a world which welcomes him as it does every child, offering identical privileges and responsibilities. If we accept this treatise, as physical educators we have an obligation to see that *all* children in the program have an opportunity to develop to the full extent of their capabilities. This obviously applies to the handicapped child as well as to the normal individual. If we believe that physical education is important to any child, it can be immediately seen that it is of the greatest benefit to the handicapped child, who may have had limited opportunity for vigorous activity and for the social development which such activity affords.

VALUE OF THE PROGRAM FOR THE HANDICAPPED CHILD

FITNESS

The physical education program is of particular worth to the handicapped child in this respect, because it may afford the only opportunity for safe, vigorous activity in an otherwise quiet daily living pattern. We know from numerous researches that vigorous activity is essential to organic development. Considering this factor, it is apparent that the activity afforded by physical education is necessary to the development of all children. Is it not reasonable to assume that the handicapped child should be included?

This is not to say that we must attempt to make a superior athlete out of each and every atypical child. Fitness is a relative thing. We can attempt to develop fitness only within the limits of medical propriety, the handicapped youngster's abilities, and the needs of the child in terms of his daily living.

SOCIAL DEVELOPMENT

Educators have long believed that physical education activities afford great opportunities for social development. That this is true has been shown in the studies by Jones (2), Kuhlen and Lee (4), Skubic (5), and others. To again single out the handicapped child, he may have few opportunities to be with other children in activities which are mutually enjoyable. Many have never shared activities with children of their own age in which they can "let their hair down." They need these advantages.

All people have basic drives to be an accepted part of a group, to be wanted and loved, and to find success. The handicapped child is no exception. He is not an oddity to be shunted aside by the physical educator; he is a child with exactly the same desires as millions of other children his age. He needs physical activity for the same reasons as these other children, but his need may be greater because of limited opportunities to meet these basic drives. He may, in many cases, never have had an opportunity to be an accepted part of a group. The alert, interested physical educator can do much to help him satisfy this need.

BUILDING THE PROGRAM FOR THE HANDICAPPED CHILD

In building the program for the handicapped child, one must, as is true of any phase of the program, start by stating the goals of the physical educator for the child. Some writers have made this a cumbersome, complicated thing. It need not be so. Once we remember that the goals of the program for the handicapped person *must* be the same as those for any other child, the problem becomes much simpler and the planned course begins to take shape. The ultimate goals of any physical education program are the same as those of education in general, as stated by an N.E.A. Committee in the Seven Cardinal Principles of Education. These principles are:

1. Health
2. Attainment of the fundamental processes
3. Ethical character
4. Worthy home membership
5. Good citizenship
6. Worthy use of leisure time
7. Vocational preparation

There are some things which must be re-emphasized in planning the program for the handicapped child. As is the case for any pupil, the program must be planned within the confines of medical safety *for that particular child.* In the case of the handicapped youngster, this obviously may impose extra restrictions on the selection of activities which are to help him meet his goals. The medical safety of the child is always the foremost precaution to be exercised when fitting the child into the regular physical education program. We would scarcely expect to find a child with serious heart trouble in an activity such as basketball or a paraplegic in a group studying wrestling. However, there are other activities which would be safe for these people, and from which they may gain a great deal. The physical educator should obtain advice from the family physician and the child's parents in determining the extent to which the child might participate. Such advice from the physician is imperative. The physician, by training and experience, is qualified to make such decisions; and the physical educator, unless he is similarly experienced, is not. The physical educator should work hand-in-hand with his medical colleague toward the well-being of the child.

SELECTION OF THE ACTIVITY

Although the physician sets the limits within which the child may participate, the development of the program within these limits is largely up to the physical educator. Because of his wide knowledge of activities, he is usually better qualified than his medical co-worker in this respect. In designing the program, the physical educator must remember the following points, which should serve as guides:

1. *The activity should never aggravate an existing injury.* The medical advisor, again, is indispensible in aiding the physical educator in determining just which activities are safe for the particular student.

2. *Activities should be appropriate to the age level of the child.* It is extremely important to make sure that the chosen activities are geared to the age level of the pupil. Nothing could be more absurd than choosing an activity like "drop the handkerchief" for a teen-age class. Such a game would destroy the student's interest in physical education and would limit the usefulness of the program for some time to come. Activities should be inherently interesting to the child; only thus can the program be useful. The physical education instructor should rely on his knowledge of activities and on his knowledge of the growth, social, and mental development patterns of children to help him find these activities.

3. *The child should be able to find success in the activities in which he participates.* All of us have a definite need to succeed. Nothing is more frustrating than continual failure in any area of endeavor. The paraplegic could hardly enjoy participation in softball, because he would never find success and thus would not care for the game. His interest would be small, indeed, and physical education would be able to do little in helping him. On the other hand, the postpolio child who finds success in swimming, and who finds that he is able to compete on an equal basis with classmates, will develop great interest in learning. He will be interested and eager, and the teacher will be far more successful in helping the child to achieve his goals under these circumstances.

4. *It is wise to select activities which have lasting recreational value.* Particularly with the older child, it is not wise to "make up something to do." The child assigns his own values to such a program. If, on the other hand, he is learning activities such as golf, horseshoes, swimming, tennis, or bowling, which he knows he will be able to enjoy when he is away from the school, his endeavors take on added meaning and are of far more value.

When adapting the activity, for these reasons, the instructor should try to approximate the true game situation as much as possible. This, of course, aids in creating a positive attitude on the part of the handicapped child in emphasizing his abilities rather than disabilities. Furthermore, the less change made in the game, the more the handicapped child feels he is an important part of the group, contributing with his teammates toward a common goal. As a result, the much sought-after feeling of belongingness can be developed on the playing field.

Some writers, in considering the principles of the adaptation of activities, have been definite in stating that the program should lead to an improvement of the disabling condition. This at first glance would seem to be a worthwhile aim. However, it should be remembered that the goals of medicine and physical education are not necessarily identical. The responsibility of the doctor is to apply medical treatment; and the responsibility of the physical educator is to educate physically, to achieve the goals of education through the medium of physical activity.

CLASSIFICATION OF CHILDREN FOR PARTICIPATION IN THE PROGRAM

When one is confronted with grouping handicapped children for participation, it is usually desirable to classify on the basis of interest rather than degree of handicap. The childrens' level of mental and social skills is much more important in regard to their success in getting along with one another.

Then too, whenever it is possible to place handicapped youngsters with the nonhandicapped it is desirable to do so, when the nature of the activity is such that he will be able to compete on a nearly equal basis. This, again, puts accent on the positive side of the ledger, emphasizing what the child can do rather than what he cannot do, and thereby creating a more favorable teaching-learning situation.

If the child is put with children of his own age, whose desires, needs, and interests are similar to his, he will be far more likely to become a valued member of the group than if he is placed with children who are older or younger. He will be far more interested and thus will learn more. Instruction, too, will be greatly enhanced if the children in a particular group possess similar interests. Successful teachers do not teach all children in the same manner nor do they always use the same techniques. All teaching must be geared to the individual student's ability to comprehend. Teaching, then, can be of a higher caliber if all students in the class are similar in age and interests.

Constantly keeping in mind all of the above principles, the physical educator, employing his professional knowledge and skills, can establish and conduct programs for the handicapped child which should result in attainment of the recognized objectives.

VALUES OF SWIMMING

According to Covalt (1), "When a handicapped person has been taught to get in and out of a pool or lake without any physical assistance, and to actually swim about in freedom and security without the impediments of braces, crutches, or wheelchairs, and use extremities that move easily in the water which they do not do on land, then this independence is a goal, the attainment of which is obvious and most pleasurable." How better might we summarize the value of the swimming program for the handicapped child? No other single activity can contribute as much to the well-being of the child as can swimming. From the point of view of the physical educator as well, swimming is a marvelous activity. This is true for several reasons. First of all, aquatic activities are fun. When a child learns to swim, an entire new world of experiences unfolds before him, ever-challenging, ever-rewarding as he learns more, and always offering new areas to be conquered. Nearly everyone can find pleasure in some phase of aquatics, whether it be wading, feeling the coolness of the water on the feet, just swimming because it is fun and exciting to do, or even lifesaving, competition, or synchronized swimming. It is possible to limit exertion to almost any level by selecting stroke and speed and limiting time of participation. Arranged in order of *increasing* energy cost, the strokes are as follows: crawl, back, breast, and side. This order maintains regardless of speed. As concerns energy cost and speed for the crawl, Karpovich (3) reports that the amount of energy spent in a given time is roughly proportional to the square of the speed. The exponent is probably greater than 2 for the other strokes. One need not be speedy to enjoy the water. As one develops skill, it becomes more and more possible to adjust effort to fit individual needs. Many instructors like aquatics for the handicapped because many of these children can enjoy swimming on an equal basis with their more fortunate friends. Handicapped people have been successful in even such a difficult area of aquatics as competitive swimming. William "Bill" M. Smith, the great Hawaiian swimmer who competed for the Ohio State University and became the 1948 Olympic 400-meter champion, had polio as a child and originally took up swimming to strengthen his weakened legs. At one time, he held nearly all the free-style world records between 200 and 1000 meters, and was many times national champion. Forbes Norris, of Harvard, who had a badly atrophied leg as an aftereffect of polio, was also a member of the 1948 Olympic team. Miller A. Anderson, who also competed at the Ohio State University, was many times national champion on the springboard. He competed after World War II with a metal plate in his leg as a result of a wartime injury. He was a member of the 1948 and 1952 Olympic teams and is still considered by many as the greatest twist diver of all time.

In addition to the fact that the handicapped child can compete in swimming activity along with the normal child, Lowman pointed out as early as 1911 the therapeutic values of swimming. Even though we recognize that the primary purpose of the physical educator is to practice physical education with handicapped children, one must be aware of the concomitant therapeutic effects in order to do full justice to the child. Swimming requires complete use of the muscular system. Various strokes encourage attainment of full range of joint motion, and there are positive conditioning effects involving primarily the heart-lung system. As in most instances when dealing with individualized sports adaptation, much of the success of the program rests with the ingenuity of the instructor. Each person is unique unto himself, and that which works well for one may not be so effective with another. The physical educator must thus use his knowledge of physiology, kinesiology, and anatomy in determining the best course to be taken with each individual.

A further advantage of swimming, with some children, is the buoyant effect of water. Frequently a person discovers that he has the ability to move an affected part when it is immersed in the water, because the buoyancy removes the necessity for the muscles to work against even their own weight. Frequently it is found that handicapped children will have more use of the involved side in the water because of this buoyancy, and because the swimming instructor sets goals for him which are more desirable to attain than those set by his therapist. A unit plan for teaching beginning swimming to the blind is presented below.

A UNIT PLAN FOR THE BLIND IN SWIMMING

The unit plan for the blind in beginning swimming can be divided into four general areas of instruction. It should be noted that this plan is similar to usual plans for normal children, except that specific points of instruction must be utilized in teaching, due to the sightless child's inability to use visual cues in the learning process.

AREA 1: ORIENTATION

This phase is of the utmost importance to the ultimate accomplishments of the sightless individual. If he is to succeed in the water, he must understand his surroundings. He should first be taken around the pool area on an exploratory trip, with the instructor calling attention to the shallow and deep ends of the pool, doors, drinking fountains, and other important landmarks. Following a thorough, well-conducted tour of the pool area, the children may be introduced to the water. All instruction should take place at the shallow end until the pupil demonstrates sufficient ability to swim in deep water. He should be taken around the shallow end of the pool, and should be shown where ladders, scum gutters, and pool ends are located. He should be taught how to tell by the slope of the bottom whether he is headed toward shallow or deep water. When a blind child is familiar with his surroundings, and has landmarks firmly located in his mind so that he is confident in his new environment, actual instruction may begin.

AREA 2: ADJUSTMENT

The purpose of this area of instruction is the removal of fear of the water. This may be accomplished by the following progression of skills.

1. Take water in the hands, place it in the crooks of the elbows, tops of the shoulders, back of the neck, top of the head.
2. Take water in hands, wash the face.
3. Place hands in water, put face in hands.
4. Repeat #3, remove hands.
5. Place face in the water without hands. A good deal of time should be spent in going over and over the above skills until they can be done with little effort. Usually the sightless person will not like to put his head in the water because when his ears are immersed, his hearing is poor and therefore the most important means of orientation has been removed. This usually leaves him confused and afraid.
6. Repeat #5 and exhale through nose and mouth.
7. Repeat #6 four or five times, inhaling out of the water through the mouth and exhaling into the water through the nose and mouth.

AREA 3: FLOATING

By this time the pupil should have no fear of putting his face in the water. He is now ready to learn the floats, which are basic to all swimming skills. These floats are learned by means of the following steps:

1. Instructor demonstrates prone float. Pupil places hands on instructor's back and pushes instructor arm's length toward bottom of pool, feels instructor rise as the buoyant effect of air in his lungs forces him back to the surface.
2. Pupil places his hands (palms down) on instructor's hands (palms up) and then bends down until the water covers his shoulders; then he places his face in the water and straightens out to prone float position. Instructor releases him so that he may float free, then helps him stand.
3. Student repeats #2 without using instructor's hands. Instructor helps him stand.
4. Instructor demonstrates recovery from prone float by drawing knees to chest, lifting head, and pushing down with hands; he then stands as feet rotate under him. This is demonstrated to pupil by having him stand to side, with one hand at middle of back so he can feel the body rotation, and other hand on shoulder to palpate arm movements of the instructor.
5. Student has felt what instructor has demonstrated, goes into and recovers from float by himself.
6. Similar steps are employed for back and tuck floats.

AREA 4: MOVEMENT AND STROKING

When the student has learned to float successfully, he is ready to add propulsion to the float to make a swimming movement. With the human stroke as an example, the following steps may be used to build a swimming skill:

1. Pupil goes into prone float, pushes against bottom with toes, glides 2-3 feet to instructor who helps him stand.
2. Student does glide, recovers by himself as from prone float.
3. Instructor demonstrates thrash kick, which is explained as a walking movement with toes pointed. Pupil standing to side has one hand on instructor's hip and the other on his thigh, so that he can feel what the movement is like.
4. Pupil tries movement combined with previously learned prone glide. Movement propels him forward.
5. Instructor demonstrates human stroke armstroke with pupil's hands on his shoulder and elbow. Movement is described as being similar to climbing a ladder with the hands.
6. Pupil tries armstroke combined with prone float. Movement propels him forward.
7. Pupil combines armstroke and legkick by beginning with prone glide, starting kick, and then adding armstroke to the kick when rhythm pattern with the legs has been established.
8. Instructor demonstrates breathing by lifting head straight to the front, exhaling and inhaling through the mouth, placing face in water. Pupil's hands are between the shoulders and on back of head during the demonstration. He can hear exhalation and thus can tell how they are timed with head movement.
9. Student tries breathing with stroke.

SUGGESTIONS FOR TEACHING SWIMMING TO THE BLIND

In teaching the blind, it is of the utmost importance to remember that they must *feel* the demonstrations. They cannot rely on sight, and explanation alone is not enough.

Generally the sightless are slower in learning to swim than their seeing friends. They should be allowed to learn at their own rate. For rushing them will halt their learning, and the activity will cease to be enjoyable. In selecting the strokes for the blind, the physical educator will find that they will usually prefer those in which the hands can be held in front of the head, such as the human stroke, breast stroke, and side stroke.

LIMITATIONS OF SWIMMING AS AN ACTIVITY

Although swimming is a truly wonderful activity for the handicapped, it is well to remember some of its limitations. For example, if instruction lasts to the point of overexertion, the pupil might actually be harmed. This is particularly true for the cardiac. Care should be taken that no disabled child becomes excessively tired or chilled while in the water. To prevent chilling, pool temperatures should be kept around 84-85 degrees. If this is not possible, teaching sessions should be shortened, because chilling and excessive tiring go hand-in-hand. It should be noted, too, that for safety's sake, the class of handicapped youngsters must be small. The instructor will find it important to pay specific attention to each and every youngster, to watch for the signs of fatigue, and to make sure that no child inadvertently wanders into danger. The actual number in each class will depend on the extent of the disabilities, but it can be said that the smaller the class, the safer and more effective the teaching.

CAMPING

Camping, like swimming, is of extreme importance in developmental physical education. Camps devoted to handicapped are becoming more numerous because parents, educators, and medical people are beginning to recognize that it can provide safe, powerful teaching situations.

One of the chief reasons that camping can be so valuable is that, like swimming, it affords a wide range of activities from the quite sedate to the vigorous, all of which are intrinsically interesting to the youngster. Camping seems destined to be of even greater future importance in physical education for the handicapped.

SUMMARY

All children have equal rights to enjoy the benefits of the physical education program. This is true of the disabled child as well as the normal one. The values of the physical education program are, if anything, even greater for the handicapped student, because he may have an opportunity for social as well as physical development that is not available to him in the other facets of his life. Physical education also affords him the chance to satisfy some of his basic needs, such as success and acceptance by a peer group.

The goals of the developmental physical education program are the same as those of the general program. These are in turn identical to those of general education, differing only in that they are met through the medium of physical activity. The goals of the handicapped program are the same as those of the regular program because the children are essentially the same. The handicapped child has the same needs as any other child his age.

In order to meet the above-mentioned goals, the careful physical educator does not attempt a medical program. He stays within his own province, trying only to educate the child physically. He builds the program, allowing the family physician, the parents, and the child's medical records to set the limits within which the youngster may participate. He then draws upon his own wide knowledge of skills, physiology, kinesiology, and the physical and social growth patterns of children to select the activities which will be used to help the child meet his goals.

In the selection of the activities to be used, the physical educator keeps the following points in mind:

1. The activity should never aggravate an existing condition. The physician and medical records are of great help in this respect.
2. Activities should be appropriate to the age level of the child to insure his interest in them.
3. It is wise to select activities which have lasting recreational value when possible.

When classes are made up, it is better to classify the children by interests rather than by degree of handicap. This insures continued interest in the class and makes for a more effective teaching-learning situation.

Swimming and camping are excellent areas available for the handicapped. This is true because of the wide range of activities that are fun, exciting, and challenging in each, but which can still be geared to the physical and social needs of almost any child.

REFERENCES

1. Covalt, Nila Kirkpatrick, "Swimming by the Handicapped," *Archives of Physical Medicine,* June, 1958, 377.
2. Jones, Harold E., *Motor Performance and Growth,* University of California Press, Berkeley, 1949.
3. Karpovich, Peter V., *Physiology of Muscular Activity,* Saunders, Philadelphia, 1959, p. 105.
4. Kuhlen, Raymond G., and Lee, Beatrice J., "Personality Characteristics and Social Acceptability in Adolescence," *Journal of Educational Psychology,* September, 1943, 34 (6).
5. Skubic, Elvera, "Studies of Little League and Middle League Baseball," *Research Quarterly,* March, 1956, **27** (1).

Chapter 5

STRENGTH

THE 434 voluntary muscles in man constitute 40 to 60 percent of his total body weight. The muscles are useful because they are able to produce motion, which is the most fundamental function of the musculoskeletal system. The action of muscles on the bony levers permits man to stand erect, carry out activities of daily living, and impart movement to other objects. This motion in the musculo-skeletal system is governed by the strength of muscles.

Responsibility for the supervision of strength-building exercises, whether for the sick, physically handicapped, or normal individual, lies with the physician, the physical therapist, and the physical educator. Therefore, it is essential that we have some understanding of the physiological principles and mechanisms which underlie the administration of an activity program. For example, the refractive characteristics of a muscle (referred to as birefringence), or the path on which light rays travel through muscle, are used as a clinical aid in ascertaining muscle status. In order to understand the principle of kinesthesis we need some knowledge of the proprioceptors. These tiny organs, imbedded in muscle and tendon, keep the brain informed as to the status of the muscle in overcoming external resistance.

For the professional person to adequately plan and conduct programs designed to increase muscular strength, endurance, and flexibility requires a knowledge of the muscles. He should know structure in order to understand function; and even though it remains a problem for future researchers to answer conclusively, the person dealing with movement should know the most recent views on how a muscle contracts.

We shall therefore study the physical properties, strength of contraction, summation, tension-length relationship, and optimal load of muscles and, finally, the effects of exercise on strength. Such knowledge will help us to form a foundation of scientific knowledge on which we may draw as we work with the physical education program.

MUSCLES

The unit of muscle responsible for contraction is the muscle fiber. Each voluntary muscle is composed of many thousands of these individual muscle fibers, which are bound together by a thin connective tissue to form primary bundles. The primary bundles are similarly grouped together to shape secondary bundles, until the complete muscle is formed.

Muscle ordinarily contracts only in response to nerve impulses passing from the central nervous system over the motor nerve supplying the muscle. If we were to count the number of motor nerves entering a muscle and calculate the number of muscle fibers within the muscle, we would find that a great difference exists between the two. There are about a quarter of a billion separate muscle fibers which make up the skeletal musculature in man, but there are only about 420 thousand motor neurones. Inasmuch as the number of fibers in a muscle greatly exceeds the number of fibers in the nerves, the individual nerve fibers must necessarily branch repeatedly so that a single nerve fiber innervates anywhere from 5 to 150 or more muscle fibers. All the muscle fibers served by the identical nerve contract and relax at the same time, working as a unit. For this reasson, the single neurone and the muscle fibers which it supplies are called the *motor unit.*

The ratio of muscle fibers innervated by a single neurone is not determined by the size of the muscle, but rather by the precision, accuracy, and coordination of its movement. Muscles which are called on to perform fine and delicate work, such as the eye muscles, may have as few as 5 to 10 muscle fibers in a motor unit; muscles requiring rather heavy work, such as the quadriceps, may have as high as 150 or more muscle fibers per motor unit.

ELEMENTS OF CONTRACTION

As early as 1868, Kuhne extracted a protein substance from muscle which he named *myosin*, and regarded it as the fundamental structural unit causing contraction. More recently Szent-Gyorgyi's laboratory staff has shown that myosin in the skeletal muscle consists of at least two proteins, actin and myosin. Today it is recognized that *actomyosin* constitutes the complex unit responsible for muscle contraction.

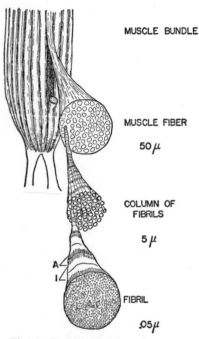

MUSCLE BUNDLE

MUSCLE FIBER

50 μ

COLUMN OF FIBRILS

5 μ

A
I

FIBRIL

.05μ

Adenosine triphosphate (ATP) is an energy-yielding substance found in the muscle; when added to the actomyosin-containing filament, it causes contraction. Szent-Gyorgyi has actually extracted actomyosin from the muscle, spun it into filaments, added ATP, and caused the filament to contract as it does in a living muscle. For a clearer understanding of the microscopic and submicroscopic structure of the skeletal muscle fiber, see Figure 1.

Fig. 1. Small section of muscle bundle illustrating approximate diameters of the fiber, column of fibrils, and the fibril. Note the anisotropic (*A*) bands and isotropic (*I*) bands along the fibril. This gives the cross striated appearance to skeletal muscle.

According to Szent-Gyorgyi, the myofilaments, first observed in the late 1800's, number some 10 million in the total fibrils of a single fiber. Containing predominantly actomyosin, these filaments are estimated to measure about 150 Å[1] in diameter; they are the smallest contractile units yet observed. Present research seems to indicate that during a contraction the myofilaments remain linear, and the shortening of the muscle comes about as a result of changes within these filaments.

To appreciate the mechanism of contraction more thoroughly we can tease out a fiber from the sartorius muscle of a frog. After placing this single fiber under a microscope we can observe the regularly alternating light and dark bands (Fig. 1). These disks are called *I* bands and *A* bands, respectively. The anisotropic *A* bands are so named because the velocity of a light wave as it passes through the fiber is not the same in all directions. Substances exhibiting this property are said to be *doubly refracting* or *birefringent*. The isotropic *I* bands are only slightly doubly refracting.

Using the fibers of a frog muscle it has been demonstrated that both *A* and *I* bands participate in the contraction process. In a static or isometric contraction, the sarcomere remains the same length, the *A* band shortens, and the *I* band lengthens. During a dynamic or isotonic contraction, the major portion of the shortening takes place in the *A* band. However, if we were to passively stretch the muscle, the *A* band would lengthen.

Explanation for the difference in birefringence between the *I* and *A* bands is yet to be made. However, it is observed that when a muscle is stretched, its total birefringence is increased. In the isotonic contraction, there is a decrease in the total birefringence. The initial length of the muscle is a key factor in determining the degree of double refraction. The birefringence decreases most at low initial lengths, and the change is hardly perceptible for the stretched muscle. The birefringent characteristic of muscle has been used in appraising the muscle's functional status.

MUSCLE, JOINT, AND TENDON PROPRIOCEPTORS

Sensory terminal devices consisting of several intrafusal muscle fibers contained in a fibrous capsule are scattered throughout the

[1] Å = Angström. 1 micron = 10,000 Å. A red blood cell is about 7 microns in diameter.

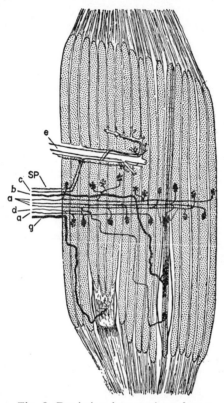

fleshy part of a muscle (Fig. 2). These are known as *muscle spindles.* Their purpose is to supply information to the central nervous system regarding the number of motor units which must come into play to overcome a given resistance during a muscular contraction. In addition, serving the same capacity are sensory nerve endings, or *tendon spindles,* located in tendons. These organs are particularly affected by the length and tension of the muscle in which they lie. Two-thirds of the motor fibers are connected to the muscle cell, and the remaining one-third supply the intrafusal cells of the muscle spindle.

Fig. 2. Depicting innervation of muscle fibers. Innervation comes over nerve fibers *a;* the muscle spindle has a large annulospiral ending *b,* with a flower spray ending connected to the nervous system by fiber *d.* Golgi tendon organ *g.* SP is sympathetic plexus with small myelinated pain fiber *c* from blood vessel *e.* (Adapted from Creed, Denny-Brown; Eccles, Liddell; and Sherington, *Reflex Activity of the Spinal Cord.* Clarendon Press, Oxford; 1932, p. 166)

Two additional types of endings are the Golgi tendon organ and the Pacinian corpuscles. The former are found among the tendon fibrils; the latter are located in the muscle fascia, particularly beneath the spot where the tendon inserts at the joint. The smooth coordinated motor movement is possible only through this regulated control from the periphery, for these muscle receptors continuously relay information to the central nervous system regarding the status of a muscle during active contraction, passive stretch, and tension. In physical education, this phenomenon is called *kinesthesis* or *kinesthetic sense*.

PHYSICAL PROPERTIES

1. Hooke's Law regarding elastic bodies states that the stress is directly proportional to the strain. For example, if a weight were hung on a spring it would cause the spring to change shape by stretching. This change is referred to as *strain*. The force causing the change is called *stress*. The individual muscle fibers are elastic bodies and therefore follow Hooke's Law; however, the entire muscle deviates from this law because of the presence of other types of tissue, i.e., fat.

2. A muscle increases in elasticity after a few preliminary stretchings. The elasticity of a contracted muscle is greater than that of a relaxed muscle.

3. The resistance of muscle tissue to tearing is from 2.6 to 12.5 kg/cm^2, depending on whether it is relaxed or contracted.

4. The power generated by muscle in contracting 1 sq. cm. of functional cross section represents a capacity to sustain a weight of 10 kg. for 1 minute. This is called a *myoton*. The functional cross section refers to a section at right angles to the fibers of the muscle.

5. As a muscle is cooled in vivo to 27 degrees centigrade by means of an ice pack, both strength and endurance are decreased. It has been reported that a cold muscle can exert a greater pulling force. This has been shown by studies dealing with fibers that have been removed from the muscle. The data in our research have shown just the reverse when using intact human muscles.

FACTORS DETERMINING STRENGTH OF CONTRACTION

Gradation in strength of voluntary contraction of a muscle is primarily dependent on two factors: (1) the number of motor units acting, and (2) the frequency of impulses to each muscle fiber.

ALL-OR-NONE LAW

A stimulated muscle fiber either contracts completely or it does not contract at all. In other words, a minimal stimulus causes the individual muscle fiber to contract to the same extent that a stronger stimulus does. The phenomenon is known as the *All-or-None Law*. Because a single neuron supplies many muscle fibers in the formation of the motor unit, it naturally follows that the motor unit will also function according to the All-or-None Law. While this so-called law of physiology holds true for the individual muscle fibers and motor units, it does not apply to the muscle as a whole. It is possible for the muscle to exert forces of graded strengths, ranging from a barely perceptible contraction to the most vigorous type of contraction, depending on the number of fibers stimulated.

The strength of a muscle contraction can also be graded by the rate of stimulation to it. For example, when two stimuli, each capable of causing a muscle to contract, follow each other in such rapid succession that the second stimulus fires during the contraction of the first, it will elicit a stronger contraction than the first. The greatest effect of the second impulse is observed when it is applied to the muscle near the height of the contraction caused by the first. In some way as yet not clearly understood, the second impulse adds to the first to produce a stronger response of the muscle. If a large number of stimuli are applied to a muscle in rapid succession, there is a fusion of the twitches resulting in a *tetanus*. The tension developed during tetanus may be four times as great as that during a single twitch.

To summarize; the strength of contraction in a muscle may be graded by two means: (1) by varying the number of motor units called into play, and (2) by varying the frequency of impulses (stimuli) to the muscle. Thus, less strength is required to lift a ping-pong ball than a 50-pound dumbbell. In each case the resistance being offered the muscle determines the frequency of stimulation which activates the number of motor units necessary to accomplish the task.

PHYSIOLOGIC FACTORS INFLUENCING MECHANICAL WORK

TENSION-LENGTH RELATIONSHIP

The actual amount of tension which a contracting muscle can develop, when all the fibers are effectively stimulated with optimal frequency, varies with the length of the fibers at the time of contraction. The contraction tension increases somewhat linearly with increasing length until a maximum is reached, after which it decreases with further elongation of the fibers. The peak or plateau where a stretched muscle develops maximum tension is called the *optimal resting length* or the *physiologic zero*. This length has been considered close to maximum extension, under normal conditions within the body. At lengths either greater or less than this, active tension of the muscle is decreased.

The tension-length relationship is of great importance in orthopedic surgery, where muscle tendon transplants are being made and immobilization procedures are required. If a muscle is immobilized in a shortened position it deteriorates, undergoes disuse atrophy, and loses strength per unit weight faster than if immobilized at the optimal resting length. This fact is also of particular importance to the physical therapist who must not only administer a therapeutic exercise program for these orthopedic patients, but also administer neuromuscular re-education techniques for paretic and paralyzed muscles. Positioning the extremity so that the involved muscle is on stretch in order to enhance maximal response is a cardinal principle in neuromuscular re-education.

SPEED AND LOAD

Rapid motion requires a great deal more energy to accomplish the same amount of mechanical work than a slow movement of identical intensity. The force developed by a contracting muscle has a decreasing linear relationship with speed. On the other hand, more energy is spent in maintaining this type of contraction and, as a result, most muscular action is done at an optimal *speed* so that the most can be accomplished without fatigue. It is also well established that, with the same strength of stimulus, a fairly well loaded muscle does more mechanical work than one which is overloaded or underloaded. The load at which maximum work is done per contraction is known as the *optimal load*. Therefore, maximum work is obtained from a muscle when: (1) the initial length is the optimal length for the development of strength, (2) the rate of contraction is at an optimal speed, and (3) the muscle contracts against an optimal weight-load.

EFFECTS OF EXERCISE ON STRENGTH

Muscular exercise is such a common experience that the more striking effects are evident to all. One need go no further than the school playground to hear the familiar challenge, "Show us your muscle," and witness the youngsters flexing their arms to compare biceps. Indeed, muscle enlargement with a corresponding increase in strength is a commonly observed phenomenon.

The enlargement of muscle, under proper conditions, is due to an increase in the cross sectional area of the individual muscle fibers (hypertrophy), not to an increase in the *number* of fibers (hyperplasia). This hypertrophy of individual muscle fibers is attributable to an increase of sacroplasm and a thickening of the connective tissue surrounding the fibers. In untrained muscle, the fibers vary considerably in their diameters. The objective of a strengthening exercise program is to bring the smaller muscle fibers up to the size of the larger ones. Rarely do the hypertrophied fibers exceed the cross sectional area of the already existing larger ones, but a great many more attain this size.

Why is there an associated increase in strength when a muscle hypertrophies as a consequence of a systematic training program? The answer appears to be in the findings of Haxton (8), who reports that muscle fibers can exert a maximum force of about 4 kg/cm^2 of cross sectional area. Under conditions of true muscle hypertrophy there is an actual increase in the cross sectional area of the fibers, hence there must be a corresponding increase in the amount of force the muscle is capable of exerting.

However, it must be kept in mind that the increase in muscle girth is also due, in part, to circulatory changes. Starkweather (18) concluded that the change in arm girth and volume resulting from doing dumbbell curls was attributable to changes in the rate of blood flow as a result of vasodilation. Petren and co-workers (16) reported changes in the number of capillaries, which in some instances was 40 to 45 percent more in the trained than in the untrained muscle. By measuring the circumference of the upper arm before and after strenuous exercises, such as arm curls with a 30-pound weight, it is easy to demonstrate the influence of circulatory changes in producing muscle girth enlargement. It is possible to obtain as much as ½ inch or more increase in size of muscle girth after doing such an exercise to fatigue.

To be sure, a muscle cannot continue to get larger and stronger indefinitely; there is a limit to its increase in size and strength. To a considerable extent, the proportion of increase will depend on the general condition of the muscle before training starts. One cannot expect as great an increase in girth and strength if the subject is in a high state of condition prior to the training program. On the other hand, if the subject is obese and in poor condition prior to the strengthening program, there may be an actual decrease in the measurement of girth while the muscle increases in strength. Extreme caution must be exercised in using size of muscle girth as an indication of muscle strength.

OVERLOAD PRINCIPLE

The physiologic principle on which strength development is dependent is known as the *overload principle*. Steinhaus (19) credits Lange with expressing in scientific literature the first views on the relationship between muscle hypertrophy and the overload phenomenon with the statement: "Only when a muscle performs with greatest power, i.e., through the overcoming of greater resistance in a unit of time than before would its functional cross section need to increase. . . . If, however, the muscle performance is increased merely by working against the same resistance as before for a longer time, no increase in the contractile substance is necessary."

Later experiments, utilizing a treadmill at controlled speeds, showed that there was a relationship between speed of work and increased hypertrophy of muscle. A classic example of this principle may be observed by comparing calf and thigh muscles of the track sprinter to those of a mile or two-mile runner. Invariably the sprinter will have tremendously hypertrophied leg muscles compared to those of the distance runner. While this relationship between speed of work done and muscle hypertrophy appears to hold true in the above-mentioned observation, it is doubtful that it holds for all types of strengthening exercises. When a muscle contracts isometrically (increases tension without shortening) there is, mechanically speaking, no work done at all; yet it is a fact that muscle strength and hypertrophy can be greatly increased by using an isometric type of contraction during exercise.

Whether a muscle is undergoing an isotonic or isometric type of contraction during an exercise program, it is fairly well agreed that only special types of exercise will develop muscular strength. These are exercises in which the muscle contracts against increased resistance. For this reason, the original version of the overload principle, as first stated by Lange, has recently been modified to what we now call the *principle of progressive resistance exercise.*

Since World War II, primarily owing to the work of DeLorme (4, 5, 6), the clinical application of the principle of progressive resistance has begun to take its rightful place in the various programs of physical medicine and rehabilitation and physical education. DeLorme maintained that activities can be classified as to purpose—whether they develop strength, endurance, speed, or coordination—and that a common error is to attempt to increase muscular strength by endurance-building exercises. He believed that strength could best be increased by progressive resistance, low repetition exercises; and that even extremely atrophied muscles would respond to such a program.

In setting forth his method of exercises for maximal development of strength, DeLorme established first a 10-repetition maximum (10 RM) which was the maximal load that the muscle could lift during 10 repetitions. The actual exercise program consisted of a total of 30 repetitions per exercise bout: 10 repetitions at one-half of the 10-repetition maximum, and a second set of 10 repetitions at three-fourths of the 10-repetition maximum, and a third set of 10 repetitions at the 10-repetition maximum. From day to day the subject tried to increase the number of repetitions while maintaining the same resistance load. The 10-repetitions maximum weight load was increased at weekly intervals. DeLorme also recommended one bout of exercise daily for only four days each week. He found by experience that five days per week was usually the heaviest schedule that could be employed without developing signs of delayed recovery from the exercise sessions.

This method of exercise has gained such popularity that even today many of those who are associated with exercise or training programs think of strength-building exercises (PRE) only as being the DeLorme method. Generally speaking, one may realize a strength increase by using the DeLorme method, for it does adhere to the principle of increasing resistance. On the other hand, it must be recognized that two-thirds of each exercise session is spent in having the muscle function against a submaximal resistance. Consequently, one cannot expect as rapid a rise in strength by using the DeLorme method as might be realized by using fewer repetitions at greater resistance. While there is no agreement regarding the details of a training program, there is one agreement in principle: if you want to develop strength, use progressive resistance exercise in the overload zone.

INDIVIDUAL DIFFERENCES

The amount and rate at which improvement in muscular strength progresses is limited by many factors. There are considerable variations from individual to individual, at differing ages, and between the sexes. Body types differ as do temperaments, and for this reason alone it would seem reasonable to expect an individual response to the standardized training program. In a recent series of investigations utilizing a common strength-building activity program. Mathews and Kruse (13) clearly demonstrated the fact that no two individuals react in the same manner to the same exercises. The success or failure of any strength-building activity depends on how well those who design and administer a training program are aware of these influences and incorporate this knowledge into their training programs.

Although the reasoning underlying individualistic responses to an activity program has never been satisfactorily explained, there is a growing belief that body type plays an important role. Anthropometric investigators have noted that growth in muscle girth is related to body type. Those with a high degree of ectomorphy appear to respond less to strenuous strengthening exercises; and the athletic type, or those with a high degree of mesomorphy, appear to respond the most. Cureton (2), while making extensive studies on body types of Olympic athletes, found that the dynamic-type athlete had an above-average component of mesomorphy combined with varying amounts of ectomorphy or endomorphy. Although most of the investigators in this area are not very definite or conclusive in their finding, they do indicate that one should be cognizant of body build when designing any activity program.

The relationship of strength to age has intrigued a number of investigators, and a considerable amount of information is now available from their work. Tests of muscular strength have been given to subjects of all ages and under a variety of conditions. In general, most of the investigations show that strength of muscle increases rapidly from 12 to 19 years, advances more slowly and regularly to about 30 years, after which it declines gradually throughout the rest of life. During periods of rapid growth in body length, exercises seem to have less of an effect on muscles than in periods when there is not this rapid acceleration in growth.

Although there are numerous studies of strength differences between the sexes, there has been very little research in the effectiveness of various exercise programs on male and female. Jones (11) reported that few girls improve in strength tests after the age of 13, whereas boys strength scores veered upward after the age of 13. Schochrin (17), in testing the strength of the extensor and flexor muscles of the lower leg, stated that women were 28 to 30 percent weaker than men; but at the age of 40 to 45 the decrease in strength was not so great with women as with men. Isikawa (10) found that females were about 70 percent as strong as males. In light of these results, and until more evidence is produced, it seems reasonable to assume that we cannot expect as great a response from a strenuous activity program for the female as we might expect for the male.

ISOTONIC VS. ISOMETRIC CONTRACTIONS

One of the primary problems confronting those interested in physical training and conditioning is whether a systematic isotonic (dynamic) and isometric (static) activity produce different effects on strength. There are conflicting reports regarding the benefits derived from these two types of muscle contraction. Darcus and Salter (3) reported that, in general, dynamic training causes a greater percentage of strength gains than static training, although the difference between the two is not statistically significant. On the other hand, Muller (14) and Hettinger (9) report that a static type of exercise produces greater strength gains. Mathews and Kruse (13) state that apparently the isometric type contraction results in greater gains than the isotonic type; and Asmussen observed that each type of activity produces approximately the same degree of improvement.

In establishing a strength-building program, it is important to be aware of these two forms of exercise. Apparently, little difference exists between the end results of the two, so that in some instances they may be used interchangeably. The time factor, a pathology, or the physical status of an individual may recommend the use of one form of activity over the other. If an increase in muscular strength is the only objective of the training program, one may take his choice between the two and realize approximately the same end results.

FREQUENCY OF EXERCISE

While the amount of strength gain appears to be independent of the type of muscle contraction utilized in a training program, the frequency of exercise periods is important. In a series of clinical investigations into the effect of varying the frequency of strength-building exercises, it was observed that groups exercising five days a week showed a greater percentage of strength increase than those who exercised two, three, or four days a week. Undoubtedly, for every individual there is an activity program that is best suited to his particular characteristics. This program will vary in intensity or amount of resistance and frequency of exercise, depending on the individual; and it is up to those who are responsible for the development of strength-building routines to decide which type of program is best suited to each person. In general, by exercising five times a week and employing the principle of progressive resistance in the overload zone, a maximal increase in muscular strength will result.

Obviously there is a limit to how far a man can develop muscular strength. Naturally, the proportion of increase will depend on the general state of the muscle before training starts. However, Karpovich (15) states that by exercising two or three times a week for two months, one may expect an increase in the girth of the biceps from $\frac{5}{8}$ to $1\frac{1}{2}$ inches; after four to six months, $1\frac{3}{4}$ to $2\frac{1}{2}$ inches. After this period, the increase is much slower. A rough estimate of the total possible increase in muscular strength would be approximately 50 percent; many factors tend to influence this potential gain in strength and may even alter the end result.

LEARNING FACTOR

Once a strength-building routine has been established for an individual, it is imperative that the supervisor of the program keep a close eye on the pattern of progress that is being made. Initially, a subject may experience a sudden rise in strength after only three or four exercise sessions. Some will interpret this phenomenon as an actual increase in muscular strength; but we should not be deceived. Even the simple task of flexion at the elbow joint against heavy resistance requires a certain amount of skill and coordination. Naturally, the more complex the movement, the greater the degree of skill and coordination needed to accomplish the task. This process of learning to do a particular motion is commonly referred to as the learning factor. Usually, after three or four practice sessions it is possible to increase one's strength scores anywhere from 3 to 15 pounds, depending on which muscle group is being tested. When establishing a maximal weight limit, such as the 10 RM in the DeLorme method of progressive resistance exercise, it is essential to be aware of this learning factor and take it into account. Everyone participating in an activity program should be allowed to practice the desired movements with resistance before determining a base line; otherwise, misinterpretation about progress of the exercise routine may ensue. Appendix A contains a well-balanced weight-lifting program for junior high school age through adulthood.

PLATEAUS IN STRENGTH GAINS

In plotting strength gains against the time factor, it may be observed that the pattern of progress is not linear in nature; it is irregular, similar to a flight of stairs with the height and depth of each step varying in dimension. Strength gains as a consequence of an activity program will vary in the same manner; there is a rise of strength, and then it will plateau for a while before going up again. The increase of strength may be steady and gradual for a period of weeks or months, or it may be rather sharp and sudden before reaching a plateau. This varies from individual to individual and, within each individual, from plateau to plateau. Actually, there is no way to predict the amount of strength gain that will take place before a plateau is reached or what kind of pattern the individual will follow. Usually, as physical conditioning progresses, the amount and rate of increase becomes slower and more gradual, along with greater frequencies of training plateau periods.

The plateau, quite frequently referred to as "the sticking point" or "going stale," occurs when one is unable to increase his physical performance, i.e., speed, strength, or endurance. It is probably the most discouraging phase of a training program, and one must always be on the lookout for it. There is no sure way of getting over one of these sticking periods; sometimes they last for days, weeks, or even months. The main thing to remember is that they *can* be overcome; but it requires patience, ingenuity, and a lot of hard work.

When a plateau has been reached, and it seems impossible to increase the physical performance, it is perhaps advisable to approach the exercise routine differently. Often varying the frequency or the amount of work will help the person to work past a plateau. Other means are (1) to increase the weight load to the point where only one or two repetitions are possible at each exercise session, (2) to reduce the resistance and increase repetitions for a week or two, and (3) to lay off training for a week or two. Needless to say, the number of ways to break through a plateau is unlimited and, as previously mentioned, it depends on the ingenuity, knowledge, and understanding of the supervisor. We can do no more than experiment to find whatever method is best suited for the individual.

As in the case of determining the amount and rate of strength gain, there is no one way to predict when an individual will start to plateau or how long he will remain at that plateau level. Usually the best policy is to forewarn the individual that these plateaus will occur sooner or later; otherwise the participant may not be inclined to believe your explanation and he may give up on the whole program. On the other hand, if he is told in advance what to expect, he may offer much greater cooperation and be more susceptible to any changes that may be necessary in the program.

MAINTENANCE OF STRENGTH

Once a desired strength level has been attained with an activity program, how do we retain this increase in strength? Do we have to continue with the same type of program for an indefinite time? Scientific study regarding the retention of strength is meager and more investigation is needed. Meanwhile, we must follow the advice of those who are more experienced in training and conditioning.

It is generally agreed that strength, once developed, subsides at a slower rate than it develops. Of course, the rate at which it declines is dependent on the customary living activities of the individual. If he lives a sedentary existence, he may expect a rapid and fairly complete loss of any strength gains he may have experienced, whereas an active individual will retain his gains for a longer time. Gallagher (7), while working with adolescent boys, who generally are quite active, observed that many of his subjects showed no loss of strength a year after exercises were stopped. Muller maintains that strength gained in youth by overnormal activity persists for life.

The difficult phase of the strength-building program is to accomplish the desired goal—the development of muscular strength! Once this has been accomplished, it is relatively easy to retain this gain. Exercise once every two weeks will probably maintain the increase in muscular strength. The importance of this is obvious, for the fact that maintaining muscular strength demands only a minimal amount of time allows the supervisor to emphasize other aspects of his program.

CROSS TRANSFER OF STRENGTH

The ramifications of a strength-building program cannot be dismissed without some mention of the cross transfer of strength theory. Many people believe that exercising one extremity results in an increase of strength in the opposite extremity. While much of the laboratory evidence appears to substantiate this cross transfer phenomenon, practical experience does not. For instance, why should an unused limb atrophy and lose strength when its counterpart has an above-normal amount of activity as is the case of patients with a fractured arm or leg? We know this happens no matter how heavy an exercise program is carried out by the active, uncasted limb. Such experiences have helped lead to a renewed interest in and increased investigations into the transfer effect of strength-building activities.

In 1955, Baer and associates (1) reported that the cross transfer of strength was of borderline significance in one experimental group and of no significance in two others; Muller reported, "We never observed such an effect in our experiments." Kruse and Mathews (12) observed a 1 to 4 percent transfer of strength from the exercised to the unexercised arm in their 120 subjects. However, when these gains were submitted to statistical testing, the results were not significant. Moreover, this 1 to 4 percent strength gain of the unexercised limb was found to be approximately the same as exhibited by their control groups. Therefore, it does not seem logical for those concerned with the therapeutic use of exercises to expect the cross transfer of strength to be effective in an activity program; there is no conclusive evidence to substantiate it.

SUMMARY

The unit of muscle responsible for contraction is the muscle fiber. These fibers are grouped into motor units and are stimulated from one motor neuron. From 5 to 150 single fibers may be grouped into such motor units. The motor units are grouped together to form a whole muscle. The strength of a muscle contraction may be graded by varying the number of motor units called into play, or by varying the frequency of nerve impulses to the muscle.

Maximum mechanical work is obtained from a muscle when (1) the initial length of the muscle is optimal for maximal development of tension, (2) the rate of contraction is at an optimal speed, and (3) the muscle contracts against an optimal weight load.

The enlargement of muscle girth as a consequence of a strength-building program is due, in part, to an increase in the cross sectional area of the fibers (hypertrophy) and circulatory changes, rather than an increase in the number of fibers (hyperplasia).

The only way to have a muscle grow stronger is to make it exercise against an ever-increasing resistance.

Many people are under the impression that PRE (progressive resistance exercise) refers to the DeLorme method of exercise. Progressive resistance exercise is not a method. It is the basic principle underlying all strength-building activities. The number of methods of doing progressive resistance exercise to increase muscular strength are limited only by the degree of imagination and ingenuity. There are scores of different methods in the literature, all of which may be justifiably referred to as PRE.

No two individuals will react to the same exercise program in the same manner. Individual differences are of paramount importance when designing strength-building programs, and standardized exercise routines should be avoided. In general, exercising 5 times a week will produce a maximal increase in muscular strength. One need only to exercise once every two weeks to maintain strength gains that were realized through an exercise program.

Where an increase in muscular strength is the only objective of a training program, one may choose between an isotonic or isometric type of contraction. Apparently there is little difference between the two in the amount of strength gains that may be realized.

While most of the early laboratory research seems to uphold the cross transfer of strength theory, practical experience and present-day research does not. There is no justification for administering a strength-building exercise program to one extremity with the intention of eliciting an increase of muscular strength in the opposite member.

REFERENCES

1. Baer, Adrian *et al,* "Effects of Various Exercise Programs on Isometric Tension, Endurance and Reaction Time in the Human," *Archives of Physical Medicine and Rehabilitation,* August, 1955, **36** (8), 496-502.
2. Cureton, Thomas K., *Physical Fitness of Champion Athletes,* University of Illinois Press, Urbana, 1951.
3. Darcus, H. D., and Salter, Nancy, "The Effect of Repeated Muscular Exertion on Muscle Strength," *The Journal of Physiology,* August 29, 1955, **129** (2), 325-326.
4. DeLorme, Thomas L., "Restoration of Muscle Power by Heavy Resistive Exercise," *Journal of Bone and Joint Surgery,* October, 1945, **27,** 645-667.
5. DeLorme, Thomas L., and Watkins, Arthur, "Techniques of Progressive Resistance Exercise," *Archives of Physical Medicine,* May, 1948, **29,** 263-273.
6. DeLorme, Thomas L., and West, Francis F., "Influence of Progressive Resistance Exercise on Knee Function Following Femoral Fractures," *Journal of Bone and Joint Surgery,* October, 1950, **32A,** 910-934.
7. Gallagher, J. R., and DeLorme, Thomas L., "The Use of the Technique of Progressive Resistance Exercise in Adolescence," *Journal of Bone and Joint Surgery,* October, 1949, **31A** (4), 847-858.
8. Haxton, H. A., "Absolute Muscle Force in Ankle Flexors of Man," *Journal of Physiology,* December 15, 1944, **103,** 267-273.
9. Hettinger, T. H., and Muller, E. A., "Muskelleistung und Muskeltraining," *Arbeitsphysiologie,* October, 1953, **15,** 11-126.
10. Isikawa, T., "Power of Grip Measured by Dynamometer," report of The Institute of Science and Labor, No. 12, Japan, 1932.
11. Jones, Harold E., *Motor Performance and Growth,* University of California Press, Berkeley, 1949, p. 181.
12. Kruse, Robert D., and Mathews, Donald K., "Bilateral Effects of Unilateral Exercise: Experimental Study Based on 120 Subjects," *Archives of Physical Medicine,* June, 1958, **39,** 371-376.
13. Mathews, Donald K., and Kruse Robert D., "Effects of Isometric and Isotonic Exercises on Elbow Flexor Muscle Group," *Research Quarterly,* March, 1957, **28** (1), 26-37.
14. Muller, Erich A., "The Regulation of Muscular Strength," *Journal of the Association for Physical and Mental Rehabilitation,* March-April, 1957, **11** (2), 41-47.

15. Murray, Jim, and Karpovich, Peter V., *Weight Training in Athletics,* Prentice-Hall, Englewood Cliffs, N. J., 1956, p. 38.

16. Petren, T., Sjostrand, T., and Sylven, B., "Der Einfluss des Trainings auf die Haufigkeit der Cappilaren in Herz and Skelemuskulatur," *Arbeitsphysiologie,* 1936, **9**, 376.

17. Schochrin, W. A., "Die Muskelkraft der Beuger and Strecker des Unterschenkels," *Arbeitsphysiologie,* 1935, **8**, 251-260.

18. Starkweather, Esther V., "On the Volume Changes of the Arm During Muscular Exercise," University of California Publications in Physiology, October 23, 1913, 4, 200.

19. Steinhaus, Arthur H., "Strength from Morpurgo to Muller; A Half Century of Research," unpublished paper presented to the Connecticut Valley International Congress of Essentials in Physical Education for Youth Research Section, Springfield College, Springfield, Mass., April 13, 1954.

Chapter 6

FUNDAMENTAL MECHANICAL
PRINCIPLES OF MOVEMENT

The mechanics of body movement is a complex but fascinating field of study. Physical educators, physical therapists, orthopedic surgeons, and doctors of physical medicine (physiatrists) are among the specialists whose responsibilities require varying degrees of knowledge in this field. An understanding of the physical laws governing body movement helps these specialists to function at near maximum efficiency. For the physical educator, such information can increase his ability to: (1) analyze game, sport, and dance skills; (2) recognize faulty mechanical development of children; and (3) plan special exercise programs.

Our first responsibility to children is based on the concept that increased variety of sports participation leads to a fuller and more enjoyable life. If a child becomes sufficiently experienced in a variety of skills, he will be more eager to participate and sports activity may become more a natural part of his daily life. Once this idea is firmly implanted, the physical education program is on the road to success. Effective classroom teaching helps to insure attainment of classroom objectives for the majority of the pupils. To be truly effective in the teaching of physical skills, we need a good comprehension of kinesiology as well as an understanding of certain laws and principles of physics which pertain to the human body. Of particular importance are those laws dealing with equilibrium and force.

EQUILIBRIUM

In the coaching of sports, it is important for us to know the mechanical principles of stability. In fact, Bunn (1) says they are probably the most significant of all physical principles involved in sports techniques. In a moment we will see how this can be true. The location of the center of gravity of a body is the key to the degree of stability it has. The center of gravity is the point at which

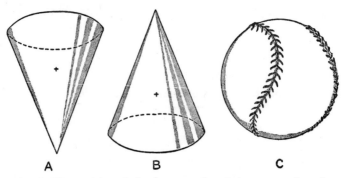

Fig. 3. Three objects being supported at their centers of gravity: *A*, unstable; *B*, stable; and *C*, neutral. (The center of gravity never falls outside of the ball.)

the mass of a body is concentrated—or the point at which a single upward force will balance the object. Figure 3 shows three objects being supported at their centers of gravity. Notice that there is no tendency for the objects to rotate about the point where the supporting forces are applied (center of gravity). It is also possible for the center of gravity to be outside the body, as in the case of a horseshoe, a tea cup, or an automobile tire, and in some cases the high jump (western roll).

Equilibrium may be described as stable, unstable, or neutral, each condition dependent on the location of the center of gravity. We think of an object being in stable equilibrium when it will return to its original position after being displaced. For example, a blocking dummy which is heavily weighted at its base (and thus has a low center of gravity) will immediately return to its upright position after being hit by a charging player; a bench, if raised and released, will at once fall back to the floor because of a low center of gravity. An example of unstable equilibrium would be a person on skates or a person on stilts; either is quite easily spilled because of his high center of gravity.

Neutral equilibrium may best be illustrated by the ball; for it has no tendency of its own to roll in any particular direction, and it does not try to return to its former position. When a ball rolls, its center of gravity is neither raised nor lowered, and the point of support on the ground or floor is always directly under the center of gravity.

Stability is related not only to the position of the center of gravity, whether it be high or low, but also to the area of its base. We have experienced this principle even though we may not have recognized it as such. For example, if someone is about ready to push you, the natural reaction is to widen your base immediately by spreading your feet. Additional stability is obtained if you flex the ankles, knees, and hips, which, of course, results in lowering the center of gravity.

There are occasions in athletics when a stable equilibrium is desired. The wrestler constantly works for a stable position by broadening his base and maintaining as low a center of gravity as possible. The football lineman is another good example, for he so positions himself to prevent the opposition from moving or upsetting him. There are also situations in athletics when the participant will want to be in an unstable equilibrium. This position would be conducive to quick starts and rapid changes in direction, as exemplified by the track start and running.

A comparison between a low center of gravity and accompanying broad base and a high center of gravity and correspondingly small base is illustrated in Figure 4. The book illustrated in *A* is in the most stable position possible; the center of gravity is low while the base is broad. In *B,* the book is standing upright, resulting in a high center of gravity and a narrow base. It would take about ten times as much effort to tip over book *A* as it would book *B.* The application of this principle is extremely important in body movement, whether it be in sports participation or in therapeutic exercise.

In terms of equilibrium, man comes in second when compared

to a bird. The bird has fused nearly all his spine and, most important of all, in the weight-bearing area its spine is one solid piece. Not so with man, for his spine is made up of 33 separate (though connected) vertebrae, in a long column with three curves in it—lots of places to hurt. Furthermore, man's spine is not a sound mechanical structure compared to that of the bird. In humans the center of gravity of the upper torso is in the region of the thoracic spine; and the cen-

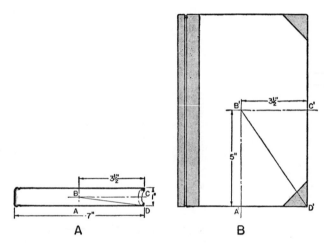

Fig. 4. A book in stable (*A*) and unstable (*B*) equilibrium.

ter of gravity is far above the hip joint, which of course is the means of support. (See Fig. 5.) In the bird, the contrary is true; the hip joint is elevated, which places the center of gravity *below* the hip joint. One of the many reasons for discussing the elementary physical principles of body mechanics is to better understand movement. In a later chapter pertaining to problems of the spinal column, particularly such symptoms as low back pain, we will take up again the principles of equilibrium.

FORCE

Forces either produce or prevent motion. In everyday parlance, a force may be either a push or pull. The locomotive exerts a force on the train by pulling; the shot-putter exerts a force on the shot as he pushes it. This is the single most important point in the physics of human motion, because our bones act as levers with the muscles to provide the force for movement. We shall therefore devote our study to levers and moments of force.

Everyone is familiar with the use of levers as aids in performing work, such as raising rocks, prying open jelly lids, and opening

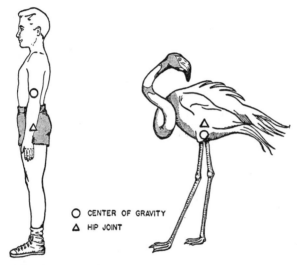

O CENTER OF GRAVITY
△ HIP JOINT

Fig. 5. Contrasting centers of gravity for man and bird. Mechanically man rates a poor second, for the slightest deviation of this point over its base of support (pelvic girdle) will cause exaggerated stress at the lumbosacral joint.

soft drink bottles. A lever is usually a rigid bar, free to rotate about a fixed point or axis called a *fulcrum*. The seesaw (Fig. 6) is a good example of a lever system, with which a small boy on the long end can balance a heavier boy on the short end. In certain physiology and kinesiology books, the approach to the study of levers is by classifying them into first-, second-, and third-class systems. However, it probably will do us more good to think of them in terms of how they are used.

In Figure 6, if we removed subject *A*, subject *B* would cause the teeterboard to rotate in a clockwise direction. To balance this rotary effect we again replace subject *A* in his original position. The system is once again perfectly balanced, or in equilibrium. The rotary effect just demonstrated is the result of something more than the size of the force or, in this case, the weight of the subject. For if we were to place subject *A*, who weighs 150 pounds, the same distance from the fulcrum or axis of rotation as subject *B*, who weighs 100 pounds, we would observe that the system of levers (teeterboard) is

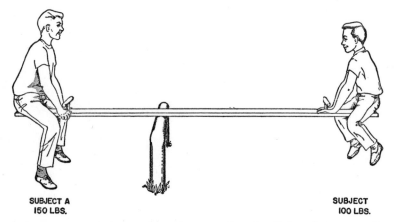

SUBJECT A
150 LBS.

SUBJECT
100 LBS.

Fig. 6. A practical use of moments so that the lighter boy can enjoy the teeter board with his heavier playmate.

once again out of equilibrium. We may conclude from this simple demonstration that the effectiveness of a given force in producing movement about a point of rotation is determined, not by the size of the forces alone or by just the distance forces are from the center of rotation, but by *the product of the force and its perpendicular distance to the line of action of the force.*

In Figure 7, the perpendicular distance from the point of rotation or axis to the force line of action is *CB,* not *CA.* We can observe that *AB* is the direction of action of the force needed to raise the weight, and *BC* is the perpendicular distance to this line. The lever arm or, preferably, the moment arm of the force is defined as *the perpendicular distance from the axis to the line of action of the force;* in this case, *BC* is the moment arm. The product of the force and its moment arm equals the moment of force, or the torque. When the length of the moment arm is expressed in feet and the force in pounds, the moment of force is reported in foot-pounds.

PRINCIPLE OF MOMENTS

We are now ready to consider an important concept known as the *Principle of Moments*. When a body is in equilibrium, the sum of the moments which tend to rotate the system in a clockwise direction

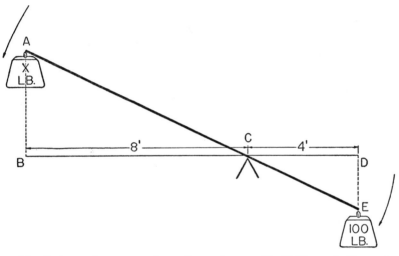

Fig. 7. Sum of moments about *C* equals zero. Or $\Sigma\ M_c = 0$. Can you compute *x*? The answer is 50 foot-pounds.

equal the sum of the moments which tend to rotate the system in a counter clockwise direction. This may be stated in the following equation:

$$\Sigma\ M_a = 0$$

(The sum of the moments about an axis is equal to zero.)

Figure 8 illustrates this principle very nicely. There are two forces in this particular example, one which tends to rotate the system in a clockwise direction and the other which tends to rotate the system in a counterclockwise direction. To meet the condition stipulated by the principle of moments, the sum of the counter-clockwise moments must equal the sum of the clockwise moments. The moment tending to rotate the system in a clockwise direction is equal to 8 × 50, or 400 foot-pounds. The product of 4 × 100 also equals 400 foot-pounds, the moment tending to rotate the system in a counterclockwise direction.

Figure 7 illustrates a problem which requires you to realize that a moment is defined as the perpendicular distance from the line of action of the force to the point of rotation. Let us compute the force

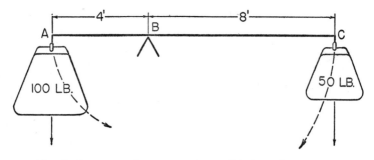

Fig. 8. A system of moments in equilibrium. $\Sigma \, M_b = 0$.

which would be necessary to balance the 100-pound weight. The moment tending to rotate the system clockwise is equal to 100 × 4 feet, or 400 foot-pounds. The moment tending to move the system in a counterclockwise direction about the fulcrum is equal to 8 × x, the unknown force. We use 8 as the length of one moment arm because, you will recall, this measure is defined as the perpendicular distance from point of rotation to *line of action of the force.* Thus:

$$(4) \ (100) \ = \ (8) \ (x)$$
$$8x \ = \ 400$$
$$x \ = \ 50 \ foot\text{-}pounds$$

The value of the lever is clear, for with a force exerted of 50 pounds, one is able to balance a rock twice as heavy. Archimedes, once said that he would be able to move the world if he had a place to stand.

Thus far we have dealt only with one force tending to rotate our system clockwise and one force acting in a counterclockwise direction. Figure 9 represents several forces acting on a bar, with the distance of the line of action of these forces to the point of rotation indicated. One force is unknown; the problem is to find force x, which will maintain the system in equilibrium. To solve this problem we must find all the forces tending to rotate the system clockwise and total them, and do likewise for the forces tending to move the system counterclockwise.

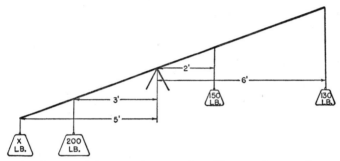

Fig. 9. Several forces acting on a bar. How much must force x be in order to maintain the system in equilibrium?

On the left of the equation, we have (x) (5) plus (3) (200); on the right we have (2) (150) plus (6) (130) or:

$$\begin{array}{cc} Counterclockwise & Clockwise \\ moments & moments \end{array}$$
$$(x)\ (5) + (3)\ (200) = (2)\ (150 + (6)\ (130)$$
$$5x + 600 = 300 + 780$$
$$5x = 480$$
$$x = 96 \text{ pounds}$$

Trigonometry and Forces

In some cases it may be necessary to compute the length of the moment arm in order to solve the problem. This necessitates the use of elementary trigonometric functions.

$$\text{sine } \theta = \frac{a}{c} \text{ or sine } \theta = \frac{\text{side opposite}}{\text{hypotenuse}}$$

TABLE 1. Trigonometric Functions

Deg.	Rad.	Sin	Cos	Tan	Cot		
0	0.0000	0.0000	1.0000	0.0000		1.5708	90
1	0.0175	0.0175	0.9998	0.0175	57.290	1.5533	89
2	0.0349	0.0349	0.9994	0.0349	28.636	1.5359	88
3	0.0524	0.0523	0.9986	0.0524	19.081	1.5184	87
4	0.0698	0.0698	0.9976	0.0699	14.301	1.5010	86
5	0.0873	0.0872	0.9962	0.0875	11.430	1.4835	85
6	0.1047	0.1045	0.9945	0.1051	9.5144	1.4661	84
7	0.1222	0.1219	0.9925	0.1228	8.1443	1.4486	83
8	0.1396	0.1392	0.9903	0.1405	7.1154	1.4312	82
9	0.1571	0.1564	0.9877	0.1584	6.3138	1.4137	81
10	0.1745	0.1736	0.9848	0.1763	5.6713	1.3963	80
11	0.1920	0.1908	0.9816	0.1944	5.1446	1.3788	79
12	0.2094	0.2079	0.9781	0.2126	4.7046	1.3614	78
13	0.2269	0.2250	0.9744	0.2309	4.3315	1.3439	77
14	0.2443	0.2419	0.9703	0.2493	4.0108	1.3265	76
15	0.2618	0.2588	0.9659	0.2679	3.7321	1.3090	75
16	0.2793	0.2756	0.9613	0.2867	3.4874	1.2915	74
17	0.2967	0.2924	0.9563	0.3057	3.2709	1.2741	73
18	0.3142	0.3090	0.9511	0.3249	3.0777	1.2566	72
19	0.3316	0.3256	0.9455	0.3443	2.9042	1.2392	71
20	0.3491	0.3420	0.9397	0.3640	2.7475	1.2217	70
21	0.3665	0.3584	0.9336	0.3839	2.6051	1.2043	69
22	0.3840	0.3746	0.9272	0.4040	2.4751	1.1868	68
23	0.4014	0.3907	0.9205	0.4245	2.3559	1.1694	67
24	0.4189	0.4067	0.9135	0.4452	2.2460	1.1519	66
25	0.4363	0.4226	0.9063	0.4663	2.1445	1.1345	65
26	0.4538	0.4384	0.8988	0.4877	2.0503	1.1170	64
27	0.4712	0.4540	0.8910	0.5095	1.9626	1.0996	63
28	0.4887	0.4695	0.8829	0.5317	1.8807	1.0821	62
29	0.5061	0.4848	0.8746	0.5543	1.1434	1.0647	61
30	0.5236	0.5000	0.8660	0.5774	1.7321	1.0472	60
31	0.5411	0.5150	0.8572	0.6009	1.6643	1.0297	59
32	0.5585	0.5299	0.8480	0.6249	1.6003	1.0123	58
33	0.5760	0.5446	0.8387	0.6494	1.5399	0.9948	57
34	0.5934	0.5592	0.8290	0.6745	1.4826	0.9774	56
35	0.6109	0.5736	0.8192	0.7002	1.4281	0.9599	55
36	0.6283	0.5878	0.8090	0.7265	1.3764	0.9425	54
37	0.6458	0.6018	0.7986	0.7536	1.3270	0.9250	53
38	0.6632	0.6157	0.7880	0.7813	1.2799	0.9076	52
39	0.6807	0.6293	0.7771	0.8098	1.2349	0.8901	51
40	0.6981	0.6428	0.7660	0.8391	1.1918	0.8727	50
41	0.7156	0.6561	0.7547	0.8693	1.1504	0.8552	49
42	0.7330	0.6691	0.7431	0.9004	1.1106	0.8378	48
43	0.7505	0.6820	0.7314	0.9325	1.0724	0.8203	47
44	0.7679	0.6947	0.7193	0.9657	1.0355	0.8029	46
45	0.7854	0.7071	0.7071	1.0000	1.0000	0.7854	45
		Cos	Sin	Cot	Tan	Rad.	Deg.

$$\text{cosine } \theta = \frac{b}{c} \text{ or cosine } \theta = \frac{\text{side adjacent}}{\text{hypotenuse}}$$

$$\text{tangent } \theta = \frac{a}{b} \text{ or tangent } \theta = \frac{\text{side opposite}}{\text{side adjacent}}$$

In each of the three equations, a knowledge of any two values will enable us to compute the third. For example, let us say angle

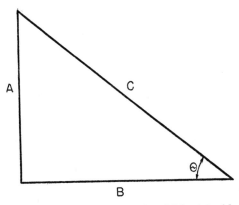

Fig. 10. Right triangle, in which A is side opposite angle θ; B is side adjacent; and C is the hypotenuse.

(θ) equals 52 degrees and side B equals 5 inches; what does side C equal? We should select the equation for the cosine in which:

$$\text{Cosine } \theta = \frac{b}{c}$$

$$52° = \frac{5}{c}$$

Referring to Table 1 of trigonometric functions (p. 88), we find the cosine of angle 52° is equal to .6157. Therefore:

$$.6157 = \frac{5}{c}$$

$$.6157c = 5$$
$$c = 8.1 \text{ inches}$$

Here is an example of how to make use of the trigonometric functions in the solution of force problems. Figure 11 depicts the elbow flexed at a right angle. The biceps is inserted at an angle of 70 degrees and 3 inches below the joint, or point of rotation. The center of gravity of the forearm is 7 inches from the point of rotation. The problem is to determine how much force will be necessary for the biceps to exert in order to just hold the forearm against

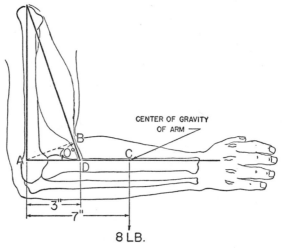

Fig. 11. Biceps flexed at angle of 90 degreees.

gravity; the forearm weighs 8 pounds. *AB* is the moment arm tending to rotate the system counterclockwise; *AC* is the moment arm tending to effect movement in a clockwise direction. *AC* is known; *AB* must be computed. Knowing the angle *BDA,* the equation for the sine of theta may be used.

$$\text{Sine } \theta = \frac{AB}{3}$$

$$70° = \frac{AB}{3}$$

$$.9397 = \frac{AB}{3}$$

$$AB = 2.82$$

Now solving $\Sigma M_a = 0$

$$(2.82) \quad (x) = (7) \qquad (8)$$

$$x = 19.8 \text{ pounds}$$

The biceps must exert a little over two times the effort in order to hold a mass of 8 pounds. The smaller the angle at which the biceps is attached, the greater will be the sustaining force required at the origin of the biceps. This should be impressive to the physical educator—think how much force is being maintained at the lumbosacral joint in supine position with legs held about 10 inches off the floor. Calculations reveal this figure to approximate 800 pounds, a conservative estimate for an adult. Furthermore, imagine the force being sustained by the biceps when exerting a force of 60 or 70 pounds as measured at the wrist joint: forces approximating half a ton. Thus we can see how a pitcher, under certain circumstances, can break his arm while throwing a ball. A thorough understanding of how to compute moments helps us to understand the forces being brought to bear at the various joints and muscle insertions during a particular exercise. As a result, we should be more alert to the manifestations of good and bad form in executing movements. For example, consider the child who exhibits an extreme lordotic curve while performing leg raises in the supine position. Certainly if this severe curve appears, the muscles which stabilize the pelvis must not be strong enough to maintain integrity at the lumbosacral joint; and a severe strain may result.

CONSERVATION OF ENERGY

Now that we are somewhat conversant with the more important principles of moments, it might be well to examine the characteristics of the levers of the body. When a muscle contracts, it moves the bone in an arc about the joint or center of rotation. All the points on the lever will move a distance exactly proportional to the distance of the selected point from the axis of rotation. Figure 12 illustrates this factor. For example, the palm holds a glass 14 inches from the center of rotation and the biceps muscle contracts 1 inch; the glass will move through a distance of 14 inches. This is true because all points along the lever move in an arc, and the distance the points move are proportional to their distances from the center of rotation. This is the law of the conservation of energy, and it may be stated

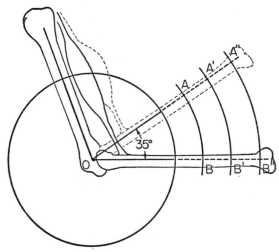

Fig. 12. Demonstrating conservation of energy. All points along the lever move in an arc. The distances the points move are proportional to the distances from the center of rotation.

as follows: Distance may be traded for force and force may be exchanged for distance; or, the longer the moment arm, the easier will it be to move the resistance, *but* the greater will be the distance through which the moment must travel.

SOME MECHANICAL APPLICATIONS

As you proceed further into the study of the physically handicapped, it will be necessary to remember your mechanical principles and to apply them constantly. To illustrate the importance of these principles we will consider several practical applications.

The glider cane, which has a four-pronged base, is now replacing the standard cane in certain situations. This is a good example of employing a broader base to gain stability. When teaching the patient to use such assistive devices in walking, instruction should include the principle of exerting the force as nearly perpendicular to the ground as possible; otherwise the cane will slip easily. Which of Newton's laws is applicable here?

When teaching crutch walking, again the instructor must employ the principles of equilibrium to insure that the individual knows not only how he is to use the crutches but also the reasoning underlying the method. In certain cases, such as paraplegia, the patient has a great feeling of insecurity when he is first placed in an upright position. Atrophy of the lower extremity, with accompanying hypertrophy of the upper regions as a result of exercise, will cause the center of gravity within the body to rise. Hence, there is an increase of instability and an accompanying feeling of apprehension.

Straight leg braces are made of exceptionally heavy steel when used with cerebral palsy children to lower their center of gravity and thus create greater stability.

Physical therapists employ what is known as a powder board when exercising patients to lessen the effects of gravity. The board has a highly polished finish, and powder is placed between the appendage being exercised and the surface of the board in order to reduce resistance to a minimum.

Throughout the field of physical medicine, extensive use of the principles of moments is employed when positioning a patient for exercise. Certain positions are designed to lessen the effect of gravity when working with weak muscles. On the other hand, there may be circumstances when the fullest possible effect of gravity is desirable. The further the center of gravity of an appendage is from the axis of rotation, the greater will be the effect of gravity.

SUMMARY

A muscle is strongest when on stretch.

The length of the lever arm does not affect the time it takes a muscle to shorten. Therefore, the length or distance through which the bone moves is directly proportional to the speed of movement which can be attained. In most levers, the resistance is applied close to the axis and the force farther away. In such an arrangement, the mechanical system gains force at the expense of distance. The bony levers of the body are built more for speed than for maximal force. The force (muscle) is applied with short lever arm (distance from axis to point of insertion) to overcome a resistance quite some distance from the axis.

The muscles pull at an angle of 20 degrees or less. The smaller the angle of pull, the farther and faster will a given amount of contraction move the bone. As the muscle shortens in contraction, the angle of pull changes. We must recognize that when speed and distance are increased as the muscle pulls at a small angle, there is a corresponding loss in force.

Three factors are the important determinents of the effectiveness of a moment system:

1. Length of lever.
2. Distance force is from axis.
3. Angle of pull.

REFERENCES

1. Bunn, John, *Scientific Principles of Coaching,* Prentice Hall, Englewood Cliffs, N. J., 1955, p. 4.

Chapter 7

THE EXERCISE PROGRAM

AMONG the most important contributions of physical education are the values derived from exercise. In this chapter we will discuss in some detail the application of exercise to handicapped children. To be sure, knowing the important principles of therapeutic exercises enables us to do a much more effective job, not only with the handicapped youngster but with the athletic squads and our regular classes as well. Good program design for those in need of therapeutic exercise can help each child lead a fuller and more effective life.

In Chapter 1 we discussed the necessity of procuring all pertinent data about each youngster who we felt required individualized attention by the physical educator. Regardless of the nature of the program, before any activity is initiated for a handicapped child, two steps must be taken: (1) all aspects of the pupil's total problem should be understood, and (2) medical clearance or approval of the child's program must be obtained *in writing* from the family physician or physician in charge. There are no exceptions to these two rules. The physician is completely responsible for counseling and directing the therapeutic program; and, most important, there are instances when an activity or exercise is contraindicated, especially when it might aggravate the condition and hence retard the youngster's rehabilitation. Furthermore, any apprehension about working with the handicapped child can be relieved through consultation, supervision, and approval by the medical doctor. Cooperation among parents, physican, guidance teacher, and physical educator results in the team approach to the child's problem; such a team can render an effective and efficient service to the handicapped youngster.

DESIGNING THE THERAPEUTIC EXERCISE PROGRAM

For all programming in physical education, we must first know and understand each child. Employing every possible source of information, we must painstakingly assemble the facts before proceeding to diagram the exercise program. Regardless of how time-consuming and difficult the task may be, good results cannot be expected unless the youngster's handicapped condition as well as associated problems are thoroughly understood. Once this has been done, the physical educator, on the basis of facts, outlines his program and submits the final draft for medical approval. This is a unique and vital responsibility of the physical educator. When dealing with the physically handicapped child, the medical record is the most authorative information.

THE MEDICAL RECORD

There should be a complete and up-to-date medical record on permanent file for every physically handicapped child who is attending school. Items of interest to the physical educator that should appear in the medical record are: (1) the diagnosis and prognosis; (2) a brief medical history; (3) areas of the body involved and the extent of involvement; (4) medical treatment; (5) notes and comments by ancillary medical personnel, including psychologists, physical therapists, and nurse; (6) special instructions by the physican; and (7) medical clearance for the youngster to participate in the physical education program.

The physical activity to be used in a therapeutic exercise program will primarily depend on the type of pathological involvement, the specific muscles affected, and the extent to which they are affected. Essentially the physician's report will contain the diagnosis (cause of the condition) and the prognosis (prospects as to recovery); however, in many instances certain additional information will be necessary. This is true because in addition to the fact that exercise may be contraindicated, the specific location of the lesion could be the determining factor as to whether one should use muscle re-education and coordination exercises rather than strength or endurance-building activities.

The physician will usually be able to explain pertinent aspects of the case. Before consulting him we should gain as complete an understanding as possible of the pupil's medical condition so that the interview will leave no question as to the particular exercise program and its place in the total rehabilitation of the child.

Certainly we cannot proceed with an exercise program until a complete muscle evaluation is made. This information should appear in the medical report prepared either by the physician or physical therapist. The ability to determine what muscles are affected and the extent to which they are affected requires special skill and knowledge. Usualy the medical doctor will delegate this responsibility to a physical therapist, and the information will appear in the medical report under the heading "Manual Muscle Test." The results are usually quite specific and include the following: names of muscles involved; grade of muscle strength as to normal, good, fair, poor, trace, or zero; limitations of motion at joints; amount of spasticity present; and degree of incoordination.

It is well for the physical educator to remember that the manual muscle test is a subjective evaluation. Doctors and physical therapists may use different methods to grade and record the information. It is our responsibility to know what the various grading systems mean and what information may be realized from the test. Naturally, it would be desirable if the physical educator could administer his own muscle test, both as an aid in designing the exercises and as a criterion for determining the effectiveness of the program. At the end of this chapter are references (2, 4) that may be consulted for more detailed information on the techniques of administering the manual muscle test.

Although the medical report contains much of the basic information necessary for planning a successful therapeutic exercise program, it is not the sole source of data to be considered. The results of psychological examinations will give a great deal of insight into the youngster's emotional, intellectual, and sociological status. Consultation with teachers, parents, and school nurse will also yield much useful information, as will the pupil interview. To have a successful therapeutic exercise program we must have complete cooperation from the person participating in the program. The maximum degree of enthusiasm is generated when the teacher fully understands the pupil and all of his problems and when the pupil is completely oriented as to the purposes of the exercise program.

TYPES OF THERAPEUTIC EXERCISE

Therapeutic exercise is the scientific application of bodily movements in treatment of disease, malfunction, or deformity. These movements fall into one of four major categories: (1) passive exercise, (2) active-assistive exercise, (3) active exercise, and (4) resistive exercise.

Passive exercise is imparted to a segment of the body by another person or some outside force, without active effort by the patient. During the application of passive exercise, the patient is requested to remain completely relaxed and inactive while the instructor brings about the desired motion. All movements should be done slowly, smoothly, and through as complete a range of motion as possible. It is a general rule in therapeutic exercise that one movement through a full range of motion is much more effective than a series of movements through a shorter range of motion. Rapid pumping movements are to be avoided. Passive exercise should be done within the limits of pain, and the teacher should immediately cease all movements when pain or muscle spasm appear. The primary object of passive exercise is to prevent contractures and the formation of adhesions.

Passive exercises also may be used to increase the range of motion of a joint. When used in this manner, they are referred to as *passive stretching*, or merely stretching exercises. In some cases, force may be applied to the extent that the movement is extremely painful for the patient. In conditions like fibrous ankylosis and "frozen shoulders," the process of forced movement to break the adhesions may be so painful that a sedative or anesthetic is required. The procedure of using forceful stretching movements while the patient is under a local or general anesthetic is called *manipulation*. It should always be performed by a medical doctor.

Active-assistive exercises are those in which the patient makes an active effort to move a segment of the body and the instructor or some other outside forces assists. They are used when for some reason—weakness or pain perhaps—the patient is unable to go through a complete range of motion by himself. It is a combination of effort in which the patient does as much as he can and then outside assistance is provided.

Usually maximum assistance is needed during the initial and final one-third range of motion. The combination of internal forces (levers and relative length of the muscle) work together in the middle phase of movement so that there is an *optimum of muscle contraction*. In the initial third, the position of the joint is such that while the muscle is on stretch and in a physiological position for maximum contraction, the angles formed by the articulating bones and the pull of the contracting muscle on bone are at a mechanical disadvantage to produce rotary motion. On the other hand, just the opposite happens during the final one-third of the movement. The angles formed by the articulating bones and the pull of the contracting muscle on bones are now at a better mechanical advantage for rotary motion; however, the muscle has now shortened to a point where it is at a physiological disadvantage. For these reasons, we usually find that most assistance is needed during the initial and final one-third of a movement. It is not uncommon to find a patient who will be unable to initiate or complete a particular movement, although he will be able to carry on completely by himself during the middle phase of motion.

There are many forms of help available to provide the outside force necessary in active-assistive exercises. Manual assistance by the instructor is perhaps the most common method of helping the patient to carry out a desired movement. The buoyancy provided by water (therapeutic pool) is often used, although the tremendous cost in money and space prevents its widespread usage. Then too, it is difficult to stabilize or isolate muscle action while the patient is immersed in water, and muscle substitution too frequently results.

Not commonly used outside the hospital situation, the powderboard (Fig. 13) is an excellent aid in applying active-assistive exercise to the extremities. It is a solid piece of plywood, about 30 × 38 inches, which has four or six collapsible legs (similar to a card table) that are 6 to 8 inches long. The surface of the board is extremely smooth and highly finished to reduce friction between the patient's arm or leg and the board. It is common practice to sprinkle talcum powder on the surface of the board to further diminish friction; hence the name *powder board*. It is used in giving active-assistive exercise to an extremity. Proper positioning of the patient permits significant reduction of gravital effects. This allows the individual to exercise actively through a complete range of mo-

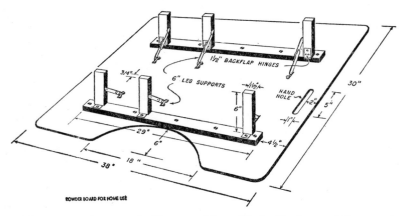

Fig. 13. Powder Board. (Courtesy Mayo Clinic, Rochester, Minnesota.)

tion entirely by himself. Resistance may be progressively increased by use of sandbags. The powder board is no longer required once the patient is capable of moving his arm or leg independently through a full range of motion.

Reduction of gravital effect is important when exercising an extremity which is controlled by weakened muscles. For example, it is not uncommon to have a patient with quadriceps so weak he cannot do knee extension against gravity even once; yet he will be able to go through a full range of motion (knee extension) on a powder board with 20 pounds of sandbags providing resistance. Powder board exercises are considered active assistive exercises because the effects of gravity are minimized.

Among the more important values of the powder board are: (1)

the patient is greatly motivated by the fact that he may be able to perform the movement without assistance; (2) improvement can be noted through the use of additional sandbags; (3) the resistance can be carefully graded with varying size sandbags; and (4) proper positioning eliminates the necessity for the patient to use his own muscles to stabilize and support himself, which permits him to concentrate on performing the specified exercise.

Counterbalanced weights, pulleys, and suspension springs are also used in active-assistive exercise to minimize gravity or to assist the desired movement. Sometimes proper positioning of the body segment will also help.

Active exercises, or free exercises, are movements performed by the subject with no assistance. These exercises are the ones most commonly used in a therapeutic program. They help to improve muscular coordination and develop motor skills, to correct postural abnormalities and muscular and circulatory disturbances, and to hasten recovery following trauma. They are of particular importance in recreational activities.

There are many advantage in using active exercise in the physical education program. Once the student has mastered the skills and is aware of the purpose, he can conduct his own program. The teacher does not have to give his undivided attention to any one student as he does with passive or active-assistive exercises. Also, the variety of activities permitted in such an exercise program helps to maintain the pupil's interest.

Resistance exercises are performed by the active contraction of the muscles against an outside resistance. Actually, resistance exercise is a form of active exercise, the only difference being that the strength of the muscle has developed to the stage where it is now capable of contracting through a range of motion against an external force. Since World War II, resistance exercises have become rather popular as a therapeutic tool and are used extensively in physical medicine and physical education programs.

VALUES OF THERAPEUTIC EXERCISE

Before proceeding to the discussion of the attributes of exercise it might be prudent to briefly consider the more important aspects of the physiological properties of muscular contraction.

Isotonic contraction, sometimes referred to as dynamic contraction, is characterized by change in the length of a muscle, thus producing motion. The alteration in muscle length may occur either as a shortening or as a lengthening contraction. When muscle contraction produces a shortening of the muscle, it is known as a *concentric contraction* or shortening contraction; an example is elbow flexion. The muscles responsible for this motion must contract with a force great enough to overcome the weight of the forearm and hand. As the attachments of the elbow flexor muscles are brought closer together, the muscle becomes shorter and thicker.

The physiological demands of the concentric contraction are high because only a small portion of the required energy is used for mechanical work. Some of the energy is used to overcome inertia and the remainder is converted into heat. While most activities of daily living require the use of all types of muscle contraction, the concentric one seems to be most common, and it is the one most often used in an exercise program.

The lengthening contraction, or *eccentric contraction,* occurs when the tension developed in a contracting muscle is less than an outside force being applied. The muscle becomes longer and thinner as its attachments are moved apart by the external force. An example of the eccentric contraction is the flexed forearm being pulled down into a position of extension by the weight of the forearm and hand. The triceps does not act to produce the motion of extension; rather, the elbow flexors increase in length slowly and under control, allowing the movement to take place. In other words, the external force actually assists the movement, and the eccentrically contracting muscles (elbow flexors) work to break the action.

Isometric contraction is sometimes refered to as a static or holding contraction because, during the active phase of contraction, tension is developed within the muscle but no movement of bones takes place. Because movement is not associated with an isometric contraction, we cannot say that mechanical work is being done. The energy developed during an isometric contraction is expended in the form of heat. The importance of an isometrically contracting muscle lies in its stabilizing effect as exhibited by the gluteus muscle in maintaining the integrity of the pelvis during ambulation, and the *erector spinae* muscles in holding the body in an upright position.

It is now generally recognized that there are four specific outcomes, or qualities, that may be realized from a therapeutic exercise program: strength, endurance, mobility, and coordination. For the most part, these qualities are interrelated; that is, with a strength-building program, endurance and coordination may also be improved. However, this overlap of qualities should not interfer with the specificity of the exercise program, for each type of exercise imparts a proponderence of the quality for which it is designed.

STRENGTH

The development of muscle bulk and strength is perhaps the most sought-after outcome of an exercise program. There is some confusion among professional workers, as well as laymen, regarding the use of the word *strength*. Terms such as *work, power, force, tension,* and *strength* are often erroneously used interchangeably. Reporting on a three-year survey of two leading journals in the field of physical medicine and rehabilitation, Cook and associates (1) found some 22 articles written about muscle activity under given conditions. Of these articles, 27 percent used work as a measure of strength and 23 percent employed the term *isometric tension*. Only six of the authors used words consistent with meanings found in related fields. We shall therefore define the following terms:

1. *Force* is that which tends to cause or change the motion of matter. It is either a push or pull and may be applied without causing actual motion. It is measured in units such as pounds.
2. *Tension* is a system of forces tending to draw asunder the parts of a body, combined with an equal and opposite system of restraining forces holding the parts of the body together. Tension is measured in units of force such as pounds.
3. *Strength* is the capacity for exertion. *Muscular strength* is the force of muscular contraction and is measured in units of force such as pounds.
4. *Work* occurs when a force moves an object through a distance in the direction of the force. It is measured in units of work, such

as foot-pounds. Thus, if you lift 10 pounds a distance of 2 feet, you perform 20 foot-pounds of work.

5. *Power* is defined as the rate of doing work. Power is measured in units such as foot-pounds per second. It is equal to the work done divided by the time required to do it. Thus, if you lift 100 pounds a distance of 2 feet in 10 seconds, your power for that feat is 20 foot-pounds per second.

Perhaps the greatest amount of misunderstanding occurs in using *work, power,* and *strength* interchangeably. Both work and power must have motion occuring; power necessitates having the time element associated with it. As muscular strength is only the force exerted during contraction of a muscle, it is not necessarily related to movement. For example, an individual pushing against a solid brick wall may exert maximum muscular strength and expend vast quantities of energy, but he is not demonstrating power. On the other hand, if the same person picks up a 10-pound weight from the floor and places it on a table 3 feet high in 5 seconds, he is exerting muscular strength, doing work, and demonstrating power.

The slogan "exercise and grow strong" is exceedingly popular and widely accepted; but it can be misleading. Those who are well informed realize that only special types of exercise will increase muscle strength; exercise based on the overload principle (commonly referred to as the principle of progressive resistance) is required to produce hypertrophy of a muscle group. The secret to a successful strength-building program is to systematically and progressively increase the resistance against which the muscles must act.

The type of exercise to be used in a strength-building program depends on the condition of the muscle. Either an isotonic or an isometric type of contraction may be used. If the involved muscle is so weak that the pupil is unable to move the segment through a full range of motion by himself, the teacher will have to begin with active-assistive exercises. As muscle strength increases, the amount of assistance will be decreased until the youngster is able to accomplish the movement entirely by himself. The degree of assistance or resistance, the duration and frequency of exercise, and the extent and rate of strength gains to be expected are variables peculiar to the individual and must be recognized as such.

The method of applying progressive resistance exercise may vary considerably, depending on time, equipment, and knowledge of the instructor. The following examples are some of the more common methods used in therapeutic exercise today.

1. *Manual Resistance.* The teacher or some other person manually offers resistance to the action of the muscle. A modification of this method occurs as an individual offers resistance, with an isometric contraction, to his own muscle with another part of his body. (The method has been commercially used in America under the term "Dynamic Tension.")

Manual resistance is extremely adaptable and can be applied to almost any muscle in the body. It is of value when dealing with very weak muscles or when the patient is confined to bed in a restricted position. On the other hand, manual resistance exercises are time consuming and fatiguing to the operator. The amount of resistance patient offers to a motion may vary from hour to hour and day to day. There is little motivation for the patient because he has little idea as to the amount of improvement being made.

2. *Weights.* External weights, such as bar bells, sandbags, pulleys, and springs, are commonly used in progressive resistance exercise. Weights are easily graded so that the rate of progress can be measured and controlled; this provides motivation for the pupil to continue his program. A great deal of money can be spent on the purchase of weights, but the teacher with a limited budget can easily make his own equipment with pipe, cans filled with concrete, or canvas bags filled with lead shot or sand.

Properly applied weight-lifting techniques can be a lot of fun and will prove to be the most rapid way to augment strength. Care must always be taken to insure that the students know the proper method of lifting. Positioning the body part to be exercised in relation to the weight is extremely important. Pupils should be encouraged to work in pairs so that proper spotting techniques may be used to prevent accidents. Be sure to see that no student attempts to lift more weight than he can handle with safety.

3. *Body Position.* Changing the body's position so that the weight of the body provides the resistance is another method of offering resistance to a muscle. For example, in attempting to do a sit-up, the pupil will find it more difficult when his hands and arms are raised over his head than when the arms are beside the body. Raising the arms and hands also raises the center of gravity within the body so that the muscles must work against a longer resistance arm. In some instances it is possible to position a body so that the insertion of a muscle remains fixed and the origin moves

toward the insertion. Thus, the contracting muscle will be moving a considerably heavier load. Resistance may also be increased by positioning the body so that the maximum effects of gravity will act against the movement. For example, to produce hyperentension of the trunk, the *erector spinae* muscles will have a greater resistance to overcome when the body is in a straight prone position than when it is in a standing or sitting position.

Any strength-building exercise requires close supervision by the teacher. Many students participating in these exercises lift and carry weights that are heavy and awkward to handle. Purely from the safety point of view, it is necessary to maintain a watchful eye. But just as important as the safety factor is the prevention of muscle substitution. There is an extremely fine line between loading an involved muscle with enough resistance to contract with maximum force and overloading a muscle so that its synergists must come into play to overcome the resistance. When the synergistic muscles take over the function of the prime mover (agonist), the condition is known as *muscle substitution*. In such cases, the prime movers grow weaker and the synergistic muscles grow stronger. At times it may be possible to eliminate substitution by positioning the involved part of the body so that the synergists are at a disadvantage and the agonist is in an advantageous position to contract. Other times it may be controlled by reducing the weight load. In any case, it is much easier to control muscle substitution in its early stages than to try to correct it after the pattern of motion has become established.

ENDURANCE

Physical endurance may be defined as the ability of the human organism to continue physical effort and withstand the stresses created by this effort. Actually, endurance may be thought of as that quality which allows an individual to perform muscular work for the longest period or greatest number of times. As such, the chief object of endurance exercise is to increase the duration and efficiency of the human body to do work. We usually think of endurance in terms of either (1) local or muscular endurance or (2) general endurance involving predominantly the heart-lung systems.

Local endurance may be defined as the ability of a muscle to perform repeated movement for a long period of time. It is sometimes referred to as *muscular endurance*. Example of such activities would be arm curls and bench presses with light weights, exercise on an ergograph, or use of pulleys. Local endurance is dependent on muscle strength and the ability of the muscle to produce and utilize energy. When a strong muscle overcomes a comparatively light resistance, relatively few fibers need to be called into action. As these become tired, other fibers in the muscle take over the work. This constant interplay of the fibers in a muscle allows the fatigued fibers to recover in order that they may resume the activity later if necessary. Strength, however, is only one aspect of local endurance. Frequently it is found that a gain in local endurance is out of all proportion to the gain in hypertrophy and strength of a muscle. Karpovich (3) believes that localized endurance training improves the quality of contraction. He suggests that this improvement may come about because fuel is made more available for contraction, fuel is stored in greater amount, and oxygen is more plentiful because of increased muscle perfusion as a result of the exercise.

General endurance may be defined as the ability of the individual to participate in an activity for prolonged periods. Athletics requiring this type of endurance include distance running and swimming events. Much needs to be learned in regard to what physiological and even psychical changes take place during an endurance training program. Only minor physiological differences may be observed between the highly trained and the unconditioned when evaluated while at rest; however, once the individuals begin to exercise, quite significant differences are noted. The following include the most classic characteristics of the highly trained: (1) he can tolerate greater oxygen debt; (2) he has increased respiratory capacity; (3) he has lower heart rate; (4) he will establish a higher work level and maintain it for a greater period of time; and (5) he will experience a more rapid recovery following the exercise.

General endurance activities will stress the heart-lung systems; and the degree of stress for a given exercise is related to the individual's condition. A half-mile walk for an athmatic child might be a stressful experience, but a distance runner would hardly give a second thought to jogging several miles. This is probably the single most important principle to consider when designing the general endurance program.

STRENGTH VS. ENDURANCE EXERCISES

Many teachers tell their students to do push-ups to strengthen the arm and shoulder girdle muscles, and to do sit-ups to hypertrophy the stomach muscles. Such blanket exercise prescriptions are hazardous, for what may be endurance-building for one person could be a strength-development program, or even sufficiently stressful to be harmful, for another person. Constant and repetitive exercises like push-ups or sit-ups will not necessarily increase the strength of the involved muscles any more than running five miles every day will always increase the strength of the leg muscles. It is true that strength and endurance exercises are similar in many respects; however, there are certain basic differences that are vital.

Although the patterns of movement to increase endurance are similar to those used to obtain strength, the demands made on the muscles are less. Exercises to bring about growth in strength require *maximum effort* but *few repetitions*, whereas exercises to develop endurance require *less effort* but *many repetitions*. In other words, strength exercises require an all-out effort of muscle contraction to lift a maximum weight a few times, but endurance exercises require an all-out effort to lift less weight but numerous times. Maximum strength gains are best achieved by exercising every day, although three times per week will yield significant results. Endurance gains are best achieved by exercising five days a week, preferably twice a day. Duration is usually the aim of endurance activities and it may be necessary to alter the load, rate, and frequency of exercise to increase the number of repetitions.

ENDURANCE ACTIVITIES

Practically every type of activity utilized in a physical education program can be adapted to develop endurance. The whole idea is to make sure that the student constantly strives to increase the amount of time in which he actually participates in the activity. Steady repetition of active movement confined to one muscle, or group of muscles, is excellent for local endurance. The level of performance may be elevated by adding resistance or increasing the speed of movement. Games and sports may be of value for general endurance; but as the student improves his skill of the game, because of increased efficiency he may actually use less energy than when he first began to play. Distance running, swimming, hiking, circuit training, and continuous and uninterrupted gymnastics are most desirable for their effect on general endurance.

MOBILITY

Movement is one of the most meaningful and important functions of the human organism. The articulations (joints) of the skeletal system, which have varying degrees of mobility, are the center for movement. The type and amount of motion possible at any one joint is determined first by the type of articulation found at the joint, and second by the condition of the fibrous tissues, ligaments, tendons, and muscles surrounding the joint. Although there is very little one can do about altering the type of bony articulation (except by surgical intervention), a well-planned and directed exercise program will markedly influence the condition of the soft tissues about the joint. Thus, the primary purpose of mobility exercise is to improve function of the body by maintaining or restoring normal joint range of motion.

MOBILITY VS. STABILITY

It is now generally agreed that joints with great mobility have less stability and those with great stability have less mobility. This rule holds true not only for the various joints in the same individual, but also for the same joints in different individuals. The hip joint, for example, has less mobility but more stability than the shoulder joint even though both joints are the ball-and-socket type. The "loose" individual does not have the stability in posture as compared with the less flexible person. The fact that stability is sacrificed to obtain mobility should be taken into consideration when designing this type of exercise.

Age plays an extremely important role in determining the amount of mobility a person has. We cannot expect to find the same degree of flexibility in the high school or college student as would be found in the first- or second-grader. Along with the growth process from childhood to adulthood, there is usually a tightening of the soft tissues and a loss of elasticity of the muscles. This change affords greater stability for the physical demands of adult life, such as long periods of standing or sitting and the lifting and carrying of heavy objects.

MONOARTICULAR AND PLURIARTICULAR MUSCLES

There are two general groups of muscles in the body relative to the joints: monarticular and pluriarticular muscles. The monarticular muscles pass over one joint and are capable of producing motion only at that joint. The pluriarticular muscle passes over two or more joints and is capable of producing movement at any one joint, all the joints, or any combination of the joints. The type of movement produced by a pluriarticular muscle depends on the circumstances at the time of contraction. For example, the *biceps brachii* will produce the motion of supination of the forearm when the elbow and shoulder joints are fixed. However, if all the joints affected by the *biceps brachii* are free, it will produce the motions of abduction and forward flexion of the arm, elbow flexion, and supination of the forearm. Another important characteristic of pluriarticular muscles is that they are not long enough to permit complete movement in all the joints at the same time. Under normal conditions, for example, complete hip flexion is impossible unless the knee is flexed; the hamstring muscles, which extend the hip and flex the knee, are not long enough to permit a complete range of motion across both joints at the same time.

GENERAL PRINCIPLES FOR MOBILITY EXERCISES

Basically, all mobility exercises are directed either to maintain or to increase joint range of motion. Inasmuch as stability is usually sacrificed for mobility, we should always strive to build a corresponding increase in strength and endurance in the muscles controlling the joint. Joint mobility is desirable, and necessary for maximum efficiency in movement; but it can also be dangerous and possibly lead to further injury or disability. It is therefore imperative to insure that every degree of mobility gained at a joint be compensated with a corresponding increase in strength.

Maintaining the existing range of motion at any one joint is relatively easy, and it should not be too uncomfortable for the individual. The body part is moved through the joint range to the point of pain. It is held at this position, usually for a count of three, and then slowly returned to the resting position. Best results are obtained when the motion is repeated 6 to 10 times per exercise session, with three or four sessions repeated regularly throughout the day. Movements should be slow and steady; extreme caution should always be taken to avoid sudden, jerky, or rapid movements which could exceed the pain threshold as well as tear tissue.

Stretching activities must be utilized to increase the joint range, and this usually involves the use of forced movements. The patient should be positioned in a comfortable manner so that he can relax as much as possible. The first few exercise sessions may be spent in feeling out the patient to determine what he can or cannot do and to gain his confidence. The exercise itself should consist of firm but gentle pressure applied in the direction of increasing range up to the point of tolerable pain. Hold this position for a few seconds. If the patient will relax and tolerate more, pressure is then resumed and the new position is held for a few seconds. Return the body part to the resting position slowly and gently.

Maximum stretch of pluriarticular muscles is best obtained when the muscle is stretched over all the joints simultaneously. Sometimes it is desirable to hold (fix) a desired range at one joint while working for a complete range of motion at another joint. Positioning and fixation of adjacent joints are extremely important factors to consider when administering stretching activities.

Always avoid excessive range of motion at a joint; it is easy to overcome the resistance offered by children, and there is great danger in overstretching and traumatizing the joint before we realize it has occurred. There should be a gradual and continuous improvement in joint range if stretching exercises are properly applied. A loss of motion or increased muscle pain and spasm may indicate that the stretching was too vigorous and should be decreased or discontinued. It is always wise to be on the cautious side when dealing with stretching activities. A large and varied number of exercises may be employed to obtain the quality of mobility.

Stretching exercises of choice are those in which the person actively attempts to make the movement. Active contraction of a muscle invokes the reciprocal innervation of antagonistic muscle, which implies that when a muscle actively contracts, it is accompanied by relaxation of its antagonist. For example, when the *biceps brachii* contracts, its antagonist, the triceps, relaxes. The greater the amount of contraction in the agonist, the greater the relaxation in its antagonist. Thus, active exercise will greatly enhance the ability to stretch a muscle, and resistive exercise, theoretically, will further augment the stretching process.

A stretching program produces maximum results when the exercises are administered on an individual basis. Stretching is a painful process, and few individuals will push themselves to the point where the exercises will do much good. Most children do not have the detailed knowledge of anatomy to know what movements to make or to detect and correct muscle substitution. In many instances, outside assistance must be given to position and fix specific adjacent joints so that stretching exercises can be effective. These and many other factors make it imperative for the teacher to have close, individual contact with any pupil who is participating in a stretching exercise program.

Coordination

As used in this text, coordination is defined as that quality whereby an individual has the ability to use the correct muscles, at the proper time, with the exact force necessary to perform a desired movement. It is primarily concerned with the functional relationship between muscles and the central nervous system. Unlike the other qualities attributable to exercise (strength, endurance, and mobility), much less is known and understood about the nature of coordination. The topic is one of the most difficult and controversial in the field of physiology. The process of learning, whereby movements which are initially clumsy and difficult become ultimately skillful and easy, has not been fully explained. Physiological knowledge is still insufficient to enable a commonly accepted and agreed upon theory of coordination or voluntary movement in man.

Coordinated movement is smooth, accurate, and purposeful. It is extremely doubtful that coordination can be taught per se, although, within limits, is is possible to improve coordinated movements through an exercise program. Coordinated movements must pass through stages, from the rather primitive to the highly developed skills. Maximum development in physical skill is possible only when all the muscles and nerve centers are intact. Coordination and the ability to do certain movements may be reduced, or lost altogether, if there is a disturbance or destruction of these centers and nerve tracts, e.g., through cerebral palsy, brain or spinal cord lesions, or paresis (weakness) or paralysis due to a variety of causes. In such cases, muscle re-education may be used to improve the chances of recovery.

MUSCLE RE-EDUCATION

Muscle re-education, sometimes referred to as neuromuscular re-education (or proprioceptive neuromuscular facilitation), is that phase of therapeutic exercise used to develop or recover voluntary control of skeletal muscles. The lack of effective muscle control may result from many different causes and may be exhibited in many different ways; but, regardless of the cause and effect, the object of muscle re-education is the same: to develop voluntary control of the muscle.

In applying muscle re-education techniques, every mental and physical effort of the patient must be guided to the movement which is being initiated. It is desirable to have the exercise area free from outside disturbances so that the patient's attention will not be distracted. The usual procedure is to carry out two or three passive movements of the desired motion, in order to stimulate the proprioceptor nerve endings in the muscle, joints, and tendons. The location, action, origin, and insertion of the muscle to be treated is described to the patient so that he will know and understand what is to be done. The patient's attention is then directed to the spot where motion begins, and the skin over the area is stroked in the direction of insertion toward the origin. The muscle should be placed on stretch at the beginning of the movement in order to realize maximum contraction. Stroking the muscle will elicit tactile stimuli to help develop an awareness in using the correct muscle. Light or heavy pressure, heat, cold, and other forms of external stimulation may also be used to augment the muscle response. Visual stimulation is provided when the patient watches the movements being performed passively. Thus, every available method of reinforcing proprioceptive stimulation to complete the movement is used.

Upon completion of the passive movements and the execution of the above procedures, the patient is instructed to do the motion along with the teacher. Sufficient assistance is given by the teacher so that the patient does not have to exert maximum effort in performing the motion. If maximum effort is made, it is usually accompanied by a great deal of muscle substitution and incordination. The purpose of muscle re-education is to develop voluntary response of muscle, and no particular attention should be given to the development of strength. (If strength is the desired quality, then the exercises should be designed to produce it.) If the wrong muscle is being called into play, it can usually be controlled by finger pressure on the desired muscle, giving more assistance to the movement, or a combination of the two. If the patient becomes tired, appears to lose interest, or becomes uncooperative, the exercise should be discontinued until a later time.

It is not to be implied that the above method is the only way to do muscle re-education. On the contrary, there are numerous methods and techniques advocated for the purpose. But the method described above is probably the most commonly accepted and widely used of them all.

SKILLS

Walking, using a typewriter, or fielding a baseball are skilled acts usually taken so much for granted that we lose sight of their complexity and forget the months or years spent in mastering them. Exercises or activities which at one time required concentration and effort become automatic; when this occurs we say the person is skillful.

The achievement of skill comes only through constant and repetitious performance of the desired act. As the pattern of motion becomes established, it is simplified and becomes more efficient; and the conduction of the necessary impulses along the neuromuscu-

lar pathways is facilitated. There is a transfer of learning from one
skill to another only to the extent that they have common elements.
Moreover, this transference is most likely to occur from the more
difficult to the easy rather than from the relatively easy to the difficult. Before we can undertake the task of teaching skills, we must be
assured that the pupil's musculature has the strength, endurance,
and mobility necessary to perform the task. It is sometimes necessary
to concentrate on these qualities before attempting to teach even
the simplest of skills.

MEASUREMENT

The whole philosophy on which therapeutic exercise is based
may be found in the slogan "Progress Is Our Most Important Product." Progress can be recognized and demonstrated only by measurement. As such, measurement and evaluation play an indispensible
role in the successful therapeutic exercise program. Through the
use of objective and valid tests, the physical educator removes program design from the realm of guess and supposition puts it on a
highly scientific level. He is able to identify those who are deficient
in the essential qualities of strength, endurance, mobility, and coordination and to plan his program accordingly. He is able to
measure the pupil's progress toward achievement of a specific goal.
One of the very important aspects of carrying out a successful
exercise program is in knowing when to redesign the activity program or what to emphasize. This knowledge can only be obtained
through measurement. If the physical educator hopes to achieve
maximum success, he must *know* and *use* measurement in his therapeutic exercise program.

SUMMARY

It is only through using therapeutic exercise that we can help the
handicapped student achieve maximum physical effectiveness. Since
all other phases of rehabilitation are built on the residual physical
disability that cannot be eliminated by medicine, therapeutic exercise must be considered the foundation of all rehabilitation proc-

esses. Success in a therapeutic exercise program is achieved through rational planning based on known facts. Knowing the "why" is just as important as knowing the "how" of exercise. Our approach to this subject has been through the fundamental knowledge basic to designing and carrying out a therapeutic exercise program rather than by developing a long list of exercises "to be done in the following manner."

In discussing therapeutic exercises, especially those of endurance nature, one cannot restrict himself to merely the physiological phenomena. The rapidity and extent with which endurance exercises increase the capacity of the body for work, suggest that changes other than physiological must take place. The full nature of these changes are unknown, but it is thought that some of the improvements are due as much to the psychological as physiological changes. Motivation in the form of competition, encouragement from teacher and classmates, and cheering usually make a student perform a little better. The fact that he understands the purpose and need for exercise as well as how to do the activities may be a contributing factor. Establishing a state of mind that encourages the pupil to do his very best contributes tremendously to improvement. After all, the child with a disability has the same desires and needs as the pupil who has no physical handicap.

Appendix A contains a weight-lifting program for all age groups; Appendix B includes a variety of exercises to use in planning an exercise program.

REFERENCES

1. Cook, R. et al, "Meaning of Strength in Physical Medicine," Archives of Physical Medicine, September, 1954, 35, 586-589.
2. Daniels, L., Williams, M., and Worthingham, C., Muscle Testing, Techniques of Manual Examination, Philadelphia, 1956.
3. Karpovich, Peter V., Physiology of Muscular Activity, W. B. Saunders, Philadelphia, 1959, p. 40.
4. Licht, Sidney (Editor), Therapeutic Exercise. Elizabeth Licht, New Haven, 1958, section by Thomas F. Hines, "Manual Muscle Examination," 159-251.

Chapter 8

THE SPINE

THE movements of the spine can be understood most readily if the regions of the spine are visualized. The following anatomical summary is presented to recall certain vertebral characteristics and muscle function. It should be kept in mind that the facings of the articular processes and the articulations, both at the arches and between the bodies and discs, present certain characteristics. The size of the vertebrae and discs and the directional location of the processes in the cervical, thoracic, and lumbar regions will in part affect the freedom and plane of movement in the spine.

DESCRIPTION OF THE VERTEBRAL COLUMN

The individual vertebrae of the spinal column are united by a series of articulations (1) between the vertebral bodies and the discs and (2) between the superior and inferior articular processes of the adjacent vertebral arches (see Fig. 14). The bodies of the vertebrae support the superincumbent weight of the mass, and each vertebra becomes progressively larger from the cervical through the thoracic and lumbar regions of the spine. The sacrum is a fused mass composed of five ossified vertebrae, all possessing identifiable vertebral characteristics. The fusion of the articular processes and of the bodies and discs accounts for the fact that the sacrum does not participate in spinal movement. The lumbosacral articulation is located at the junction of the movable and immovable spine, and is recognized as the weak link in the spine, since stresses and strains tend to be magnified at this joint.

The posterior articulations of the ribs with the bodies, discs, and transverse processes of thoracic vertebrae, and the anterior attachments of the ribs to the sternum, form the thoracic cage. The thorax provides a stable skeletal structure for muscle attachments and support and protection of the heart, lungs, vital structures of the mediostinum, and the nerve trunks within this area. One of the more important functions of the thorax is its association with the movement of the ribs in repiration.

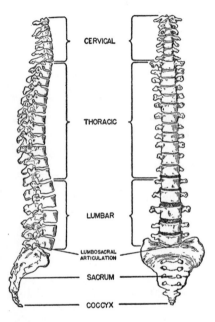

The spine is a flexible rod characterized by normal curves in the anteroposterior or sagittal plane. These curves convex forward in the cervical and lumbar regions and concave forward in the thoracic and sacral areas. The normal curves add to the stability of the column and to the complexity of certain spinal movements. In the presence of pathological conditions, traumatic injuries, or developmental disorders, the gravital force may contribute to asymmetrical problems of balance.

Fig. 14. Lateral and rear view of spinal column.

MOVEMENTS OF THE SPINE

Movement at the vertebral arches, between the superior and inferior articular processes of contiguous vertebrae, is gliding or arthrodial in nature. The range of motion at each articulation is not extensive; however, the cumulative effect of individual motion between the 24 vertebrae of the movable spine results in a relatively extensive range of movement between the skull and the sacrum. The amount of motion between the bodies and intervertebral discs is minimal; however, the variations in thickness of the discs in the cervical, thoracic, and lumbar regions have some effect on the degree of freedom. In addition, the range of spinal movements may be dependent on individual differences in skeletal and ligamentous structure, previous experiences in physical activity, and the presence of anomalies or a pathological condition.

Movements of the spine in the anterposterior plane include forward bending (flexion), the return to the erect position (extension), and backward bending (hyperextension). The cervical and lumbar normal curves are obliterated in acute flexion as the thoracic forward concavity is increased. The reverse pertains in extension and hyperextension since the normal convexity forward in the cervical and lumbar regions is increased, with a corresponding decrease of the thoracic curve, within structural limitations.

CERVICAL SPINE

The first cervical vertebra, the atlas, articulates with the occipital condyles and supports the head. The movement at the atlanto-occipital joint is forward and back in the sagittal plane; it is used when nodding affirmatively.

The articulations between the first and second cervical vertebrae (the atlantoaxial joints), are between the superior and inferior articular processes laterally, and in the median line between the odontoid process of the axis (which functionally becomes the missing body of the atlas) and the anterior ring of the atlas. The toothlike dens is supported by ligaments, and the horizontal plane of movement, turning the skull to the right or left, is suited to this vertical axis. The functional action at this joint is depicted when saying "no" by shaking the head.

The facing of the articular processes of the remaining cervical vertebrae gradually changes from upward-downward to forward-backward. The vertebrae gradually increase in size and the intervertebral discs become relatively larger. The cervical spine permits movement in all directions—flexion, extension, lateral flexion, and rotation.

THORACIC SPINE

The surfaces of the articular processes face forward-backward, which permits lateral flexion with rotation, flexion, and extension. Hyperextension in the thoracic spine, particularly above the ninth vertebra, is limited due to the downward slant of the spinous processes. The intervertebral discs are relatively thin in this region, and this factor, magnified by the restrictive nature of the thoracic cage, results in limited freedom of movement.

LUMBAR SPINE

The intervertebral discs are thicker in the lumbar region than in the cervical or thoracic spine. Freedom of movement is greater in those regions having larger and thicker discs. The articular surfaces are larger, and this influences the range of motion. However, in the lumbar spine the articular processes have a medial-lateral facing. This prohibits rotation of the vertebral bodies and serves as a protective mechanism, limiting mobility beyond the range of safety. Flexion, extension, hyperextension, and side bending have a relative degree of freedom in the lumbar spine, although side bending has less freedom than the movements in the sagittal plane.

LOCALIZATION OF MOVEMENT IN THE SPINE

LATERAL FLEXION

Side bending, or lateral flexion, is a compound movement accompanied by rotation of the verterbal bodies. Since the normal curves of the spine are located in the anterposterior plane, and lateral flexion is in the lateral plane, concomitant torsion or twisting of the vertebral column occurs with side bending. Lateral flexion in the cervical, thoracic, and lumbar spine will in part be governed by the degree of flexion or extension present in the anteroposterior plane. Side bending in the acutely flexed position occurs in the thoracic spine, since the lumbar region is locked to lateral flexion in this position. Side bending in hyperextension is located below the eleventh thoracic vertebra in the lumbar spine, since there is impingement of the downward-pointing thoracic spinous processes in the hyperextended position. Side bending in the erect position is most marked below the tenth thoracic vertebra and in the upper lumbar spine.

ROTATION

Rotation of the spine, or trunk twisting, is accompanied by lateral flexion, since this is a compound movement. Rotation of the spine is accompanied by lateral flexion, and lateral flexion is always associated with rotation of the spine; one movement does not occur without the other. The localization of rotation in the spine follows the general pattern of lateral flexion. According to Lovett (3), "Rotation, therefore, is located highest [in the spine] in the flexed position, lower down in the erect position, and lowest in hyperextension in the model cadaver, and child." (A basic understanding of movements of the spine is of paramount importance to the physical educator, physical therapist, occupational therapist, and other paramedical people who specialize in therapeutic exercises.)

SPINAL MUSCULATURE

The symmetrical development of the musculature of the trunk may become impaired from a variety of causes; congenital disorders, developmental asymmetries, habitual stresses during periods of rapid growth, traumatic injuries, infections, and pathological conditions may be causative factors. The student of preventive and corrective physical education should be aware of Wolff's law of bone growth: "Bone changes its internal architecture and external shape according to the manner in which weight is borne or stress applied." This may operate to the detriment of normal bone and joint development. Habitual malpositions may affect normal development of the joint or bone with concomitant stretching of the spinal musculature unilaterally and contractures of the antagonists. Habitual unilateral stress, which is muscular in nature, or weight bearing, together with gravital force may result in a gradual developmental deformity of the bones, discs, and joints.

SPINAL EXTENSORS

All movements involving partial or total spinal extension, either against the force of gravity or with gravity eliminated, activate the great muscle mass of the dorsal spine, the sacrospinalis. We need to visualize this muscle in order to understand its functions. Horizontally, the sacrospinalis is composed of three main sections: the iliocostalis, the longissimus, and the spinalis divisions. The most lateral section is attached to the ribs near their angles and, in the cervical spine, to the transverse processes (iliocostalis lumborum, dorsi, and cervicis); the middle section is attached to the ribs and processes of vertebrae (logissimus dorsi, cervicis, and capitis), and the medial divisions attach to transverse, articular, and spinous processes of vertebrae (spinalis and semispinalis).

The vertical sections of the muscle are attached to the sacrum, ilia, lumbodorsal fascia, the ribs, and vertebral processes and extend upward to the mastoid processes of the temporal bones and the occipital bone. The directional arrangement of the fibers indicates the functional areas of extension, i.e., lumborum (the lumbar spine), dorsi (the thoracic spine), cervicis (the cervical spine), and capitis (the head). A person may flex his lumbar spine acutely and extend the thoracic, cervical, and head; or, from the acutely flexed lumbar spine position, lateral flexion is possible in the regions above; and other regional combinations of movements are possible. The arrangement of the fibers of the sacrospinalis makes possible a greater variety of movements in the anteroposterior, lateral, or horizontal planes, and enhances the participation of the axial skeleton in total body movements.

The deep sections of the spinal extensors are located between contiguous vertebrae, more specifically between the lateral processes and the spinous processes (multifidus); between the transverse processes and laminae (rotatores); between contiguous transverse processes (intertransversari); between the spinous processes (interspinalis); and between the tips of transverse processes from the seventh cervical through the eleventh thoracic to the rib below (levatores costarum). In addition to extension of the spine in symmetrical action and development, the five deep muscles participate asymmetrically in rotary movements of the spine.

A discussion of the spinal extensors would be incomplete without mentioning the superficial neck muscles, the splenius cervicis and capitis. Functionally, these muscles working together extend the head and neck. With unilateral contraction, they rotate the head and laterally flex it to the same side.

SPINAL FLEXORS

The prime movers in flexion of the spine, located anterior and lateral to the spine, are associated with the abdominal musculature in trunk and thigh flexion. From the supine position, flexion of the spine is initiated by the anterior head and neck muscles (primarily the prevertebral muscles and the sternocleidomastoid). The abdominal muscles are the stabilizers of the pelvis when the trunk is curled upward against the gravital force. The psoas major, attached laterally to the bodies and discs of lumbar vertebrae, acts in conjunction with the iliacus and is one of the prime movers in trunk and thigh flexion. Performing these movements with the knees flexed minimizes the tension on the iliopsoas and reduces the hazard of low back strain. The function of the abdominal muscles during trunk and thigh flexion is to stabilize the pelvis. When these muscles contract effectively and stabilize the pelvis, they prevent a forward tilt of the pelvis, usually associated with hollow back. Trunk flexion should be observed carefully, for detection of an arch in the lumbar spine and a slight lateral bend to one side as the movement is performed.

Trunk flexion accompanied by a twisting motion of the trunk to the right activates the left external oblique and the right internal oblique muscles. In trunk twisting to the left, the opposite abdominal obliques are the prime movers.

INCLINATION OF THE PELVIS

The frontal plane of the pelvis is described as the vertical relationship of the anterior superior spines of the ilia to the superior border of the pubis. These two landmarks are in vertical alignment in normal postures.

The transverse plane of the pelvis is approximated by the relationship of the anterior superior spines and the posterior superior spines of the ilia. These two landmarks are approximately in horizontal plane in the balanced standing position.

The angle of inclination of the pelvis is the angle formed to the horizontal plane of the body from the posterior inferior spines of the ilia and the superior border of the *symphysis pubis*. In normal postural relationships of the pelvis, this angle should approximate 50 to 60 degrees from the horizontal.

Antigravity Muscles

The body in stance and in locomotor activities is supported and balanced by a series of muscles from the skull to the feet supporting the superincumbent body mass. These muscles, because of their function, have received the group designation: antigravity muscles. Briefly stated, the antigravity muscles are the extensors of the spine, hip joints, knee joints, and ankle joints, the abdominal muscles, and the retractors of the shoulder girdle.

THE TRUNK ON THE PELVIS

The trunk is stabilized over the pelvis in the erect stance by the sacrospinalis and splenius muscles posteriorly and the abdominal muscles anteriorly. The sacrospinalis is the great spinal extensor muscle. These two muscle groups are the stabilizers of the spine in erect posture.

The abdominal muscles have their attachment to the anterior portion of the pelvic girdle and are the prime stabilizers and movers of the trunk on the pelvis. These muscles of the trunk attached to the pelvic girdle are the antigravity muscles of the trunk and pelvis, and are concerned with the balance of the trunk in stance and of the axial skeleton when the body is in motion.

SHOULDER GIRDLE

The shoulder girdle is an incomplete bony girdle. The posterior portion is completed by the insertion of the rhomboids and the trapezii muscles to the scapulae, from their fixed points of origin on the spinous processes of thoracic and cervical vertebrae. There is a tendency for a downard and outward force on the shoulder girdle in the presence of forward head and round upper back, which places the rhomboids and trapezii muscles on stretch and weakens their supportive action. In normal posture the yoke formed by the clavicles and scapulae is balanced on the upper thoracic cage with a minimum of muscular tension.

The antigravity muscles of the body in stance are the sacrospinalis, gluteus maximus, quadriceps, gastrocnemius and soleus, rectus abdominis and the internal and external obliques, and the shoulder girdle retractors. Since these muscles serve to balance the body segments with their supportive action as indicated previously, they receive the group designation of antigravity muscles. It is interesting to note that the antigravity muscles of the axial skeleton receive the major developmental attention in the event of anteroposterior postural deviations.

Brown (1) has discussed the factor-of-safety motion in joints, a principle one needs to consider carefully in teaching body mechanics. "Since no two spines are alike," he says, "each one must be judged on its own individual structure. Whatever the anatomical shape of the bones, there is always an optimum position for function of that particular variety of spine, and that position is one in which none of the spinal joints are used at the extreme of flexion or the extreme of extension. The range of motion from this optimum position is entirely dependent upon the anatomical structure of the bones."

HIP JOINT

The position of the hip joint in normal stance is one of extension. Hyperextension in the hip joint is negligible, and what may appear to be hyperextension of this joint is due to an overextension of the lumbar spine. The principle muscle for stabilizing the hip joint and preventing the trunk from flexing acutely on the thigh is the *gluteus maximus*. A subject may stand with his weight on both feet without the participation of the *gluteus maximus*, providing the trunk is displaced backward slightly beyond the gravital line. However, if the trunk is displaced forward over the base of support or in the position of readiness for forward locomotion, the balance of the trunk over the femoral heads is lost without the supportive action of the *gluteus maximus*, and forward collapse of the trunk over the hip joint will occur if the *gluteus maximus* is weak or absent. The line of gravity changes forward or backward as adjustments to slight flexion or extension of the hip joints occur in stance, and this slight motion is associated with an increase or decrease in the pelvic inclination.

The action of the abdominal muscles is one of stabilizing and holding the pelvis upward while the *gluteus maximus* and hamstrings tend to pull downward, each muscle group acting to stabilize the forward or backward shift of the pelvis. As the angle of pelvic inclination increases, there is an increase in the lumbar lordosis. As the angle of pelvic inclination diminishes, the lumbar spine tends to flatten and the hip joints tend to extend toward complete extension. Both the abdominal and the *gluteus maximus* muscles are stabilizers of the pelvis in the sagittal plane.

KNEE JOINT

The gravital line lies in front of the knee joint, and the quadriceps muscles prevent the knee from collapsing forward provided the joint is not fully extended. However, the hyperextended knee is one which may violate the factor-of-safety motion in joints, and stress placed on the posterior ligaments and muscle attachments may gradually affect the normal function of the knee joint. The hyperextension of the knee contributes to an increase in the forward inclination of the pelvis or lordosis of the lumbar spine.

ANKLE JOINT

In the erect stance, the center of gravity lies in front of the ankle joint, and the gastrocnemius and soleus muscles aid in balancing the extremity over the base of support. The greater the forward lean of the trunk, the greater the action of the calf muscles to maintain the mass over the base of support.

REFERENCES

1. Brown, Lloyd T., "The Mechanics of Lumbosacral and Sacroiliac Joints," *Journal of Bone and Joint Surgery*, 1937, 19, 770-775.
2. Cobey, Milton C., *Postural Back Pain*, Thomas, Springfield, Ill., 1956.
3. Lovett, Robert W., *Lateral Curvature of the Spine and Round Shoulders*, 3rd ed., Blakeston, Philadelphia, 1916, Chap. 3.
4. Steindler, Arthur, *Kinesiology of the Human Body Under Normal and Pathological Conditions*, Thomas, Springfield, Ill., 1955.
5. Willis, Theodore Alan, *Man's Back*, Thomas, Springfield, Ill., 1953.

Chapter 9

DAILY LIVING ACTIVITIES

In order to apply the mechanical principles to the body in motion or to the resting state, one must direct his attention to the laws of motion, equilibrium or balance, leverage, and gravity as they pertain to movement efficiency and to static positions. In Chapter 6 we studied a basic approach to the laws and principles of mechanics and forces. In this chapter will discuss the performance of activities associated with daily living as they relate to these physical laws and mechanical principles. All individuals, children and adults, have a wide variety of experiences in day-to-day living. None escape from some form of activity within the total range of minimal to maximal physical exertion. Individual differences in age, maturation level, sex, health status, and occupational pursuits influence the intensity and duration of the activity.

Glassow (3) has presented a classification of static and dynamic postures which has stimulated physical educators to relate movement to its functional aspects or main purpose, namely: moving the body, moving objects, stopping moving objects, and maintaining equilibrium. During the course of the day a person moves his body or its parts frequently from one place to another, performing such activities as walking, running, skipping, hopping, sliding, climbing, stooping, and reaching. He may move other objects through the application of force supplied by his moving body as in pushing and pulling, or he may have the object become part of his body mass as in lifting and carrying.

In organizing our thoughts with respect to all activities, we should be aware of balance and maintenance of equilibrium as an integral part of the static positions the body assumes and the movements it performs.

MAINTENANCE OF EQUILIBRIUM

The stability of an object is dependent on the following factors:

1. *The size of the base of support with respect to the body or mass.* A person has greatest stability in the lying position. He is more stable in the sitting position than in standing with the feet together. The size of the base, while standing, may be increased by assuming a forward-stride or side-stride position.

2. *The relationship of the gravital line to the base of support.* The body has greatest stability when the gravital line falls within the center of the base of support, is less stable as it approaches the margin of the base, and loses stability when the gravital line falls outside the base. In locomotor activities, we recognize the loss of stability followed by recovery in a sequential pattern.

3. *The height of the center of gravity.* The center of gravity is located anteriorly in the area of the second sacral vertebrae. The exact location varies with the concentration of body weight. The individual possessing a heavy trunk and superior extremities, and proportionately less concentration of the mass in the lower extremities, will have a higher center of gravity. One may deliberately lower his center of gravity by bending the knees and hips and assuming a crouch position.

4. *The weight of the body or mass.* The greater the weight of the body, the greater the stability, providing the three above-named factors pertain.

STATIC POSTURES

Static postures are those wherein the body is not moving from one place to another, and one may assume the body is at rest. A minimum of muscular effort is needed for the reclining position. There is a slight increase in energy cost while sitting, and the standing position calls for an additional increase in energy output. Sitting postures call for some action of the trunk-balancing musculature; and in the standing position, the effort of the balancing mechanisms is magnified by the height of the center of gravity, postural sway, and the position of readiness for movement.

Lying Positions. The stability is greatest in the supine or prone positions. The body is relatively stable when side lying with the supportive leg flexed, and least stable in the side lying position with the legs straight and no supportive action from the hands and arms. Side lying, with a blanket roll or pillow placed along the trunk for support and the knees and hips flexed slightly involves an increase in the size of the base, improving the stability.

SITTING POSITIONS

The *long sitting position,* with knees extended, is the least stable because the ischial tuberosities support the trunk and there is a tendency to flex the trunk in attempting to move the weight inside the margin of support; there may also be flexion of the knee joint due to the tension placed on the hamstring muscles.

Hook sitting, with the knees flexed and the feet on the floor, alleviates the hamstring tension; however, the trunk tends to shift forward over the ischial tuberosities.

Cross sitting, with the knees flexed, the lower legs crossed, and the thighs outwardly rotated, widens the base laterally and thus improves stability. Another position, sitting on the floor, which we often observe in children and occasionally in young adults, is with the knees together and the feet to each side. In this position, the thighs are placed in inward rotation. The contact of inside borders of the feet with the floor places strain on the medial knee joint structures, and obviously this position should be discouraged.

Chair sitting: the prime requisite for efficient sitting is the selection of a chair with certain specific features which contribute to the comfort of the individual and make it possible to maintain the correct and efficient sitting posture. Anthropometric measurements of men, women, boys, and girls reveal a relatively wide variation of individual structural differences. For the adult, these differences include height, trunk length, upper leg and lower leg length, and body build. For the growing child, additional factors include age, sex, maturation level, and grade level for which furniture is selected. No one can decide that the sitting surface of the chair should be a certain number of inches from the floor for all persons, nor can anyone state the correct depth of the seat or the height of the back support—beyond an approximation for the average of the group.

Posture chairs which are adjustable for sitting height and support for the low back are standard equipment for secretaries and other office workers. Many elementary schools and junior and senior high schools have installed adjustable furniture. For the college student, there is a tendency to utilize standard design furniture without adjustable features. The important points to be considered are: Who adjusts the furniture, what adjustments may be made, and what are the criteria for adjustment?

Keegan (6) has presented some evidence that the trunk-thigh angle should approximate no less than 105 degrees in high-backed chairs. In addition, he has stated that the depth of the seat should never be greater than 16 inches and, as the height is increased, the depth of the seat is proportionately decreased. This suggestion is made in order to preserve the trunk-thigh angle, minimize the seat pressure in back on the lower thigh, and insure the feet-on-floor position.

General principles for correct seating include the following:

1. The trunk should be supported on the ischial tuberosities and buttocks.
2. The depth of the chair should support approximately one-half to two-thirds of the thigh; the front edge of the seat should be curled downward slightly. These two features minimize the pressure on the popliteal area located posteriorly in the lower one-third of the femur; they are conducive to comfortable sitting and enable the feet to be placed under the center of gravity when rising from the chair.
3. The height of the seat should permit placing both feet flat on the floor and changing the leg position occasionally. This will minimize the pressure of the anterior margin of the seat on the posterior thigh.
4. The backward slope of the seat should be approximately 5 degrees, to prevent slipping forward and aid in keeping the low back in contact with the support.

5. As the height of the seat is increased, the depth should be decreased.
6. The back support should be adjusted to the lumbar region of the spine.
7. There should be a place for the posterior buttocks and coccyx between the seat and the back support.

The exact height of the desk or workspace cannot be prescribed for all individuals; however, a few general principles may be useful. A desk or workspace which results in hunching or elevating the shoulders is too high; conversely, one that results in lowering the shoulders, rounding the back, and lowering the head, is too low. The shoulder and back musculature should be free from tensions, and the elbow joints should approximate a right angle when the hands are placed on the desk. The distance from the eyes to the desk top should be approximately 16 inches.

Adjustments in the functional aspects of nonadjustable furniture can be made. A foot support can be made with a "toe-toucher." A small pad may be placed to support the low back or to decrease the depth of the sitting space, and thus preserve the trunk-hip angle, allow the feet to reach the floor, and permit the forearm to be placed correctly on the desk. Other adjustments may be made as the need is apparent. For the homemaker, the selection of furniture should be made with the idea of permanence conducive to efficient and comfortable living.

DYNAMIC POSTURES

In order for the body to move from one place to another, a loss of balance or equilibrium occurs; and the principles of inertia and momentum apply. Loss of balance may result in recovery or in a fall, in which case the body meets a resistance which impedes further motion in the same direction. The law of opposite and equal reaction indicates that the resistance will strike back with the same amount of force it received from the object. As the body and the resistance approach in the termination of the fall, the gradual absorption of the force by the body or its parts is a planned safety procedure. When the body falls from a great height, the acceleration rate is magnified as it descends. Unless the resistance which is met has some resiliency and will allow gradual absorption of the force (as in a net, trampoline, or similar device), the body is unable to absorb the greater force in sequential order rapidly enough, and injury results.

The laws of equilibrium or stability, inertia and momentum, action and reaction, and acceleration are interrelated for the body in motion. In efficient movement, the action sequences may have certain differences or similarities in space, time, and force relationships; and the laws and mechanical principles pertaining to movement will relate and interrelate to all motion and action no matter how simple or complex.

WALKING

Walking is an activity in which we all participate in daily living. (Exceptions would include infants, wheel-chair patients, or people with handicaps or disorders that require a recumbent position.) The ability to move from one place to another is accepted as a normal function. Rarely does the *how* of this activity appear to be of equal significance to the individual as is the *where, when,* and *with whom* he walks. Yet we can observe individual characteristics in the movements of various people. In fact, we often are able to recognize from a distance certain friends or members of the family because of particular locomotor habits; we may even recognize a person's footsteps without seeing him.

Walking is a rhythmical action. There is a sequential repetition of body movements, including the alternation of the arm swing with the leg swing. There is a loss of balance as the swinging phase commences, and a recovery as the heel contacts the surface and the weight is transferred forward. The pattern is swing, contact, support, propel—repeated in alternation. The interrelationship of movements of the pelvis, upper leg, lower leg, ankle joint, and foot, with the opposition of arm and leg in the swinging phase, presents an extremely complex problem in describing the sequence of actions involved in locomotion. In individual evaluation of walking efficiency, we must shift our attention from one segment of the body to another and then return to the total pattern as we attempt to discover the deviations from the easy, rhythmical, effortless gait.

ANALYSIS OF THE PATTERN OF MOVEMENT IN WALKING (9, 10, 11)

1. The inertia of the body is overcome through the forward displacement of the body mass over the supporting leg as the opposite leg swings forward.

2. The forward swing is accompanied by flexion of the hip, knee, and ankle, with rotation of the pelvis and slight outward rotation of the hip. The knee is directed forward. As the leg swings forward, it is accompanied by the forward swing of the opposite arm.

3. As the heel of the moving leg contacts the floor, the knee joint is extended and the ankle joint is flexed. This is the restraining phase of locomotion, and the commencement of the period of double support when both feet have contact with the floor. The knee joint begins to flex as the foot meets the resistance of the floor.

4. In this period of double support, the center of gravity (located in the region of the second sacral vertebra) is at its lowest point in the movement sequence.

5. The lower leg moves forward over the ankle joint to the standing phase. The heel and the heads of the metatarsals assume the body weight. This is the middle of the stance phase of the supporting leg and the high point of the vertical ascent of the center of gravity. The lateral displacement of the center of gravity moves horizontally over the supporting leg. The amount of horizontal shift of the pelvis or adduction of the femur is influenced by the tibiofemoral angle.

6. The lateral and vertical pelvic displacements do not differ appreciably in degree of movement and occur in orderly sequence concomitantly, thus smoothing the gait in locomotor activities.

7. At this point the break in the contact of the heel occurs, and this is the commencement of the propulsive phase of movement in the supporting leg; the ball of the foot or the metatarsal heads are the contact area with the floor.

8. During the propulsive stage, as the heel of the opposite foot contacts the surface, the knee joint is extended and the digital action of the toes and the calf musculature give the final propulsive effort. This leg then swings forward. The pattern is repeated by the opposite leg to complete the cycle.

SUMMARY OF ANALYSIS OF WALKING

The synchronized sequential movements of the pelvis, hip joint, knee joint, ankle joint, and digits reduce excessive efforts, tension, and fatigue, and contribute to the efficiency of walking.

1. The sequential knee joint positions
   a. At the heel contact with the floor the knee is straight.
   b. As the weight is transferred to the supporting leg, the knee bends slightly.
   c. At the end of the propulsive stage, the knee extends.
   d. During the swinging phase, after the completion of the propulsive phase, the knee bends.
2. Ankle joint arc of motion
   a. At the heel contact, there is dorsal flexion.
   b. The tibia swings forward, gradually reducing the tibial-torsal angle to the near right angle as the foot assumes the standing phase.
   c. Extension of the ankle joint takes place in the propulsive stage as the calf muscles elevate the heel.
   The movement sequence simulates a rocker-type motion from the heel to the metatarsal heads and to the final digital action. We can visualize the probable effects of even minor limitations of motion in the ankle joint and, in so doing, become aware of the importance of ankle joint flexibility to efficient walking.
3. The pelvic adjustments of rotation, tilt, and lateral displacement are synchronized to reduce excessive motion, allay fatigue, and otherwise influence locomotor efficiency. These movements are dependent on the rotation and adduction of the hip joint. Restrictions of hip joint motion interfere with the adjustments of the pelvis essential to efficient walking.
4. The opposition of arm and leg pendular motions contributes to

the balanced position of the shoulders in alternation with the pelvis and associated with the swinging phase of the leg.

The mechanical principles and laws of which we must be aware in the evaluation of walking are those pertaining to motion, equilibrium, action and reactions, the pendulum and leverage; we must also recognize tensions as revealed by movement.

INDIVIDUAL DIFFERENCES IN GAIT

Observations of individual differences in walking pattern may reveal certain deviations from the basic factors previously described as essential to efficiency and ease of movement. The following procedure and points of stress are stated as a guide to making such observations.

1. Give particular attention to the total movement pattern. Does the gait appear to exhibit qualities of smoothness, coordination, and poise? Do the hips lead, with the shoulders overhanging the sacrum? Does the body in motion appear to have many angles, or is there segmental balance? Do you observe arm and leg opposition in the swinging phase of the total movement? Is the total effect of the body line and form pleasing, as you observe the subject walk toward, away from, or diagonally from the position you have selected?

2. Shift your attention rapidly to such specific parts of the total movement as follows:

   a. Observe knee position in various aspects of the movement. Is the subject a "heel pounder"? If the answer is yes, then check the knee position following the heel contact with the floor. Does the knee "give" slightly, or bend? If not, suggest that the heel touch the floor with less emphasis. It is interesting to note that as the weight is transferred to the whole foot, the knee will "give" to an easily flexed position. No conscious effort should be directed specifically toward knee flexion.

   b. Look for efficiency in the functional use of the foot.
      (1) Does he throw his foot to the side as he swings the foot and leg forward?
      (2) Are the feet placed too far apart and markedly everted,

resulting in noticeable side-to-side body sway?

(3) Do you observe heel-ball-toe action? Can you see the sole of the foot as he completes the propulsive phase of the movement?

Functional foot exercises practiced before a mirror are valuable in the correction of many of these habits. These exercises are primarily for the development of the "feel" or kinesthetic awareness of foot balance, weight transference, ankle joint flexibility, and the position of "knee over the foot" as the knee joint flexes in locomotor activities.

c. Direct the attention toward the key area for locomotor efficiency—the pelvis.

(1) Are you aware of an unusual amount of pelvic oscillation? Does the pelvis appear to swing noticeably from side to side, forward and back, or up and down?

(2) Does the individual appear to be "heavy footed," so that you observe a seeming collapse of the trunk into the pelvis?

These divergencies of gait in nonpathological subjects can be recognized readily by the novice in body mechanics. Consider these suggestions as a starting point, for not all the divergencies of gait are included in this discussion.

IMPROVEMENT OF GAIT

Improving the tonus and control of the abdominal musculature and the muscular ties between the pelvis and the femur may be your choice of specific conditioning exercises. Concomitantly, functional activities should be performed in the correct movement pattern, preferably before a mirror during the initial stages of the gait training program.

In order to modify or change a habit pattern and improve gait efficiency, here are several logical steps:

1. The person must have an intellectual concept of the pattern— a concise, clearly stated explanation.
2. He must have an accurate visual concept of the activity—a correct demonstration of the movement is basic to teaching the skills.
3. He must develop kinesthetic awareness or the "feel" of the move-

ment—experience the movement and receive constructive advice.
4. There must be frequent repetition of the correct movement pattern.

Gait training follows an orderly procedure of basic understanding, visualizing, experiencing, and practicing. Satisfactory results are obtained only when conscious effort and repetition of the correct movement pattern is employed.

WALKING IN HIGH HEELS

Wearing high-heeled shoes presents many problems of balance and ease of carriage to the young girl when she selects her first pair. The initial trial may not give her the same feeling of security she experiences when the foot is in its normal position; but high heels are a *must* for particular social functions, and they will be purchased and worn. If the group has designated heels for a specific occasion, the pain from being different causes greater pangs than the insecurity of "walking on spikes." Several factors which decrease stability in high heels are:

1. The height of the center of gravity is increased, which reduces stability.
2. The size of the base is decreased, which further decreases stability.
3. The high heel places the ankle joint in plantar flexion (extension), and the weight is shifted forward to the metatarsal heads and toes.
4. The freedom of the ankle joint motion is reduced, since the ankle joint is held in partial plantar flexion.
5. Lateral stability is reduced because of the small high heel, and is revealed by the lateral-medial wobble of the foot of the supporting leg.

Walking in high heels will therefore necessitate certain adjustments in the described movement pattern. Since stability is decreased, the following adjustments are necessary:

1. The length of the stride is decreased in order to preserve the margin of support under the center of gravity. Develop the kinesthetic awareness of stability rather than giving exclusive

attention to shortening the stride.

2. The arm swing is decreased, as are the oscillations of the pelvis, as the length of the stride is decreased. (As the step is lengthened, there is greater knee joint flexion, lowering the center of gravity). Concomitantly the arm swing, in opposition to the leg swing, and pelvic oscillation are more accentuated.

3. The time unit for heel contact is reduced to nearly simultaneous heel-ball contact at the beginning of the support phase. This change (from heel contact and the forward rocking motion as the weight is transferred forward) is necessary because the high heel has placed the foot in plantar flexion. Knee joint flexion of the supporting leg is increased in order to adjust to plantar flexion of the ankle joint, and the center of gravity is lowered, which improves stability.

4. Some subjects add an additional angulation through forward bending from the hips to accomplish greater stability and reduce the possibility of falling.

5. Other subjects may hold the arms away from the body to insure greater stability.

Some of these adjustments will enable a young girl learning to walk in high heels to develop control, ease of carriage, and security. Other adjustments mentioned will detract from the personal appearance and will give the impression that walking in high heels is a laborious, ungainly means of locomotion. If women are going to wear "spikes," and they will occasionally, they should learn what adjustments in gait are necessary and why these adjustments should be made. Practice is of paramount importance in order to develop the "feel" of stability, and at the same time to learn to create the illusion of complete body control and ease of movement. No additional effort or noticeable extraneous movements should be apparent when walking in high heels.

CARRYING OBJECTS

Certain adjustments in body alignment and in walking patterns are necessary when an additional weight becomes part of the body mass during locomotion. The principles of stability previously mentioned (which include the size of the base, the height of the center of gravity, and the relationship of the weight to the gravital line) are applied when a weight is carried. The size, shape, and weight of the object should be compatible with the principles of stability if strain is to be avoided. Maintaining the center of gravity of the mass as near the gravital line as possible, will lessen the movement force through a shortened movement arm. We must remember that the movement arm will be zero when the center of gravity of the mass is directly over the gravital line. It becomes greater the longer the distance between the gravital line and the center of gravity of the given mass.

A number of objects may be carried on the head in order to approximate the gravital line; others may be balanced on the hand above the head or on the shoulder. In making these adjustments for carrying certain weights, the center of gravity has been raised. In order to counteract this factor, which reduces stability, the knees are partially flexed, the feet may be placed farther apart, and the heel-ball-toe action reduced. When the weight is supported to one side of the gravital line, the trunk lean is toward the opposite side in order to adjust the weight over the base of support.

A heavy load carried in one arm or on one side of the body should have some of the weight distributed to the opposite shoulder near the root of the neck. This adjustment, which may be made with a padded shoulder strap, a heavy shawl, or a similar attachment, will place the weight close to the gravital line and over the margin of support. A small child may be carried with his head over one shoulder; however, if carried lower than the shoulder and to one side of the body, some of the weight may be transferred to the opposite shoulder through a supportive sling. This adaptation minimizes the possibility of strain inherent in the lateral shift of body weight while supporting an object. Adjusting to a heavy weight carried by one arm without support from the other shoulder will cause one to lean the trunk to the opposite side, elevate the opposite arm, or a combination of both movements to counterbalance the effect of the load.

A load carried in front of the body will result in a backward lean to the trunk in attempting to approximate the gravital line within the base of support. The reverse movement, or forward bending of the trunk, occurs when carrying a load on the back.

In order to minimize the possibility of strain when carrying objects, one should be aware of the following evident factors:

1. The length of the stride is decreased.
2. The center of gravity is lowered through knee flexion.
3. The whole foot is used as a unit to insure stability.
4. The walking speed is variable—rapid if the distance is minimal, and slower if carrying a load for a distance.
5. The stability is reduced if both arms support the object.

CLIMBING STAIRS

Ascending and descending stairs is performed so frequently in our daily living experiences that we pay little attention to how we climb from one level to another. The method of progression, the rate of ascent, and the regular repetition of the movement pattern should be considered in developing efficiency of performance. Extraneous movements and malalignment of the body detract from personal appearance and safety and, together with alternation in pace from rapid to slow, increase the energy cost of climbing. The speed with which a person moves depends on the height or distance he must elevate his body, the necessity for a rapid time-saving ascent, and his health status.

Climbing stairs increases the energy cost approximately 15 to 17 times the cost of walking the same distance on level ground. The optimum rate of ascent has been calculated to approximate 1.3 seconds per step for the average height step (5). In other words, greater efficiency in energy cost is possible if three steps are negotiated in 4 seconds. However, for people who have been cautioned to perform only light exercise, the rate of ascending a few steps is appreciably lowered.

MECHANICS OF CLIMBING STAIRS

1. Place the whole foot on the step. The size of the base is greater with total foot contact, and the action of the calf musculature is reduced.
2. Forward momentum is produced as the center of gravity moves

over the contact foot. There is a slight forward lean of the body in line with the supporting leg, associated with the propulsive phase of the foot.

3. The upward thrust or elevation comes from the contraction of the hip and knee joint extensors. The final propulsive effort from the calf muscles comes during the period of double support.

4. The knee moves from flexion to incomplete extension, which lowers the center of gravity and increases the stability. Complete extension may be associated with forward lean of the trunk from the waist, which detracts from total efficiency.

5. Rapid stair climbing changes the foot and knee position in that only the ball of the foot and toes are placed on the step and there is greater knee joint flexion of the supporting leg.

6. If the width of the step is not great enough to accommodate the total foot, a person may ascend the stairs by placing the foot on the step slightly on the diagonal. Allowing the heel to hang over the edge of the step may be conducive to stumbling as the foot is moved to the next step.

DESCENDING STAIRS

1. The supporting leg bends at the hip, knee, and ankle joints. Knee flexion is approximately double that of the hip and ankle joints in order to minimize pelvice oscillation and lower the center of gravity.

2. As the body is being lowered, the center of gravity moves over the base of support as it is established.

3. The foot of the moving leg is in extension as it reaches for the step, landing toe-ball-heel, with the knees gradually bending as the weight is assumed. This position allows the foot, ankle joint, and knee joint to gradually absorb the force of the lowered body, and in addition lowers the center of gravity and improves the stability.

4. To increase the feeling of security, a hand should be placed on the rail at hip level.

FAULTS TO OBSERVE

1. Is the body moving in balanced alignment?
2. Do the knees appear to be straight and stiff, or easy and relaxed?

3. Are the arms held away from the body for balance, or are they relaxed at the sides?
4. Is there noticeable pelvic oscillation, or does there seem to be balance and control?
5. Does the subject incline slightly backward over the supporting leg, or does the body move as a unit over the established base of support?
6. Does the foot strike the step with undue forcefulness, or is the base established quietly and effectively?
7. Is the foot placed on the step in eversion with pronation, or does the knee cover the foot as lowered to the toe-ball-heel contact?

STOOPING AND LIFTING

Almost no one who is ambulatory can escape from some sort of lifting. Violations of the mechanical principles of lifting may be observed frequently in the home, in transportation terminals, in markets and shops, or on the job. Consequently many employers today provide specific job training for personnel. This is an economically sound practice from the standpoint of time, motion, and conservation of energy, in addition to the prevention of injury.

Activities in the home that require some form of lifting are many and varied. The homemaker frequently performs tasks which, if done incorrectly, are contributing factors to either acute or chronic strain or injury to the lower back. We can observe this as people in the home perform tasks like lifting a baby from its crib, opening or closing windows or doors, removing a heavy container from a low oven, or stooping to pick up toys, papers, or magazines from the floor. The basic principles of stooping and lifting are applicable whether one is lifting a pin or a small child from the floor.

Stooping and lifting have common elements, and the same mechanical principles pertain to both activities. Stooping requires both lowering the body and lifting the body to the erect position. The same levers and muscle groups are used in both movements. The extensor muscles support the joint through lengthening (eccentric) contraction as gravity takes over to lower the body, and by shortening (concentric) contraction in lifting the body to the erect position. The principles for efficient movement are identical whether an individual picks up a magazine from a low table or removes a 20-pound turkey from a low oven.

The maintenance of equilibrium or stability is enhanced by widening the base and lowering the center of gravity. The individual who picks up an object from the floor with his knees relatively straight must rock backward on his heels to balance the weight pulling him forward. When stooping and lifting are performed in this manner, the trunk is the moving lever, the weaker back muscles must lift the trunk, and the danger of injury to the low back is imminent. When an additional weight is added to this lever, the force is magnified many times. Numerous injuries from lifting are attributed to this fault in lifting mechanics.

PRINCIPLES OF STOOPING AND LIFTING

1. To lower the body in stooping, increase the size of the base. This may be done by placing one foot backward to improve stability.
2. Lower the center of gravity—bend the hips, knees, and ankles, with slight forward lean of the trunk and the back straight. Keep the hips low; the knee should cover the foot in the squat position. The slight forward lean of the trunk moves the center of gravity over the base of support.
3. Lifting the body to the erect position requires extension of the knee, hip, and ankle joints. As the body approaches the extended position, the trunk moves slightly backward to keep the center of gravity over the base.
4. When lifting objects from the floor, keep the weight near the gravital line. Stand close to the object to be lifted. Step backward slightly to widen the base and bend the hips, knees, and ankles as explained in step 2. Grasp the object with the forearms in supination of in the mid-position. Lifting explained in step 3. Some people prefer to touch one knee to the ground in lifting an object with floor lever. The one-knee support may be admissable for certain heavy objects; however, it is usually better to receive the power for the lift from both legs.
5. If the object to be lifted is in front of the body, the step is to the side, feet in line with shoulders. The object is grasped between the feet and knees with the arms straight and held close to

the body. The feet should be directly beneath the hips and the knees over the feet.

6. Avoid lifting heavy weights, or those of unusual size and shape. Two or more people may lift a heavy load, provided the object is balanced and the lift is performed in unison. Girls should use extreme care in lifting heavy weights, since their body structure indicates a lower degree of the mesomorphic component. Women in industry are protected by law in some states from lifting loads over 25 pounds. A general rule for women is that the lift should not exceed one-fourth to one-third their own body weight, and for men one-half their body weight. Of course some people should not attempt to lift this maximum, and others may exceed these figures with adequate conditioning or training.

REACHING

This is an activity performed from a stable base. One may reach upward, diagonally forward, forward, backward, and to the side. Reaching downward is associated with lifting; and when this pertains, momentum is imparted to the object through action of the leg musculature.

1. The base is widened by the forward-stride position when reaching upward, forward, backward, or forward-upward. Widen the base laterally when reaching to the side.
2. The position of the pelvis is held in its normal relationship through muscular control. Avoid arching the low back in reaching, a tendency for a person who lacks pelvic control as the arms move into a forward or upward position.

PUSHING AND PULLING

The mechanical principles pertaining to pushing apply equally well to pulling. The direction the person faces is governed by the particular activity. Ordinarily, in pushing the force is directed forward, and in pulling the weight is transferred backward. Among the activities to which the principles apply are opening heavy doors, opening and closing drawers, vacuuming, moving furniture, raking leaves, or assisting in the care of people who are bed patients or semi-invalids.

PRINCIPLES OF PUSHING AND PULLING

1. Stand close to the object to be moved, on a firm surface.
2. Stand with one foot in advance of the other to increase the size of the base.
3. Lower your own center of gravity in line with the weight center of the object to minimize friction. Hips, knees, and ankles are flexed and the trunk is in line with the driving force of the legs.
4. Place your hands on the object near the weight center, hands in front of the shoulders and elbows bent. (Meeting a sudden resistance with straight elbows may cause an injury to the shoulder or elbow).
5. The force should be applied near the center of weight in the direction the object is to be moved.
6. The strong leg muscles supply the force.
7. The force is transmitted from foot contact with the ground through the central axis of the body to the hand contact with the object. Body weight and gravity augment the force of muscle action.

PUSHING, PULLING, AND HELPING OTHERS

One specialized area of action which utilizes these principles in a combination of pulling and lifting, is in the case of moving the bed patient or semi-invalid. If the patient is in the home, the height of the bed is one of the first considerations. For purposes of illustration, say the patient is to be turned from back lying to side lying. If the patient is large and heavy, two people may execute the movement without strain. Two movements are necessary: (1) move the patient toward the side of the bed, (2) turn the patient on his side.

1. When moving the patient from the center of the bed:
    a. Stand close to the bed, one foot in back of the other, hips and knees flexed slightly and the back relatively straight.
    b. Place the hands under shoulders and pelvis and thighs and lower legs, and step backward as you lower your hips. The

pulling force for moving the patient is supplied by the leg muscles, the momentum imparted to your body, gravity, and the weight of your own body. The patient can be moved by one person, pulling the upper and lower segments in sequence.

2. When turning patient to side lying:
   a. Cross his legs in the direction of the turn. Stand close to the bed on the side the subject will face.
   b. Place the hands slightly back of the shoulders and hips.
   c. Step backward and lower your hips to utilize your own leg action, momentum, and body weight, assisted by gravity, in order to execute the turn.

Aged persons who have been ill, or the handicapped, may need assistance in moving from a chair to the standing position, or in sitting down in a chair. Severe backstrain can result when a person assists in this simple procedure because the mechanical principles have not been known or properly executed. Assisting a person (1) to the sitting position and (2) from sitting to standing may be done as follows:

1. Assist to sitting position:
   a. Be certain the chair is stable.
   b. Subject stands ready to be lowered with one foot back of the other and slightly separated.
   c. The assistant stands close to and in front of the subject with a similar foot position.
   d. The patient places his hands on the assistant's shoulders and the assistant supports the subject under the arms and on the upper posterolateral rib cage.
   e. Both assistant and subject bend their knees and hips and lower the hips simultaneously as the subject's weight is transferred to the rear foot, then to the chair. Gravity is assisting to lower the subject, and the counterforce of the assistant's pulling action retards and smooths the descent.

2. Assist to standing position:

The reverse action of that in step 1 above takes place, with the exception that the weight of the assistant is moving backward and over the rear foot support. In the event the subject's knees may be insecure and tend to flex as the weight is assumed, the assistant's forward knee is in a position to momentarily support the subject's knee without strain.

The activities of pushing and pulling employ the laws of gravity, inertia and momentum, leverage, action and reaction, and the effective force from muscular contraction. A wide variety of activities in daily situations require the application of these principles if movements are to be performed efficiently.

SUMMARY

We have just discussed the performance of daily living activities as they relate to physical laws and mechanical principles. Every individual has a variety of movement experiences each day. Proper application of the laws of physics that deal with motion results in effective teaching of an activity, whether it be a giant swing on the horizontal bar or walking in high heels.

All children in the physical education program must be taught the fundamentals of movement associated with daily living activities. Special attention must be given to the child with a physical handicap when assisting him with such movements as walking, carrying objects, climbing stairs, stooping, lifting, reaching, and pushing and pulling.

If the physical educator overlooks the mechanical laws that govern movement, a number of problems may arise, such as (1) the development of unilateral imbalances which may result in curvatures; (2) unaesthetic postures; (3) undue stress around joints, which causes stretching of ligamentous structure and results in loss of integrity at the joint; and (4) general inefficiency of movement.

REFERENCES

1. Bowen, Wilbur P., and Stone, Henry A., *Applied Anatomy and Kinesiology*, 7th ed., Lea & Febiger, Philadelphia, 1953, pp. 347-352.
2. Fash, Bernice, *Body Mechanics in Nursing Arts*, McGraw-Hill, New York, 1946.

3. Glassow, Ruth B., *Fundamentals of Physical Education*, Lea & Febiger, Philadelphia, 1932, pp. 20-55.

4. Howorth, Beckett, "Dynamic Postures," *Journal of the American Medical Association*, 1946, **131**, 1398-1404.

5. Karpovich, Peter V., *Physiology of Muscular Activity*, 4th ed., Saunders, Philadelphia, 1953, p. 85.

6. Keegan, Jay J., "Alterations of the Lumbar Curve Related to Posture and Seating," *Journal of Bone and Joint Surgery*, 1953, **35A**, 589-603.

7. Lee, Mabel, and Wagner, Miriam M., *Fundamentals of Body Mechanics and Conditioning*, Saunders, Philadelphia, 1949, Chap. 7.

8. Metheny, Eleanor, *Body Dynamics*, McGraw Hill, New York, 1952.

9. Morton, Dudley J., *Human Locomotion and Body Form*, Williams and Wilkins Baltimore, 1952, Chap. 11, pp. 19, 21.

10. Saunders, J. B. DeC., Inman, Vern T., and Everhart, Howard D., "The Major Determinants in Normal and Pathological Gait," *Journal of Bone and Joint Surgery*, 1953, **35A**, 543-558.

11. Steindler, Arthur, *Kinesiology of the Human Body*, Thomas, Springfield, Ill., 1955, pp. 635-638.

12. Wells, Katherine, *Kinesiology*, 2nd ed., Saunders, Philadelphia, 1955, Chap. 17, p. 27.

Chapter 10

EVALUATION OF BODY
MECHANICS[1]

TEACHING efficient use of the body in the skills of standing, walking, and sitting is a valuable part of the physical education program, particularly on the elementary and junior high school level. This is as true for the normal child as it is for the youngster with a physical handicap. When this phase of the curriculum is neglected, a grave injustice is done to the pupils. We know that a body characterized by firm musculature and esthetic movement can be acquired through physical training.

When working with children who are physically handicapped, we need to be very much aware of the child's body mechanics; and we must spend sufficient time with the pupil to make him understand the principles involved in practicing good mechanics. It is far too easy for children with braces, weakened musculature, or prosthesis to use compensatory mechanisms to assist them in standing and walking. When this occurs, muscle imbalances may easily result, complicating the entire picture.

Recognition and appreciation of good body mechanics in the early years of schooling will significantly reduce the number of pupils in the corrective classes. Howland (17) says that grownups move in patterns of body movement that were developed early in childhood. Many of them slump and slouch without knowing it.

[1] This chapter was taken from: Donald K. Mathews, *Measurement in Physical Education*, Saunders, Philadelphia, 1958.

150

Then, in most instances, by the time poor alignment and inefficient body mechanics are recognized, it is difficult to ameliorate the deficiency. "As the twig is bent, so grows the tree" is an age-old truth. It is during childhood that attention must be given to the development of fundamental motor movements to insure lifelong benefits of efficient body mechanics.

POSTURE

No one will argue the value of good posture as it contributes to personal appearance. Thus, a primary purpose for teaching body mechanics is an esthetic reason. However, some authorities extol the health values associated with good posture. A great deal of controversial material appears in the literature, some authorities supporting a positive relationship and others stating that no relationship whatsoever exists. To illustrate a few of these differences, some of the statements and sudies relative to this problem are given below.

Klein and Thomas (21), in summary of a Chelsea, Massachusetts study, report the following effects on health and efficiency of teaching good body mechanics to over 1700 grammar school children:

1. Improvement of body mechanics was associated with improvement of health and efficiency.
2. Improvement of body mechanics was associated with improvement in school work.
3. Improvement in retraction ability of the lower abdomen resulted in elevation of the stomach and intestines.

Carnett (5), using X ray and administering barium or bismuth to adult subjects, found that the stomach commonly elevated 3 to 4 inches when the individual changed from a slumped to an erect posture.

The effect of dropped chest on the action of the diaphragm was studied by Goldthwait and associates (16) through the use of fluoroscopic tracings. The results of the study showed that in the correct standing position, with the chest held up, the diaphragm is also held up in its fullest possible motion.

The Baruch Committee on Physical Medicine (32) reports that many ailments and disabilities, some accompanied by severe and crippling pain, may have abnormal posture as their causative factor—perhaps many more such cases than is currently realized— and therefore the patients may be benefitted by having this functional abnormality corrected.

The studies reported above fail to show *specific* relationships as to how improvement of posture objectively affects physiological function. In most cases, the statements are generalizations, quite vague in terms of specifically correlating posture and health.

Karpovich (20) tells us that lordosis may be associated with orthostatic albuminuria (slight loss of protein in the urine). However, there is no scientific proof that improvement in posture leads to definite improvements in physiological functions of the body. In commenting on the claims that visceroptosis (sagging of the bowel) depends on posture, Karpovich states that this has yet to be proved.

In summary then, Howland (17), in a comprehensive search of the literature relative to the relationship between posture and health, has concluded that no writer seems to disclaim the health values of posture in their entirety. Some reject the health claims because of lack of scientific proof, yet all appear to believe that some correlation between posture and health does doubtlessly exist. It remains for the future to prove or disprove this correlation scientifically and to ascertain in what aspects of health and in which pattern of posture the correlation significantly exists. Writers, on the whole, are in accord (though expressed empirically) with the opinion that faulty posture is conducive to some inefficiency in body functioning and organic fitness.

Regardless of the relationship between health and posture, whatever it may be, the esthetic as well as functional values resulting from proper fundamental patterns of movement warrant the inclusion of good posture as a vital part of the physical education program. Through the use of scientific measuring devices, youngsters needing extra work in body mechanics can be discovered and steps may be taken to ameliorate the condition.

WHAT IS GOOD POSTURE?

Obviously, before measurement can take place, what you are going to measure must be defined. The definition, or description, of what good posture is actually becomes the criterion for measurement. That is to say, the description indicates the norm or standard on which we base our measurements and hence are able to state whether or not this particular position would be considered normal or a significant deviation from the norm. In terms of posture evaluation, this isn't easy. Each individual is unique; and this makes it difficult to establish what you might call an objective standard. For example, some people may have a more pronounced lumbosacral curve than others; yet both groups are quite normal. Because of this uniqueness of body structure, it not only becomes difficult to establish definitive standards but also it actually may be contraindicative to the best interests of the individual to try to make him conform. As an illustration, one early physical education teacher stressed the flat lower back for *every* student. The class worked hard to obtain this flat lower back, which is actually contrary for most individuals to the normal structure of the spinal column. To further illustrate the uniqueness of body structure, McCloy (30) reports that the shapes of vertebrae vary from those that necessitate a hyperstraight vertebral column to those that necessitate a fairly great degree of curvature in the vertebral column.

Additional studies (3, 18) indicate individual differences in the structure of the pelvis and lumbar spine as they are related to body mechanics. Thus we may conclude that individual structural differences must be recognized when defining "good" posture. Massey (27), in a comprehensive analysis of the literature, came to the conclusion that there seemed to be a general agreement on the criteria used to describe "good" posture. He also concluded that postural definitions fall into two categories, those that are descriptive and those that are anatomical.

DESCRIPTIVE DEFINITION

The principal segments of the body should be balanced evenly over the base of support. The feet are slightly separated, the toes point straight forward or slightly outward, the weight of the body is borne mainly over the middle of the foot. There is easy extension of the knee and hips. The pelvic bones should be in such a position that they balance the weight directly over the acetabula, with the spine functioning as a poised column with the weight distributed about it. This involves the preservation of a moderate curve in the lumbar region and an easy backward position of the shoulders, to bring the weight on the spine rather than on the chest. In this position, the shoulder blades are approximately flat, the chest is carried moderately high but not thrust forward, and there is normal tonus of the abdominal muscles. The head is erect and balances easily without backward tension or forward stretch. The position is alert, and the individual is capable of movement in any direction. The position does not represent an artificial, arbitrary, or complex combination of postural adjustments, but the most natural, comfortable, and perfectly poised position that the body can assume in standing.

ANATOMICAL DEFINITION

The standards for normal anteroposterior posture are defined by Steindler (37) in the following manner: Beginning approximately at the mastoid process, the line of gravity passes downward posteriorly to the vertebrae of the neck, intersecting the spine near the seventh cervical vertebra, passes anteriorly to the dorsal vertebrae, touches the spine again at the lumbosacral junction, passes behind the lumbar spine, passes in front of the sacroiliac junction to the center of the hip joint, then passes in front of the knee joint and drops to the base of support at the feet directly in front of the ankle joint. Balanced in this way, with the shoulders retracted, minimum moments of force are in effect for bending the body segments out of the line of balance.

These definitions are the basis for postural appraisal. Thus, before proceeding further into the evaluation of posture, the reader should have two definite facts in mind: (1) posture is unique to the individual; and (2) regardless of whether a posture test is classified as subjuctive or objective, in the final analysis the criterion must be derived from expert opinion.

EARLY POSTURE TESTS

For the most part, early attempts at evaluating posture were based on the reasoning that each body segment—the head, trunk, and lower limbs—has a center of gravity; and when the centers of gravity of all segments are perfectly aligned over one another, the gravitational forces acting on the body are in equilibrium. That is to say, as gravity is a constant force which we must offset in the upright position, it becomes necessary to describe body alignment in such a way that the moments of force tending to bend the body segments out of line must be brought into equilibrium. Authorities claim that the body is in good balance when a perpendicular line may be passed through the following five landmarks: lobe of ear, middle of tip of shoulder, middle of greater trochanter, just back of the patella, and in front of outer malleolus.

As might be expected, there are some differences of opinion as to the exact points through which this gravital line passes. For example, Steindler (37) places the line of gravity 4 cm. in front of the ankle joint, whereas Fox and Young (14) experimentally determined this line to lie just anterior to the center of the ankle joint or, to be exact, 0.95 cm. in front of the anterior border of the tibia.

Early posture tests made use of the gravital line by the examiner hanging a plumb line, or standing a pole, beside the subject. In this manner, the traditional five body landmarks, as well as exaggerated spinal curvatures, were described in terms of deviations from what was accepted by the examiner as normal.

Bancroft's vertical-line test and triple-line test (1) as well as the Crampton wall test (8) and Lowman's (25) method of examination were a few of the initial endeavors making use of the gravital line in measuring posture. This type of evaluation may be criticized because of its highly subjective nature. The test in essence becomes as good as the examiner's ability to determine deviations from normal. The plumb line, however, may serve as a useful instrument in teaching body alignment, for it is simple to make and is tangible evidence to the pupil of the gavital line.

Following the plumb line tests, a great deal of interest was exhibited in using silhouettes for posture appraisal. In this type of evaluation, silhouettes were taken of a large number of subjects; then judges graded the silhouettes, thus permitting the experimenter to establish scales or letter classification for posture.

Recent Posture Tests

Recent developments of postural appraisal techniques have been in the direction of more precise and specific measurement. Precision instruments are used in measuring such factors as segmental angulation relative to the gravital line and the longitudinal axis from photographs, silhouettes, and X rays. Even though considerable progress has been made, it presently appears that true validity of these tests must still rest, in the final analysis, with the skill of the examiner. We shall see, as we study the tests to follow, that perhaps in no other area of physical education is the instructor asked to bring into focus and apply his knowledge of such courses as physiology, kinesiology, and anatomy, as in the evaluation of body mechanics. It is here that the physical educator truly demonstrates his ability in appraising human body structure so that deficiencies may be noted and proper steps taken to ameliorate the conditions.

The application of evaluation of body mechanics to the physical education program may be classified into four categories:

1. *Static anteroposterior posture tests,* which include appraisal methods designed to measure deviations associated with the lateral or side view of the child in a standing position. Such deficiencies as poked head, kyphosis, lordosis, shoulder overhang, and protruding abdomen may be evaluated in this type of test.

2. *Functional appraisal methods,* dealing with the subjective evaluation which accompanies the classroom instructional unit of body mechanics. For example, the immediate ability of the child to stand, walk, sit, climb and descend stairs, raise and lower weights, and walk in high heels are examples of skills which may be taught during the body mechanics unit. Here the instructor may be subjectively evaluate these specific activities as the program progresses, making functional appraisal and teaching a continuous and interdependent process.

3. *Screening tests,* which are rapid forms of posture appraisal

used to select subjectively those children with marked mechanical deficiencies. Such tests are usually administered at the beginning, or during the first few weeks, of school in order to select those children who are in need of additional, individualized attention.

4. *Refined posture appraisal,* which deals more with quantitative measurement and evaluation, such as angle of pelvic tilt, amount of spinal curvature, and differences in leg lengths. This type of evaluation is used on those children selected, from the results of a screening test, as markedly deficient. Refined appraisal is more definitive and time-consuming; hence, it is logical that such measurement be used only on those youngsters who have been referred as a result of the screening test.

STATIC ANTEROPOSTERIOR POSTURE TESTS

These tests may be further divided into two groups. The first group consists of silhouettes or shadow prints for lateral standing posture. This method of evaluation generally begins with taking a silhouette of the pupil and subjectively comparing it with a standardized set of prints. The second group might be called objective anteroposterior tests, in which photographs are taken and various landmarks on the prints are measured. The term *objective* is used because the measurements are quite precise, requiring the use of protractors, calipers, and certain other specially designed instruments.

BROWNELL TEST OF SILHOUETTES

Brownell (4) made use of judges who arranged, in order of merit, 100 silhouettes of pupils' postures. Through appropriate statistical treatment of these data, a scale of thirteen silhouettes was finally developed. This scale is arranged in rank order with numerical units ranging from 20 to 120 assigned to each picture.

To use the scale, the teacher compares the pupil's silhouette with each type of posture appearing on the scale. The procedure is to first start at the bottom of the scale with the silhouette in question and work toward the top; then start at the top and work toward the bottom. By averaging the two comparisons, a posture grade for the pupil may be obtained.

CROOK'S SILHOUETTES OF PRESCHOOL CHILDREN

Crook (19), applying for the most part Brownell's technique for establishing a scale to measure anteroposterior posture, constructed a similar standard for the preschool child. Fifty judges evaluated 100 silhouettes, resulting in a norm for grading purposes. Scoring is accomplished by moving the silhouette to be graded along the scale until the standard type of posture most similar in quality is found. This is done from each end of the scale. The average of three separate comparisons is taken as the individual's posture grade. The grade recorded is the number below the standard type of posture on the norm most closely corresponding to the sample.

Some posture characteristics of the preschool child observed by Crook during this study are as follows:

1. Hyperextension of the knees. This deficiency is perhaps due to very flexible joints or easily stretched hamstring tendons, and is the first postural fault to become evident.
2. The pelvic angle tends to become larger with increased hyper-extension of the knees.
3. As a result of the above, a hollow back and protruding abdomen are apt to become more pronounced.
4. A compensatory curve may give rise to round shoulders.
5. Finally, the head is thrust forward to preserve the balance and the entire body alignment is in maladjustment from foot to head.

HUBBARD'S SILHOUETTE TECHNIQUE

One fault of the silhouette is that it blots out many significant features of body form which probably should be recorded. To eliminate this problem, Hubbard (19) used additional lighting devices placed in front of the screen. A battery of three 200-watt lamps is placed at each side of the subject and practically all the light is thrown on him. To the 1000-watt lamp behind the screen, a 500-watt lamp is added to throw more light down to the region of the ankles and arches. The camera is placed 10 feet in front of the subject. The lights are placed 3 feet in front of the subject and a little to each side so as not to obstruct the view of the subject from the camera.

The material used in this type of silhouette is the same as in the original—5 × 7-inch photographic printing paper. The time required to take and develop the pictures is also the same as for the silhouette. Some of the advantages of Hubbard's method are:

1. Difference in height of shoulder blades is clearly shown.
2. Direction of spine is portrayed without special marking.
3. Muscular development is easily seen.
4. A check on pronation of the feet is made possible.
5. Negatives which can be photostatically reproduced and enlarged are available in case there is need for further and more detailed study of the individual.
6. The silhouette becomes sufficiently clear for the examiner to measure and record findings at his leisure, saving the time usually consumed in making detailed measurements when the individual is being examined.

CHRISTENSON'S TECHNIQUE OF EVALUATING SILHOUETTES

Christenson (6), in attempting to provide an improved technique for evaluating antersposterior posture, superimposed silhouettes on Brownell's posture standards by means of a projecting machine. Four judges were used and the comparison of judgments through superimposition by projection resulted in very close agreement. In the same study, the ability of the judges to compare silhouettes directly to Brownell's standards was related to the judges' ability to evaluate silhouettes superimposed over the standard. The results are most interesting and seem to indicate that, when a well-defined criterion is used, subjective postural appraisal becomes much more objective. For when the judges' evaluations of silhouettes were directly compared to Brownell's standards, the range was 90 and the mean deviation 26.7, as compared to a range of 20 and a mean deviation of 2.85 for the judges' evaluation of the silhouettes superimposed on the enlarged standards.

KORB'S TECHNIQUE OF RECORDING SILHOUETTES

Korb (22), in a study somewhat similar to that of Christenson's, developed the Comparograph to permit the evaluation of silhouettes against a common standard. This is accomplished by placing an outline of the selected posture standard on the curtain before which the subject stands. Thus, the silhouette of the subject has an outline of excellent posture surrounding it in the final picture. The norm used on the outline as the standard of excellent posture was that of Klein's.

Korb found that this method of silhouette analysis increased the validity by 47.5 percent as determined by use of 76 judges. The reliability of the analysis, using the mean square contingency, showed C was .79 and, when corrected for broad categories, increased to .91. This method is adaptable to both sexes and to subjects of all ages.

OBJECTIVE ANTEROPOSTERIOR TESTS

CURETON-GUNBY CONFORMATEUR

Cureton (12), seeking the answers to effects of corrective exercises on the spine, recognized the need for valid and reliable instruments to measure anteroposterior spinal curvature. The conformateur (Fig. 15), the spinograph (Fig. 16), and the silhouette were studied in terms of reliability and validity.

The conformateur consists of a wooden upright erected from a base, the former having a number of spindles sliding horizontally through holes bored in the upright. The spindles are locked into position by a system of springs attached to cords woven in and out between the spindles. The subject stands with his back toward the rods so that when the rods are gently tapped in place, the tips of the rods just touch the spinous processes of the vertebrae.

In using the spinograph the subject's spine is lightly traced by the pointer, which simultaneously records the spinal contour on a black-board.

As a result of this investigation, Cureton found that the conformateur and spinograph gave comparable results, whereas the silhouette measurements were in error. The data taken from the silhouettes showed: (1) exaggerated thoracic curvature, (2) smaller lumbar curve than actually existed, and (3) exaggerated displacement of the posterior spine of the sacrum.

In commenting on the profile error of the silhouette, Cureton claims that the individual differences in development of the posterior back muscles becloud the true measurement. Furthermore, the position of the hands has much to do the profile view. In the event that a small error of just a few millimeters is made in measuring the picture, there results a much larger error if the measurements are multiplied by the enlargement ratio.

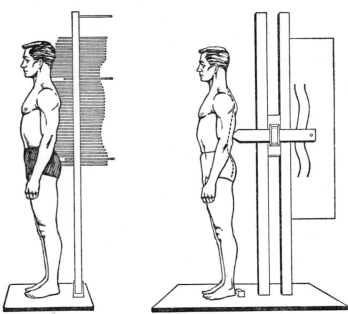

Fig. 15. The Cureton-Gunby Conformateur.

Fig. 16. Spinograph.

To eliminate error resulting from inconsistencies of subjects assuming exact positions in a series of trials, a manikin was measured with the various instruments. On the basis of these results, the Cureton-Gunby conformateur was devised. It is a combination conformateur, spinograph, and stadiometer with the following features:

1. Metal rods, precisely machined to uniform length and proper diameter, plated with cadmium to prevent rusting and having tapered ends.

2. Locking device which permits rods to be clamped into position as they are adjusted to the subject standing in a normal position.
3. Clamps are provided as an aid in certain studies.
4. Rods at the bottom to allow the location of the internal malleoli.
5. A plumb bob and line to allow the curve obtained to be related to the internal malleoli as a point in the base of support. The adjustable plumb line allows a vertical to be erected to any portion of the curve.
6. A leveling attachment to guarantee that the instrument is true vertically in relationship to the plumb line for anteroposterior measurements.
7. Holes are placed the entire length of the column to permit measuring a person of any size or measurement in the sitting posture.

Cureton recommends a combination of the conformateur and the silhouette for best results. Deviations of the spine can be measured with an experimental error as small as 1 percent. The complete measurement, including the picture, can be made in four minutes.

WELLESLEY POSTURE TEST

MacEwan and Howe (26) constructed the Wellesley posture test for women, which consists of making three measurements from a photograph: (1) the amount of anteroposterior curvature in the dorsal and lumbar spine, (2) the amount of segmental angulation and body tilt, and (3) the position of the head and neck. The sum of these measurements, which are weighted, becomes the posture grade. Grading is based on a scale from 1 to 25, which may be converted into a letter grade from A+ to E− inclusive.

To obtain the above measurements from the photograph, 11 aluminum pointers, 9 cm. long, 4 mm. wide, and 0.25 gram in weight, are affixed to the skin by means of short and narrow strips of adhesive tape. The pointers stand at right angles to the surface of attachment and indicate the real character of the anteroposterior curve and the point of flexure change. By measuring inward the proper distance from their tips, the actual position of the chest and spine can be drawn on the picture regardless of projecting scapulae, arms, and breasts. In appraisal of the photograph, three celluloid scales are used for each of the three measurements.

Eight judges were used in validating the Wellesley method; 858 subjects were photographed and eight prints of each subject were made. The judges, who were authorities in the field of posture, evaluated the pictures according to their own standards. In addition, a questionnaire was sent to each judge, the results of which indicated the importance of evaluating head and neck, upper and lower back, and weight distribution.

Validity of the test is claimed on the grounds that the battery of measurements is in agreement with the composite judgment of a group of physical educators who are outstanding in specialized study and experience in the area—posture of women.

In the final analysis, using 834 cases, the multiple correlation with reference to the criterion was .812. A regression equation was written as follows:

$$X_0 = 1.022X_1 = 0.128X_2 - 0.241X_3$$

0 = Criterion Measure (gross score of judges).
1 = Sum of depths of dorsal and lumbar curves.
2 = Segmental angulation and body tilt.
3 = Position of head and neck.

Today the Wellesley staff does not use this method of grading posture because of certain inadequacies (2). As an example, it is possible to obtain a much higher grade by bending the knees to reduce the lumbar curve, and by leaning well forward. It was found in numerous instances that the objective grade did not appear indicative of the picture, making it necessary to regrade the photograph subjectively. Furthermore, the amount of time necessary to put adhesive tape on the pointers and the number of staff members needed to handle the test seemed out of proportion to the results obtained. On this basis the staff at Wellesley has been experimenting with a subjective method of grading posture, but at the present writing it is not ready for drawing definite conclusions.

WICKENS AND KIPHUTH POSTURE TEST

Wickens and Kiphuth (40), working with Yale students, constructed a test to determine objectively the anteroposterior spinal curvature or segmental alignment from photographs. Before the student is photographed, the following points are marked with a black flesh pencil to serve as landmarks in the evaluation: tragus of the ear, front tip of the shoulder, acromion, greater trochanter, styloid process of fibula, and center of external malleolus. To determine the amount of anteroposterior spinal curvature, five aluminum pointers are attached to the back by means of 1-inch strips of adhesive tape. The pointers are located at that spinous process of the seventh cervical vertebra, the greatest concavity backward of the lumbar curve, and the most prominent part of the sacrum. To determine carriage of the chest, one pointer is placed at the lower end of the sternum. When it becomes obvious that the flesh pencil mark on the acromion will not show in the picture, another aluminum pointer is placed at this point to aid in the study of shoulder position. The student is then positioned for the picture, next to the plumb line which falls through the external malleolus. The plumb line is of help when determining body lean, as well as serving as a guide for drawing lines on the photograph.

After the picture is printed, the various measurements are taken. Because the pointers are of a known length, it is possible through measurement to locate the point of attachment. The aluminum pointers eliminate inaccuracies caused by projecting scapulae, heavily developed posterior muscles, or position of arm or elbow on the side facing the camera—all of which may be responsible for inaccuracies of the silhouette. Bow dividers are used for this procedure, and a small perforation is made at the location of attachment of the pointers. Also, a small perforation is made through the flesh pencil marks as well as at the flesh line of the most protuberant part of the abdomen. The glossy side of the picture is laid face down on the glass surface of a mimeoscope illuminated from underneath. This causes the picture to show through, allowing all the measurements to be made on the back of the picture. The lines are drawn with a hard pencil and angles are measured with a protractor. Linear measurements are read in millimeters from a vernier caliper.

HEAD AND TRUNK (Fig. 17). The position of the head and neck is determined by scaling the angle made by a horizontal line through the seventh cervical vertebra and a line from the seventh cervical vertebra through the tragus of the ear (angle E). The seventh cervical vertebra serves as a relatively immovable landmark with respect to the head. As the head and neck are thrust forward or backward, varying the position of the tragus, there is a change in the size of the angle. In the case of the poke neck, the angle is smaller as compared to the head being carried in a retracted position, when the angle becomes larger.

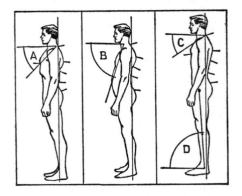

KYPHOSIS (Fig. 17). The amount of kyphosis is determined by scaling the angle made by a line from the greatest convexity backward to the dorsal curve through the seventh cervical vertebra and a line from the greatest convexity backward through the inflection point (angle *H*).

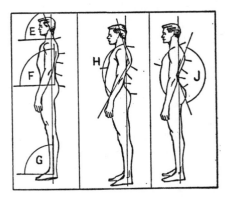

Fig. 17. Wickens and Kiphuth posture test.

LORDOSIS (Fig. 17). The lordosis angle is formed by a line from the greatest concavity backward of the lumbar curve through the inflection point and a line from the greatest concavity backward through the most prominent part of the sacrum (angle *J*).

In measurement of the upper and lower back, the straight spine will give an angle approaching 180 degrees. As the curvature is increased, the angle becomes smaller. When an individual has a reverse curve, a hollow in the dorsal region, and a prominence in the lumbar region, the reading will exceed 180 degrees.

CHEST (Fig. 17). It is generally accepted that the habitual position of the chest should be about halfway between full inspiration and complete expiration. As the chest is elevated on inspiration, it enlarges from front to rear as well as laterally. The front of the chest and sternum is carried upward and away from the spinal column. On the photograph, the angle formed by a horizontal line through the seventh cervical vertebra and a line from the seventh cervical vertebra through the end of the sternum gives a measure of the carriage of the chest (angle A). Men carrying their chests in an elevated position show a smaller angle than do individuals having a flat chest.

ABDOMEN (Fig. 17). In determining how the abdomen is carried relative to the chest, note if the abdominal line is straight and does not extend beyond the sternum. The angle formed by a line from the most prominent part of the abdomen through the end of the sternum and a horizontal line through the seventh cervical vertebra will be 90 degrees or greater. If the abdomen extends beyond the sternum, the angle will be less than 90 degrees (angle B).

SHOULDERS (Fig. 17). The shoulder angle is determined by scaling the angle made by a horizontal line through the seventh cervical vertebra and a line from the seventh cervical vertebra through the front tip of the shoulder (angle C). Measuring with vernier calipers the horizontal distance between two vertical lines erected through these points gives a line rating of shoulder forward. This is difficult to determine, since the shoulders cannot be measured relative to the head because both are quite movable.

TRUNK (Fig. 17). This is measured by using the angle formed by a horizontal line through the sacral point and a line from the sacral point to the seventh cervical vertebra (angle F). As the trunk leans forward, the angle becomes less than 90 degrees; in overcarriage, it increases from 90 degrees. This is important in segmental alignment, for it indicates the lean of the trunk forward or backward as it is balanced on the hip joint. The term *overcarriage* is applied in faulty mechanics of the trunk when the trunk's weight is carried backward so that a vertical line through the seventh cervical vertebra falls outside the prominent part of the sacrum.

HIPS (Fig. 17). The position of the hips is measured by the degree which the greater trochanter of the femur is carried forward or backward relative to the external malleolus (angle D). In the case of forward thrust, the angle formed by a horizontal line through the external malleolus and a line from the external malleolus through the greater trochanter of the femur is less than 90 degrees.

KNEES (Fig. 17). An idea of knee posture with regard to flexed knees or hyperextended knees may be obtained by scaling the angle formed by a horizontal line through the external malleolus and a line from the external malleolus through the styloid process of the fibula (angle G). In flexed knees, the angle will be less than 90 degrees; with hyperextended knees, greater than 90 degrees.

OBJECTIVITY AND VALIDITY. To determine the objectivity of attaching the aluminum pointers, of taking the measurements from the photo, and the relationship between the original photo measurements and those obtained from an enlargement (four times the original), 30 subjects were photographed and then rephotographed.

Objectivity coefficients for attaching the aluminum pointers were as follows: .721 for head and neck, .854 for kyphosis, and .730 for lordosis. Precision of measuring photos for the same three body segments ranged from .962 to .966. Objectivity coefficients obtained by comparing the original measurements to an enlargement for head and neck, kyphosis, lordosis, and chest ranged from .945 to .975.

Validity of the test was determined through comparing, when possible, other objective posture grading methods. One hundred and thirty-three subjects were photographed first with the conformateur (patterned after the one developed by Cureton) and then with the aluminum pointers. In the case of the spinal curves, angle measurements similar to those used with the pointers were applied to the corresponding points on the conformateur rods.

Here are the results of this analysis:

1. Relationship between conformateur and aluminum pointer method for following measurements:

$$\text{Head and neck} \quad r = .619 \pm .035$$
$$\text{Kyphosis} \quad r = .786 \pm .024$$
$$\text{Lordosis} \quad r = .838 \pm .018$$

2. The combined objectivity and reliability coefficients of the shoulder measurements were:

$$\text{Angular measurements} \quad r = .825 \pm .029$$
$$\text{Linear measurements} \quad r = .877 \pm .022$$

These measures apparently are influenced to a great extent by the slope of the shoulders, for the intercorrelation of these two measures was $r = .233 \pm .062$. Also, the size of the angles of the chest measurements must depend a good deal upon the carriage of the chest as the following intercorrelations indicate:

Chest normal $r = .76 \pm .041$
Chest expanded $r = .91 \pm .018$

MASSEY POSTURE TEST

Massey (27) had devised a usable and accurate method of measuring standing anteroposterior posture. In the construction of this

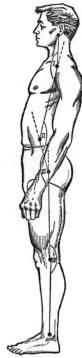

test, silhouettes were taken of 200 male students. A criterion was developed through the combined ratings of three qualified judges and through the further use of the methods of paired comparisons. A number of angles and indices were scaled and measured from the silhouettes, which were then correlated with the criterion. Elimination of certain of the variables was on the basis of low correlations with the criterion and in favor of convenience and precision of measurement. The remaining variables were combined statistically, and a posture formula expressed in regression form was devised. However, since the sum of the final test variables correlated .97 with the criterion, and since the weighted items in the regression equation raised the correlation only slightly (.985), the extra work of computing the grade from the posture formula doesn't make it worthwhile.

The following are the instructions for obtaining the posture angle measurements from Figure 18.

Fig. 18. Posture angle measurements for Massey posture test.

ANGLE I: Lines connecting the tragus to a midpoint bisecting a horizontal line drawn from the suprasternal notch to the spine, and to a midpoint bisecting the horizontal lumbar-anterior abdomen line.

ANGLE II: Lines connecting the midpoint of the suprasternal spine line to the midpoint of the lumbar-abdominal line and to the greater trochanter.

ANGLE III: Lines connecting the midpoint of the lumbar-abdominal line to the greater trochanter and to the styloid process of the fibula (midpoint of the knee joint).

ANGLE IV: Lines connecting the greater trochanter to the midpoint of the knee and to the lowest point of the external malleolus.

The angles are recorded in terms of deviation in degrees from a straight line. That is, if angle *I* is 170 degrees, it would lack 10 degrees of being a straight line. Therefore, the 10 degrees is recorded. Direct recording of the angles may be made by extending the drawn lines as indicated by the broken extensions in Fig. 18.

To obtain the posture grade, compute the sum of the angles and find the appropriate grade in Table 2.

TABLE 2. Posture Grades Based on the Approximate Steps of One Standard Deviation Above and Below the Mean

Total Degrees Angulation and Equivalent Posture Grades	
Sum of Angles I, II, III, IV	Posture Grade
8°–22°	A
23°–36°	B
37°–51°	C
52°–65°	D
66°–78°	E
79°–93°	F

SOURCE: Wayne W. Massey, "A Critical Study of Objective Methods for Measuring Antero-Posterior Posture with a Simplified Technique," *Research Quarterly*, March, 1943, 14 (1).

As a basis of comparison, Massey correlated several postural tests with his final criterion. The obtained coefficients of correlation with the Goldthwait test was .71; with the MacEwan and Howe, .560;

and with the Kellog test ("head angle," "chest ratio," and angle of "pelvic obliquity"), .855. On the basis of this analysis, one may conclude that the Kellog test and the Massey test measure approximately the same thing, and either could be used as an accurate measure in the appraisal of anteroposterior posture.

HOWLAND ALIGNOMETER

Howland (17) developed a technique for measuring and teaching structural balance of the body trunk in standing. This was accomplished by determining the balanced relationship between the tilt of the pelvis and the upper trunk, indicated by two anatomical landmarks: the center of the sternum and the superior border of the symphysis pubis.

It was found that when the sternopubic landmarks formed a perpendicular line parallel to the long axes of the separate parts of the body, as they approximate the vertical balance line (line of gravity), structural alignment of the trunk occurred. The technique was validated by use of radiographs, photographs, and a constructed measuring instrument called the *alignometer* (Fig. 19).

Study of the radiographs of experimental subjects revealed the following items.

1. Disalignment of the body trunk:
   a. The sternopubic landmarks were disaligned.
   b. The spinal column assumed exaggerated curvatures.
   c. The pelvic tilt presented a forward-upward direction at the symphysis pubis, with a flattening of the lower back.
   d. The thorax lowered, the head and neck inclined forward, and the upper back rounded.
   e. The knee joints appeared disaligned, either in hyperflexion or hyperextension.
   f. The weight-distribution line appeared to fall anterior or posterior to the supporting base between the feet (midway between the naviculars).
2. Assumed alignment of the body trunk:
   a. The sternopubic landmarks were aligned (vertically), and by linear measurement a rectangular parallelogram occurred between these landmarks and the plumb line (line of balance).
   b. The spinal column appeared to assume its natural curvatures.

c. The head, thorax, and upper back appeared balanced over the pelvis.

d. The pelvic tilt appeared to assume its midway position at a normal angle with the horizontal plane of the pelvis.

e. The knee joints appeared to assume a closer proximity to the 180-degree angle between the articulating segments.

The alignometer (Fig. 19) was designed by Howland for the purpose of measuring objectively the ability of a person to assume trunk alignment in accordance with the development technique. It is also used as a teaching device through which the technique may be more readily interpreted and practiced. The instrument consists of a simple arrangement of two sliding, calibrated pointers attached to a perpendicular steel rod. The rod is firmly supported on a wooden plank. The two sliding pointers used to locate the center of the sternum and the superior border of the symphysis pubis have a calibrated extension from their supporting arms, which slide along the perpendicular rod to meet the varying heights of tested subjects. Additional similar, but noncalibrated, sliding pointers are located above and below the sliding pointer indicating the center of the sternum. A vertical calibrated rod connects these two additional pointers; it is used in determining the exact center between the upper pointer, which

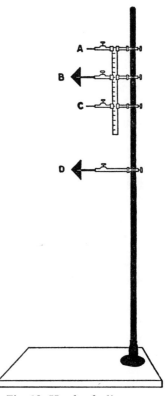

Fig. 19. Howland alignometer. *A*, pointer for locating center of sternum; *C*, pointer for locating base of sternum; *D*, pointer for locating the symphysis pubis. (Courtesy of I. Howland.)

locates the superior border of the sternum, and the lower pointer, which locates the base of the sternum. The sternal center is found by measuring the half distance between the upper and lower pointers on the sternum. The central sliding pointer is then set at the center of the sternum.

When the subject is in balanced trunk alignment (center of sternum directly over the symphysis pubis) the difference in readings, between the calibrated pointers at the sternal center and the superior border of the symphysis pubis, should be zero.

The objectivity of the instrument was determined by the test-retest method, which resulted in a correlation of .923. The relationship between the sternopubic line and this criterion (traditional lateral landmarks) was determined by computing the linear distances between them and correlating the line lengths. A high relationship was found between the sternopubic line and the distance between the acromion process of the scapula and the greater trochanter of the femur, $r = .889$. This is interpreted as meaning that when the center of the sternum and the center of the symphysis pubis are aligned, the upper and lower portions of the body trunk are considered aligned to a high degree.

The Howland technique, as taught and as measured by the alignometer, appears to represent the most encouraging scientific advancement in the appraisal and teaching of standing structural balance that has been proposed for some time. The following advantages of this method seem to overcome many problems characteristic of testing:

1. The alignometer is a teaching as well as a testing device.
2. The instrument is simple to construct and the subject is quickly and easily measured.
3. The technique takes into consideration the uniqueness of body structure regardless of age, size, or sex.
4. The test is valid in terms of the criteria as well as being objective.

CENTER OF GRAVITY TEST

Cureton and his associates (11) investigated the center of gravity in subjects as related to posture, fitness, and athletic ability. Cureton's center of gravity test, adapted from Renold's and Lovett's (33) original work, indicates the distance that the center of gravity is being balanced in front of the internal malleoli.

The test (Fig. 20) is administered in the following manner:

1. The subject is asked to step on the balance board, facing in the direction of the length of the board.
2. The internal malleoli are lined up even with a vertical pin located in the exact center of the board. The board is supported at both ends from the center of each scale.

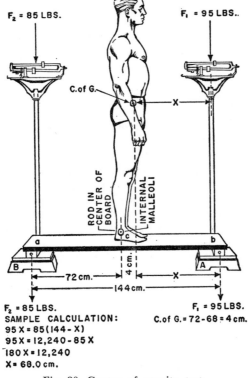

F_2 = 85 LBS.

F_1 = 95 LBS..

C. of G.

X

ROD IN CENTER OF BOARD

INTERNAL MALLEOLI

a   c   b

B   A

4 cm.

72 cm.

X

144 cm.

F_2 = 85 LBS.
SAMPLE CALCULATION:
$95X = 85(144 - X)$
$95X = 12,240 - 85X$
$180X = 12,240$
$X = 68.0$ cm.

F_1 = 95 LBS.
C. of G. = 72-68 = 4 cm.

Fig. 20. Center of gravity test.

3. The scales are balanced—first the forward one, then the rear scale—until both have their lever arms swinging freely between the guide stops. (Toledo scales facilitate this measurement.) The subject is then instructed to step down from the balance board. The scales are read and both readings recorded. One-half the weight of the board is deducted from each reading.
4. The calculation is made in accordance with the procedures appearing

in the illustration, the result being the distance that the center of gravity is being balanced in front of the internal malleoli.

With expert examiners, the objectivity of the Cureton center of gravity test is .91 as reported on 74 seniors.

In order to determine the significance of the test, the outcome was correlated with a number of measurements of posture, physical fitness, organic condition, and athletic ability. The results of these experiments are as follows:

1. There is a definite trend for men who habitually stand with their weight more forward to have straighter upper backs than do those who held their weight less forward.
2. There is a slight indication that men who stand with their center of gravity relatively more forward tend to have lower arches. This seems to bear out Cureton's original observation that stronger men have slightly flatter footprints.
3. Of outstanding interest are the correlations with the Rogers Strength Index and PFI. A correlation of .506 was obtained between the SI and the center of gravity test, while correlations of .75, .59, and .505 were obtained between the center of gravity test and the PFI. It appears that men in better condition as indicated by the strength tests stand habitually with their weight carried relatively farther forward of the vertical line through the malleoli.
4. The correlation between the center of gravity test and the Sargent vertical jump was .490, indicating that the men who stood with their center of gravity relatively more forward are better athletes as measured by the Sargent test.

Cureton suggests that this simple center of gravity test opens up the way for many possible studies, including:

1. The effect of high-heeled shoes on the carriage of body weight with relation to the base of support.
2. Typical weight balance of extremely fat persons, hunchbacks, pregnant women, old men bent with age, people with foot trouble, etc.
3. Norms for erect standing balance for all ages and both sexes.
4. The relationship between weight balance and foot defects.

The center of gravity may also be measured through the use of one scale instead of two. In this case, the subject stands at the center of the board, which is balanced at the point of two triangular blocks

1 meter apart. One block rests on the platform scale, and the other block rests on a support standing at the identical height of the platform scale. The following formula is applied to determine the distance in centimeters that the center of gravity is in front of the point resting on the block:

$$\frac{\text{Weight of subject on board} - \text{Weight of board on scale}}{\text{Weight of subject}} \times 100$$

Since the distances that the heel and toe are from the center of the board can be measured, the relationship of the center of gravity to the foot may be determined.

SCREENING TESTS

Washington State College Screening Test (35)

The posture screening test is used to select those subjects from the total group whose body statics indicate a need for a more detailed examination. Subjective ratings are made by the examiner of anteroposterior and lateral balance, and alignment of the feet and legs in the standing position. In addition to static balance, the efficiency of the gait is evaluated. Each subject is observed from the side, back, and front positions.

GENERAL PROCEDURE

In order to screen a group of students in a minimum period of time, a series of numbers (from 1 to 40 or 50) should be placed on the floor in a single line. Each student writes his name on a card and then assumes his position immediately back of a number. The examiner and a recorder write the number on the student-held card and collect all cards.

The recorder is provided with a master card for the total group. On this card a series of numbers (also from 1 to 40 or 50) has been placed under each of the following categories:

1. Anteroposterior. Combinations of obvious deviations such as marked fatigue slump, shoulder overhand, and imbalance of the

segments such as the head, shoulders, back, and legs are observed from the side view of the subject.

2. Lateral deviations. The subjects are observed with either face or back toward the examiner.
   a. Head tilt to one side.
   b. Shoulder height (one shoulder higher).
   c. Hip prominence (one hip more prominent).
   d. Rib prominence (one side of rib cage more prominent).
   e. Leg alignment (knock-knee, bowleg, tibial torsion, or inward rotation of thighs).
   f. Feet (pronation, supination, short heel cord, hammertoes, hallux valgus).

Throughout the static balance screening test, the frequent change of position from side view to front view to back view will be noted. These changes of position are desirable for the student because they facilitate circulation and minimize fatigue.

SPECIFIC PROCEDURE

1. The students, facing the examiner and standing behind a number, make a quarter turn right or left as indicated by the examiner. The recorder and examiner then move along the line about 6 feet from the subjects, and, as a noticeable imbalance is detected, the correct number is circled under *AP* by the recorder.
2. The students turn and face the examiner. Again the same procedure is used. Head tilt right or left and shoulder high right or left are recorded when observed.
3. Each subject stands with his back toward the examiner, who moves down the line and observes whether the hip line is symmetrical. An *R* or *L* is placed at the appropriate number if one hip appears to be more prominent than the other.
4. Assuming the same position as in step 3, the feet are separated approximately 2 inches, with the heels in horizontal alignment (one foot should not be in advance of the other). As each number is called, the designated subject curls his trunk forward with head, shoulders, and arms relaxed forward, finger tips reaching midway between the knees and feet; he then returns slowly to the erect

standing position. The examiner keeps his eyes on a level with the back, noting any protrusion of one side of the rib cage. The recorder indicates R or L on the number if asymmetrical rib prominence is present.

5. The subjects face the examiner, who checks for knock-knees, bow-legs, tibial torsion, inward rotation of thigh, or other imbalance in the transmission of body weight to the base of support.

6. The subjects stand with backs toward the examiner, with feet separated slightly. Observations are made for deviations of the heel cord from a straight line, and whether the weight thrust is greater to the medial or lateral side of the foot. Pronation or supination of the foot is noted and, if present, R, L, or bilateral (bil.) is recorded; if the condition is severe, marked (mkd.) is added.

OBSERVATIONS OF GAITS

A right-angle triangle is marked by placing two objects on the floor at two of the angles while the examiner stands at the right angle. The distance of the two sides of the right angle is approximately 20 feet in length. This arrangement will enable the moving subject to be viewed from the back, side, and front.

Efficiency of gait is rated on the following points:

1. Functional foot use—heel, ball, toe action.
2. Flat feet or marked pronation.
3. Increased pelvic oscillation.
4. AP balance while walking on the diagonal.
5. Repeat of observations 1, 2 and 3 as the subject walks toward the examiner.

With efficient organization of the procedure, approximately 40 subjects may be screened in a 45-minute period.

Following the screening, the findings may be recorded on the student's card (Fig. 21) from the master sheet. The students in need of a more thorough evaluation are located at the beginning of their physical education class work.

FUNCTIONAL POSTURE APPRAISAL

As has been previously indicated, this type of measurement employs a check list of selected criteria used in evaluating the body subjectively, in both a static and a dynamic state. The tests are referred to as being functional because the pupil is appraised on the specific skills which are taught and practiced in the classroom.

Name			Age	Height	Weight	
Standing			*Walking*			
	Slight	*Marked*			*Slight*	*Marked*
AP Imbalance			Lateral Balance			
Lat. Imbalance			AP Balance			
Hip Prominence			Pelvic Oscillation			
Left						
Right			Func. Use of Foot			
Rib Prominence						
Left			Pronation of Feet			
Right			Remarks:			
Leg Imbalance						
Foot Imbalance						

Fig. 21. Individual body mechanics screening card used at Washington State College for all incoming freshman girls.

Figure 22 shows a score card which may be used in making such an appraisal. Figure 23 depicts a suggested floor plan for conducting the functional test. This particular method of evaluation was worked out over a period of years and was found to be quite efficient in that 8 to 10 pupils may be carefully evaluated in 30 minutes.

The following outline gives the order in which the evaluation is made, as well as notations of the more important mechanical factors which should be observed.

1. In the standing posture, the examiner from the side view looks for such traits as are listed on the card appearing in Figure 22 under "Standing AP Posture."

2. The subject makes a quarter turn and the examiner then evaluates lateral balance in accordance with the items appearing in Figure 22.
3. The pupil is now asked to walk to the chair (Fig. 23) and be seated. The examiner looks for control of the weight over the rear foot and segmental alignment of the body as the subject lowers himself to the

Name	Score			Age	Height Score				Weight		
Standing AP Posture				Leg imbalance							
Shoulder overhang				Foot imbalance							
Forward head				Mechanics of Sitting							
Round back				Down							
Hollow back				Up							
Hyper knees				Walking AP Posture							
Pron. ft.				Lateral balance							
Lateral Balance				Pelvic control							
Shoulder height Lt.				Foot position Heel-ball-toe							
Rt.				Reaching Mechanics							
Hip Prominence Lt.				Stair Climbing Up					Rating Scale: 1—Excellent		
Rt.				Down					2—Good		
Rib Prominence Lt.				Lifting Mechanics Lowering weight					3—Fair 4—Poor		
Rt.				Raising weight							
				Rope Skipping							

Fig. 22. A functional scoring card.

sitting position. One foot should be to the rear of the other; hands and arms should remain relaxed and comfortable.
4. In the "up movement," once again the examiner makes note of transfer of body weight from the rear or supporting foot as the body is moved forward and up.
5. The tester now moves to position himself to observe the child from the rear as he walks the length of the room. He notes and records

such faulty mechanics as hip oscillation, whether the foot follows through in the heel-ball-toe movement, and whether the weight is thrust to the medial of the foot.

6. As the subject nears the end of the room he turns to his right and walks three-quarters of the distance across the room. This permits the examiner to check walking mechanics from the side or AP position. He notes the segmental balance and general carriage of the body.

7. At approximately three-quarters of the distance across the room, the pupil is asked to stop and reach upward and slightly forward. The examiner notes control of the pelvis and its relationship to the upper extremity, in order to determine mechanical efficiency of the body in this extended position.

8. The child is then asked to continue walking across the room and to be seated in the chair (Fig. 23). Once again the examiner checks for weight transfer and body position, as in step 3, for sitting and step 4, for rising from the chair. (While the subject remains seated, the examiner may take this opportunity to recheck his recording of deficiencies noted up to this point.)

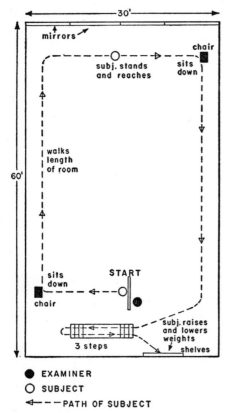

Fig. 23. Floor plan for conducting functional posture test.

9. The examiner then asks the pupil to rise from the chair and walk toward him. This permits observation of performance of the foot and leg function in walking, hip oscillation, erectness of carriage, and head tilt.

10. The pupil is now asked to climb and descend the stairs while the examiner watches for the proper transfer of body weight alignment of the body parts. This is repeated in order that the examiner may observe the subject from the side, front, and back. In the up movement, first the ball of the foot and then the heel should make contact; there should be an easy extension of the body weight over the supporting foot as the next step upward is made. In the down movement the observer notes particularly the pelvic control and whether the pupil bends the supporting leg adequately as the toe touches in order to allow the foot to be lowered with a minimum hip oscillation.

11. The child is then tested on lowering a weight of approximately 5 to 8 pounds from a shelf above his head to the floor and returning it to its original position. A series of shelves arranged from the floor to a height of about 7 feet facilitates this evaluation. Particular note is made of segmental balance, the manner in which the legs are used in moving the weight, and whether or not the pupil holds the weight to the gravital line of the body.

12. The final test consists of having the pupil skip rope. The examiner observes segmental alignment and the control and coordination that the pupil exhibits in this activity. A quiet landing, as the youngster skips, is indicative of good control.

REFINED POSTURE APPRAISAL

These tests are generally used on children who, from the results of a rapid screening process, have been referred to a special class in body mechanics. It now becomes the duty of the instructor to investigate thoroughly the underlying causes of the deficiency. For example, you have discovered that little Mary Jones in the fourth grade has a scoliosis. Certainly, before you being a training program for her, you must determine is this curvature is structural or whether it is the result of bad posture habits. If the cause of a deficiency is not completely understood, it is possible to do more harm than good. Hence, all structural deviations or conditions about which you are doubtful must be referred for medical or orthopedic diagnosis. When referral is made, you, as a physical educator, should determine, through a conference with the nurse, doctor, and parent, if you might assist the child on an individualized program under the supervision of the physician. In such cases, the more refined and specific instruments of evaluation may be employed to determine status and measure progress. Also, such objective evidence as gained through the use of measurement will be a valuable motivator for the child and for the instructor.

KRAUS-WEBER REFINED POSTURE TEST (23)

The Posture and Corrective Exercise Clinic of Babies Hospital and the Vanderbilt Clinic, during 20 years of experience, found that in systematic evaluation of body mechanics, measurement must include:

1. Sufficient morphologic (body form and structure) information.
2. Sufficient functional data (physiologic tests).
3. A clear picture of the condition.
4. Simple procedures, economical to administer.
5. Only simple instruments, to save expenses and to adhere to the above four steps.
6. Only necessary tests.

In an effort to work out a scientific evaluation of posture, the structural and functional measurements made according to the following outline have been successful.

1. Directions
   a. Measurements are taken with the subject in the standing position unless otherwise noted.
   b. The subject stands with feet 1 to 2 inches apart.
   c. The weight of the subject's body is evenly distributed on both feet; the knees are straight.
   d. The subject looks straight ahead at the mark on the wall opposite to him, at eye level.
   e. The subject's body is relaxed and inactive, his arms are hanging at his sides.
   f. The subject stands in the above position for 2 minutes to allow him to sink into habitual alignment before starting the test.
   g. The examiner marks anatomical points on the subject in order to test with facility. (Skin pencil or lipstick may be used.)
2. Structural measurements (using body landmarks)
   a. Chest expansion (in inches over xyphoid bone)
      (1) In neutral or midway position.

(2) On extreme inspiration.

(3) On extreme expiration.

b. Scapulae spine distance (in inches, using caliper and ruler)

   (1) From posterior process of the dorsal vertebrae, at level of the inferior medial angle of the scapula, to the inferior medial angle of the same scapula.

   (2) The above measurement is repeated for the other scapula.

   (3) The caliper is used to find the distance; the distance is measured with the ruler.

c. Level of the scapulae (caliper and water-level ruler) (Fig. 24)

   (1) The water-level ruler is placed horizontally so that it touches the inferior angles of the scapulae.

   (2) If not on a horizontal level, the level is held horizontal at the lower scapula and extended across the back beneath the other scapula. The caliper is used to measure distance from the water-level ruler held at the lower scapula to the highest scapula.

d. Level of the anterior superior spine of the ilium

   (1) The water-level ruler is placed on the level of the anterior superior spines of the iliac bones.

   (2) If it is not level, the same procedure is used as in the scapulae test.

e. Length of legs (use steel tape to measure)

   (1) The subject is supine on the table.

   (2) The distance from the anterior superior spine of the ilium to internal malleolus (medial) is measured.

Fig. 24. Measuring level of scapula.

f. Angle of pelvic tilt (protractor measurement) (Fig. 25)

   (1) The protractor is held against the lateral aspect of the hip joint so that the straight line (0 to 180 degrees) is parallel to the long axis of the femur. The knees are kept straight. The protractor is adjusted so that it is parallel with the sacrum. The obtuse angle between the 0- and 180-degree line and the arm of the protractor is then read. (Normal reading: 160 to 165 degrees).

g. Dorsal kyphosis and lumbar lordosis (plumb line and calibrated water-level)
  (1) The subject is placed with his back to the plumb line, which is suspended from the ceiling.
  (2) The distances from the plumb line to each of the following points is measured, using the calibrated water-level ruler:

Fig. 25. Measuring angle of pelvic tilt.

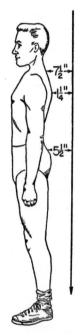

Fig. 26. Measuring dorsal kyphosis and lumbar lordosis.

  (a) Posterior process of seventh cervical vertebra.
  (b) Posterior process of vertebra at the apex of kyphosis.
  (c) Posterior processes of fifth lumbar vertebra.
  (3) Dorsal kyphosis and lumbar lordosis degrees are computed by taking the apex of the kyphosis as reference 0 reading and subtracting its distance to the plumb line from other distances.

EXAMPLE:

Readings of Rule	Subtract Kyphotic Apex	Referred to Apex 0
7th cervical 8½″	1½″	7″
Kyphosis apex 1½″	1½″	4″
5th lumbar 5½″		

3. Functional measurements (muscle tests of elasticity and strength). The length of the muscles, measured by the maximum degree of active joint range, indicates muscle elasticity.

   a. Total elasticity of the pectoral muscle (protractor)
      (1) This is indicated by the angle formed by the arm when fully raised and parallel with the long axis of the thorax.
      (2) The subject raises his arm in the forward direction as high as possible.
      (3) The protractor is held laterally against the subject's shoulder joint, with the straight line of 0 to 180 degrees parallel to the long axis of the thorax.
      (4) The arm of the protractor is adjusted parallel to the length of the axis of the humerus, and the obtuse angle read.
      (5) The above steps are repeated on the other shoulder joint.
      (6) Normal muscle reading: 170 to 180 degrees.

   b. Total elasticity of hamstring muscles
      (1) This is measured by the angle to which the legs may be lifted from the supine position without causing a motion in the fourth and fifth lumbar vertebrae.
      (2) The subject lies completely relaxed in the supine position on the table.
      (3) The protractor is placed with the straight line of 0 to 180 degrees on the table next to subject's hip joint.
      (4) The examiner places his fingers lightly on the posterior spinous processes of the fourth and fifth lumbar vertebrae under the subject's back.
      (5) The assistant slowly lifts the subject's legs, holding them at the heels (preferably one at a time).
      (6) The instant that the examiner feels motion in fourth and fifth lumbar vertebrae, the full length of hamstrings has been reached. Further movement of the legs upward causes movement of the lumbar region in a posterior direction.
      (7) When the examiner feels motion, the assistant stops lifting and holds the angle.
      (8) The arm of the protractor is adjusted parallel to the length of

the axis of the femur, and the acute angle between the table level and the femur is read; 30 degrees is a normal reading.

MUSCLE POWER AND HOLDING POWER MEASUREMENTS[2]

Muscle power (strength) is tested according to its ability to overcome gravity by assuming a test position. The holding ability of the muscle is measured by the time the subject can hold the position. The first five Kraus-Weber tests of minimal muscular fitness appear below.

ADMINISTRATION

There should not be any warm-up prior to taking the tests.

In the description of the six tests which follows, the words *upper* and *lower* are used to indicate test movements rather than any specific areas.

TEST 1 (FIG. 27)

In this test, the strength of the abdominal and psoas muscles is determined.

DESIGNATION.   "Abdominals plus psoas" or *A*.

Fig. 27. Strength test of abdominal and psoas muscles.

---

[2] This is a misnomer, as "power" denotes time rate of doing work, i.e., Power = Force × Acceleration × Time. "Strength" would be a more appropriate term. See p. 103.

POSITION OF PERSON BEING TESTED. The subject is supine, with hands behind neck; the examiner holds the subject's feet down on the table.

COMMAND. "Keep your hands behind your neck and try to roll up into a sitting position."

PRECAUTIONS. If the person being tested is unable to perform this movement at first try, it may be because he has not understood the directions. Help him a little, and then let him try again. Watch for a stiff-back sit-up. This may indicate that either the subject has not understood you and needs a further explanation with emphasis on "rolling up," or that he has very poor abdominals and is doing most of the work with his psoas.

Watch also for a twist of the upper body as the subject sits up. If one is noted, it may be due to unequal development of the back muscles.

MARKING. If the person being tested cannot raise his shoulders from the table the mark is 0. If, unaided, he is able to reach a sitting position, the mark is 10. If the examiner must help halfway to the sitting position, the mark would be 5. The distance from supine to sitting is marked by 0 to 10.

TEST 2 (FIG. 28)

This is a further test for abdominal muscles.

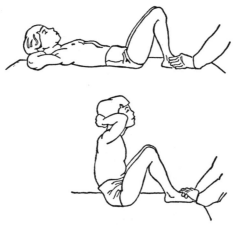

Fig. 28. Abdominals minus psoas strength test.

DESIGNATION. "Abdominals minus psoas" or *A* —.

POSITION OF PERSON BEING TESTED. The subject is supine, with hands behind neck and knees bent. The examiner holds the subject's feet down on the table.

COMMAND. "Keep your hands behind your neck and try to roll up into a sitting position."

PRECAUTIONS. The precautions are the same as for Test 1; but as Test 2 is usually more difficult, the tendency toward stiff-back sit-up will be even more pronounced. There is also a tendency to use an elbow to help with the movement.

MARKING. Same as Test 1.

TEST 3 (FIG. 29)

This tests the strength of the psoas and lower abdominals.

DESIGNATION. "Psoas" or *P*.

POSITION OF PERSON BEING TESTED. The subject is supine, with hands behind neck and legs extended.

COMMAND. "Keep your knees straight and lift your feet 10 inches off the table. Keep them there while I count." The count is 10 seconds. (Adding any three-syllable word after each number makes the count fairly reliable as to time. For example, "One chimpanzee, two chimpanzee, etc.")

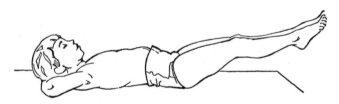

Fig. 29. Strength test of psoas and lower abdominal muscles.

PRECAUTIONS. If the person tested has not understood your command, he may try to raise his chest when he raises his feet; he will then need further explanation. Watch for an extremely arched back, which may indicate very weak abdominal muscles, or postural habits contributing to sway-back or lordosis.

MARKING.   Holding for 10 full seconds is passing and is marked as 10. Anything less is recorded as that part of the ten seconds that was held: 4 for 4 seconds, 7 for 7 seconds, etc.

TEST 4 (FIG. 30)

This tests the strength of the upper back muscles.

DESIGNATION.   "Upper back" or *UB*.

POSITION OF PERSON BEING TESTED.   The subject is prone with a pillow under his abdomen, but far enough down to give the body the feeling of being a seesaw, one end of which could be held in the air if the other end were weighted. The commands will aid in getting the subject in the proper position.

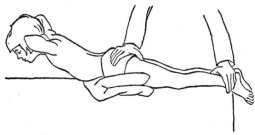

Fig. 30. Upper back strength test.

COMMANDS.   "Roll over onto your stomach and lift up the middle so that I can slide this pillow under you." (Be sure the pillow is large enough to really support the subject.) "Now I am going to hold your feet down while you put your hands behind your neck and raise your chest, head, and shoulders. Hold them up while I count." The count is ten seconds.

PRECAUTIONS.   Do not let the person being tested drop his chest onto the table or rest on his elbows. Watch for pronounced muscular development on one side of the spine. If this condition is present, the back should be checked from time to time to guard against scoliosis (curvature of the spine).

MARKING.   Holding for 10 full seconds is passing and is marked as 10. Anything less is recorded as that part of 10 seconds that was held. For example, a person staying up for 4 seconds would get the mark of 4.

TEST 5 (FIG. 31)

This tests the strength of the lower back.

DESIGNATION.   "Lower back" or *LB*.

POSITION OF PERSON BEING TESTED.   The subject remains prone over the pillow, but removes his hands from behind his neck, places them down on the table, and rests his head on them.

COMMANDS.   "I am going to hold your chest down on the table; try to lift your legs up, but do not bend your knees." There may be

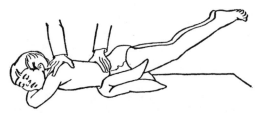

Fig. 31. Lower back strength test.

a tendency to bend the knees or even to support the legs by keeping the toes on the table. It may be necessary to assist the subject to the required position. "Now, hold this position while I count." The count is 10.

MARKING.   Holding for 10 full seconds is passing and is marked as 10. Anything less is recorded as that part of the 10 seconds that was held; for example, 4 seconds would be 4.

TEST 6 (FIG. 32)

This tests the length of back and hamstring muscles.

DESIGNATION.   "Back and hamstrings" or *BH*. (Total elasticity of back and hamstring muscles.)

POSITION OF PERSON BEING TESTED.   The subject stands erect in stocking or bare feet, with hands at his sides.

COMMANDS.   "Put your feet together, keep your knees straight; now lean down slowly and see how close you can come to touching the floor with your finger tips. Stay down as far as you can for a count of 3. *Do not bounce."*

PRECAUTION. Watch out for bouncing. The furthest point reached without bouncing and held for 3 counts is the marking point. The examiner should hold the knees of the person being tested in order to prevent any bend.

MARKING. Touch is designated with *T.* Touch is only given when the floor-touch is held for 3 counts. Less than touch is marked by the distance in inches between the floor and the finger tips. For example, a person unable to touch the floor by 2 inches would be marked "−2."

Fig. 32. Length of back and hamstring muscle test.

INTERPRETATION OF MEASUREMENTS TAKEN

STRUCTURAL MEASUREMENTS (USING BODY LANDMARKS)

1. The chest expansion measurement. This is of value in determining the relative expansion and breathing capacity.
2. The scapulae-spine distance. If this is unequal, a lateral curvature of the dorsal spine is a possibility.
3. Level of scapulae. If this is uneven, there is a lateral curvature of the spine or a disturbance of tension in the muscles of the shoulder girdle.
4. Level of the anterosuperior spine of the ilium. If this is not horizontal, there is a lateral tilt of the pelvis, possibly due to scoliosis in the lumbar region.
5. Comparison of leg lengths. One leg shorter than the other may indicate a lateral tilt of the pelvis and a curvature in the lumbar spine, with the apex of the curve on the side of the shorter leg.
6. Measurements of the angle of the forward pelvic tilt. If the angle is less than 160 degrees, increased lumbar lordosis is a possibility; if it is more than 170 degrees, this is indicative of a flat back.
7. Measurements for dorsal kyphosis and lumbar lordosis. These show an increase of the curves in direct proportion to the increase in distance between the seventh cervical and fifth lumbar vertebrae, to the apex of

the curve marked 0, and a corresponding decrease if these distances decrease.

1. Pectorals. If the angle is less than 170 to 180 degrees, there is a possibility of shortened pectoralis muscle group, which is associated with anterior displacement of the shoulder, a narrow chest, restricted range of motion in the shoulder joint, and possible dorsal kyphosis.
2. Hamstrings. If the angle measured is less than 30 degrees, this indicates a shortness of the muscle group of hamstrings.
3. Erector spinae and hamstrings. In the bending test, the distance from the finger tips to the floor gives an indication of the length of both muscle groups. Comparison with 2 above indicates whether the erectors or the hamstrings are contracted.

EVALUATION OF THE FEET

Seldom is attention given to the feet until they begin to pain. Many shoes worn by women are particularly harmful to foot health. There is a minimum of scientific evidence basic to the present shoe design; beauty and personal appeal essentially dictate shoe construction. The most glaring example of foot abuse is the spike heel on women's shoes. Such construction causes the weight of the body to be shifted forward over the balls of the feet, resulting in restricted movement of the Achilles' tendon, perhaps eventually causing it to shorten. Then, too, high heels frequently are the cause of hard calluses appearing on the soles of women's feet as a result of the body compensating for this unnatural weight placement. Data from the American Foot Care Institute indicate that about 85 percent of all foot troubles come from faulty footwear.

Bancroft (1) claims that from 57 to 61 percent of flat feet are serious enough to be discovered between the ages of 10 and 25, indicating need for special training in hygiene of the feet during this time when the neuromuscular system is immature and weight is rapidly increasing. Stafford (36) found, in examinations of school groups and army recruits, that 6 to 13 percent of those examined had true flat feet or sunken arches and 73 to 78 percent had weak feet.

FOOTPRINT

One of the early methods of evaluating the feet was by means of the footprint. The most convenient method for recording the footprint is by use of the pedograph. Directions for the use of this instrument are as follows:

1. The subject should be in his bare feet.
2. The machine should be properly inked so that the print is clear. It will be necessary to re-ink the machine for approximately every 50 pupils.
3. The stamping cover is pulled over clean paper. The subject is instructed to place his bare heel against the steel plate of the pedograph and then stand firmly on the stamping cover. There should be no extraneous movement of the foot, which might result in an inaccurate print. The opposite foot should be removed from the floor so that the full weight of the subject is brought to bear over the foot being tested.
4. The subject is instructed to step off the stamping cover. The sheet is then removed. The subject's name and the date of print are recorded.
5. The procedure (steps 1-4) is repeated with the subject's other foot.

CLARKE'S FOOTPRINT ANGLE

Schwartz (34 originated the footprint angle, which is a measure of the height of the longitudinal arch. Clarke made slight modifications of Schwartz' original work, with the resulting objectivity coefficient of .968. Figure 33 illustrates the Clarke footprint angle, which is scored in the following manner:

1. Line A is drawn to represent the medial border of the footprint between the imprint of the head of the first metatarsal bone and the calcaneus.
2. Line B is drawn from a point where line A first touches the imprint of the inner side of the big toe to the point just touching the edge of the print on the inside of the arch. This line represents the slope of the metatarsal border of the longitudinal arch. No white paper should show between this line and the print.
3. The angle at junction of lines A and B is measured with a protractor.

The average for college freshmen, according to Clark's data, may be considered to be 42 degrees. Clarke claims that anyone with angles below 30 degrees may definitely be considered a proper subject for individual foot corrections. Students with angles between 30 and 35 degrees may be considered as borderline subjects, and should be given a re-examination to determine the possible need for corrective treatment.

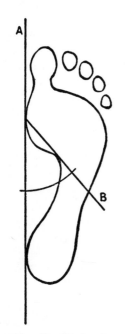

Fig. 33. Clarke footprint angle.

OBJECTIVITY AND VALIDITY OF FOOTPRINT ANGLE

Cureton (10) studied the validity of the footprint angle method of measuring the height of the longitudinal arch by comparing the vertical depth of the arch imprint in moist sand (sandbox method) to the Clarke footprint angle. The correlations between the arch angle and the arch height on two separate sets of data were .857 ± .016 and .958 ± .007.

In order to determine the validity of footprints as a measure of the functional efficiency of the foot, Cureton selected such events as running, jumping, weight-bearing, shot-putting, lifting, and balancing on the balance beam to correlate against the height of the arch. This type of event was selected because it was felt the foot is used vigorously in its execution.

Twenty-one correlations of the longitudinal arch with the selected skills showed that there was some positive correlation with 440-yard running. This might indicate that the men with the flatter prints have a tendency to fatigue more quickly, which Cureton feels may be true of most big-muscled men.

Of the 600 men tested, Cureton reported that 150 had arch angles under 21 degrees and only four or five men complained of pain. Apparently the height of the longitudinal arch does not represent either strong or weak feet. Actually, on the basis of Cureton's findings, the footprint angle serves no other purpose than to motivate the pupil in directing attention to the feet.

THE PEDORULE (13)

The pedorule was devised to measure the position of the foot in relation to the leg, as contrasted to the footprint angle which measures the height of the arch. By use of the pedorule, those subjects with abnormally low arches would not be given a misdiagnosis of weak feet, thus negating the obvious weakness of the footprint angle.

The pedorule is a rectangle of heavy plate glass, 7 inches wide and 9 inches high, with the surface scored in parallel lines $\frac{1}{10}$ inch apart. It measures the amount of deflection that the Achilles' tendon makes from a straight line. In weak feet, the lower portion of the tendon appears to be deflected outward.

Directions for measuring with the pedorule are as follows:

1. The pedorule is placed immediately behind the foot being measured, and two points are established by ink marks: (1) the midpoint of the Achilles' tendon as high on the calf of the leg as possible, and (2) the midpoint of the back of the heel.
2. The center line of the pedorule (which for convenience should be colored) should, on the normal foot, bisect these two ink marks.
3. In making observations, one eye should be closed; the examiner should be in such a position that the open eye will be approximately 24 inches directly behind the center of the pedorule.
4. From this position (above) three readings can be made: (1) the distance from the extreme tip of the external malleolus to the center of the tendon, (2) the distance from the internal malleolus to the center of the tendon, and (3) the distance from the center of the tendon to the center of the pedorule. (The center line of the pedorule will coincide with the center line of the tendon of Achilles if the arch is neither flat nor weak.)

A second method of determination of flat-footedness by the pedorule consists of:

1. Placing the center line of the pedorule directly behind the center of the tendon at the point where it is bowed inward the farthest.

2. Counting the number of lines from this point to the tips of the
   malleoli and subtracting the distance from the tendon to the internal malleolus from the distance from the center of the bowed-in
   tendon to the external malleolus. The distance that the tendon of
   Achilles deviates from the perpendicular will thus be found.

Danford recommends this latter method, for it is less confusing
and more efficient than the one first described. The perfect foot
would be "zero" thus showing the tendon to be equidistant between
the malleoli throughout its entire length. The objectivity coefficient
was found to be .94.

VALIDITY OF THE PEDORULE

Danford intercorrelated three methods of evaluating the feet: (1)
between two subjective examiners, (2) between the pedograph and
the pedorule, and (3) between each of the instruments and the
examiners.

The relatively high correlation existing between the subjective
examiners and the pedograph (.54 and .50) is attributed to the fact
that, in judging subjectively, an examiner notes the portion of the
foot not touching the floor and the pedograph print merely shows the
ground plan of the foot. Thus, in both examinations, to a great extent, the ground plan of the foot is studied without taking into
consideration whether or not the foot was normal or that it had
become flattened.

The correlation between subjective examiner #1 and the pedorule was .38; and that between the subjective examiner #2 and the
pedorule was 4 points lower. This may be explained by the fact that
subjective examiner #1 had included in his records the position of
the Achilles' tendon in relation to the foot.

The low correlation of .30 between the pedograph and the pedorule indicates that these instruments are not measuring the same
thing. The pedograph measures the footprint angle, and the pedorule is measuring the distance that the tendon has departed from
its normal position, which indicates how much the arch has flattened.

Two extreme cases of disagreement between the pedograph and
the pedorule tests were selected for more careful analysis. A subject
with a footprint angle of 11 degrees and pedorule reading of zero

for both feet was questioned as to any discomforts which might be caused by his feet. It was learned that the subject believed that he had fallen arches because of information given him. However, he never suffered any pains in his feet, legs, or back that could be attributed to flat feet.

In another extreme, where the pedograph had recorded a footprint angle of 42 degrees, which is supposedly average, the pedorule score was "five-tenths" for the right foot and "four-tenths" for the left. Because of this sharp discrepancy, the subject was asked if he had ever had any trouble with his feet; it was found that he could not take hikes, play basketball, or stand on his feet very long at a time because of severe pains in his feet, legs, and back. He also reported frequent headaches.

These two cases, of course, are not sufficient to validate the pedorule completely. However, these facts support the idea that measurement of deflection of the Achilles' tendon is a better method of evaluating feet than merely recording the footprint. This study clearly illustrates that the greater bowing-in of the tendon, the flatter the arch, although arches were often recorded as flat by the pedograph when the tendons were not bowed in.

When either the pedograph or pedorule is used, both feet should be measured; for in some subjects, the right foot might be markedly pronated or flat while the left foot is apparently normal. Rogers reports a correlation of only .28 between the right and left feet, using the footprint angle.

TRUSLOW'S FOOT RATIO

Truslow (38) has found, through clinical experience, that the ratio of the height of the arch to the length of the foot is a valid determinant in regard to the functional efficiency of the foot. From numerous foot measurements, Truslow found a normal mean ratio between the height of the arch and length of the foot to be from 7.7 to 8.3 percent. The computation is simply the height of the arch in centimeters divided by the length of the foot in centimeters times 100.

The equipment used for the measurements consists of a small draftsman's triangle (about 12 × 12 × 18 cm.) measured off on one of its shorter sides into half centimeters; and a shoe dealer's foot-measuring rod, rescaled from the heel post forward into half centimeters.

The measurements taken are as follows:

1. Height of arch with subject standing. The subject stands with feet parallel and about 12 inches apart. The examiner places the measured side of the triangle against the inner side of the foot, at the position of the scaphoid (navicular) bone; then places his pencil point beneath the bone and reads the height on the triangle. He records this for the right foot, and then measures the left.
2. The height of the arch for both right and left feet is also measured with the subject in a sitting position.
3. The length of the foot is measured with the subject in a sitting position. The reading at the tip of the great toe is noted and recorded for both the right and left feet.

The measured height of the right foot with the subject standing is divided by the measured right-foot length and the quotient recorded. The same calculations are made for the left foot (using the left-foot length) and also for both right and left feet with the measurements made with the subject sitting.

Objectivity and reliability of this method have not been recorded. The validity of the test rests with the clinical validation obtained from numerous measurements made on men, women, and children.

The interpretation of results, according to Truslow, are as follows:

1. A standing ratio of 8 percent is a fair average of efficient feet. Lacking other harmful factors, a standing range of 7 percent to 9 percent may safely be considered as constituting military or civilian efficiency.
2. The higher the figure of standing ratio (above 8 percent) the more it is an expression of existing hollowfoot (*pes cavus*), a condition which may become quite as disabling as flatfoot.
3. The lower the figure of standing ratio (below 8 percent) the greater is the indication of the existence of flatfoot (*pes planus*).
4. A fairly low standing ratio compared with a high sitting ratio indicates a temporary muscular weakness.
5. A standing ratio, at whatever low level, compared with a sitting ratio which is but little, if any, higher than the standing ratio points to

spasticity of the feet, which may be correctable by prolonged treatment.
6. Marked discrepancy between the right and the left foot lengths, or between the right and left ratios, calls for more careful study on the part of the examiner, who may expect to find antedating pathologic or traumatic causes for such discrepancy.

Truslow takes note of the importance of other factors in foot efficiency, but insists that the use of this form of foot measurement can be an important aid in the evaluation of the effectiveness of military registrants as well as individuals in civilian life.

FLEXIBILITY

Flexibility has long been recognized as an important factor associated with proficiency in athletics. The definition of this term is most frequently given as "the range of movement about a joint." However, we must recognize that the degree of joint flexibility depends on physiological characteristics underlying the extensibility of the muscles and ligaments surrounding the joint. Not only is flexibility significant in performing skills, but also recent advancements in physical medicine and rehabilitation indicate that flexibility is important to general physical fitness. Particularly, if a person maintains a satisfactory degree of flexibility, he is less susceptible to certain muscular injuries.

Exactly how much flexibility an individual should possess has not yet been scientifically demonstrated. In the Kraus-Weber floor-touch test, which involves the extensibility of the erector spinae, gluteals, hamstrings, and gastroc muscles, a passing grade is the ability to touch the floor. The only reported validity for this test is the evidence gained from examining numerous patients by the medical people who have assisted Kraus. However, in two studies dealing with college women and elementary school boys, Mathews et al. (28, 29), demonstrated length of lower limb to be independent of hip flexibility.

LEIGHTON FLEXOMETER TESTS

Leighton (24) has contributed the most comprehensive technique for measuring objectively the flexibility of 30 joint movements. The instrument used in making the measurements is called the Leighton flexometer (Fig. 34). It has a weighted 360-degree dial and a weighted pointer mounted in a case. The dial and pointer operate freely and independently; the movement of each is controlled by gravity. The instrument will record movement while in any position that is 20 degrees or more off the horizontal. The zero mark on the dial and the tip of the pointer move freely to a position of rest, and coincide when the instrument is placed in any position off the horizontal, as indicated. Independent locking devices are provided for the pointer and the dial, which stop all movement of either at any given position. While in use, the flexometer is strapped to the segment being tested. When the dial is locked at one extreme position (e.g., full extension of the elbow), the direct reading of the pointer on the dial is the arc through which the movement has taken place. In addition to the flexometer, a projecting wall corner, a long bench or table, and a low-backed armchair are also required.

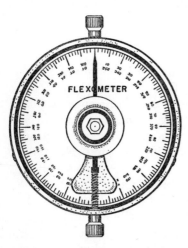

Fig. 34. Leighton flexometer.

Validity of these tests is based on the now clearly recognized and defined segmental joint movements of the body. Reliability was determined by the test-retest method, using 120 boys. Coefficients of correlation ranged from .913 to .996.

LATERAL FLEXION. *Starting position.* Sitting position in low-backed armchair, back straight, hands grasping chair arms, upper arms hooked over back of chair. Instrument fastened to back of head.

Movement: Count (1) head moved in arc sideward to the left as far as possible, dial locked; (2) head moved in arc sideward to the right as far as possible, pointer locked; (3) subject relaxes, reading taken.

Caution: Position in chair may not be changed during movement. Shoulders may not be raised or lowered.

ROTATION. *Starting position.* Supine position on bench, head and neck projecting over, shoulders touching edge, and arms at sides of bench. Instrument fastened to top of head.

Movement: Count (1) head turned left as far as possible, dial locked; (2) head turned right as far as possible, pointer locked; (3) subject relaxes, reading taken.

Caution: Shoulders may not be raised from bench.

SHOULDER

FLEXION AND EXTENSION. *Starting position.* Standing position at projecting corner of wall, arm to be measured extending just beyond projecting corner, arms at sides, back to wall; shoulder blades, buttocks, and heels touching wall. Instrument fastened to side of upper arm.

Movement: Count (1) arm moved forward and upward in an arc as far as possible, palm of hand sliding against wall, dial locked; (2) arm moved downward and backward in an arc as far as possible, palm of hand sliding against wall, pointer locked; (3) subject relaxes, reading taken.

Caution: Heels, buttocks, and shoulders must touch wall at all times during movement. Elbow of arm being measured must be kept straight. Palm of hand of arm being measured must be against wall when dial and pointer are locked.

ADDUCTION AND ABDUCTION. *Starting position:* Standing position with arms at sides, left (right) side of body toward wall, shoulder touching same, left (right) first doubled with knuckles forward, thumb side of fist touching hip and opposite side of fist touching wall, feet together, knees and elbows straight. Instrument fastened to back of right (left) upper arm.

Movement: Count (1) palm of right (left) hand pressed against side of leg, dial locked; (2) arm moved sideward, outward, and upward in an arc as far as possible, pointer locked; (3) subject relaxes, reading taken.

Caution: Left (right) fist must be kept in contact with the body and wall at all times. Knees, body, and elbows must be kept straight throughout movement. Arm must be raised directly sideward, not forward or backward. Heels of feet may not be raised from floor.

ROTATION. *Starting position:* Standing position at projecting corner of wall, arm to be measured extended sideward and bent to right angle at elbow, shoulder extended just beyond projecting corner, opposite arm at side of body, back to wall; shoulder blades, buttocks, and heels touching wall. Instrument fastened to side of forearm.

Movement: Count (1) forearm moved downward and backward in an arc as far as possible, dial locked; (2) forearm moved forward, upward, and backward in an arc as far as possible, pointer locked; (3) subject relaxes, reading taken.

Caution: Upper arm being measured must be held directly sideward and parallel with the floor during movement. Heels, buttocks, and shoulders must touch wall at all times.

ELBOW

FLEXION AND EXTENSION. *Starting position:* Squatting or sitting position, facing table or bench, with upper portion of arm being measured resting, back down, across nearest table corner so that the elbow extends just beyond one edge and the armpit is resting against the adjacent edge. Instrument fastened to back of wrist.

Movement: Count (1) wrist moved upward and backward in an arc to position as near shoulder as possible, dial locked; (2) wrist moved forward and downward until arm is forcibly extended, pointer locked; (3) subject relaxes, reading taken.

Caution: Upper arm may not be tilted or moved during measurement.

MEASUREMENT TECHNIQUE

NECK

FLEXION AND EXTENSION: *Starting position:* Supine position on bench, head and neck projecting over end, shoulders touching edge, arms at sides. Instrument fastened to either side of head over ear.

Movement: Count (1) head raised and moved to position as near chest as possible, dial locked; (2) head lowered and moved to position as near end of bench as possible, pointer locked; (3) subject relaxes, reading taken.

Caution: Shoulders may not be raised from bench during flexion, nor back unduly arched during extension. Buttocks and shoulders must remain on bench during movement.

RADIAL-ULNAR

SUPINATION AND PRONATION. *Starting position:* Sitting position in standard armchair, back straight, forearms resting on chair arms, fists doubled and extended beyond ends of chair arms, wrist of arm to be measured held straight. Strap is grasped in hand, fastening instrument to front of fist. (Common chair and table of suitable height may be substituted for armchair.)

Movement: Count (1) thumb side of fist turned outward and downward as far as possible, dial locked; (2) thumb side of fist turned upward, downward, and inward as far as possible, pointer locked; (3) subject relaxes, reading taken.

Caution: Body and forearm must remain stationary, except for specified movement, throughout measurement. No leaning of the body may be permitted.

WRIST

FLEXION AND EXTENSION. *Starting position:* Sitting position in standard armchair, back straight, forearms resting on chair arms, fists doubled and extended beyond ends of chair arms, palm of hand to be measured turned up. Instrument fastened to thumb side of fist. (Common chair and table of suitable height may be substituted for armchair.)

Movement: Count (1) fist moved upward and backward in an arc as far as possible, dial locked; (2) fist moved forward, downward, and backward in an arc as far as possible, pointer locked; (3) subject relaxes, reading taken.

Caution: Forearm may not be raised from chair arm during movement.

ULNAR AND RADIAL FLEXION. *Starting position:* Sitting position in standard armchair, back straight, forearms resting on chair arms, fists doubled and extended beyond ends of chair arms, thumb side of hand to be measured turned up. Instrument fastened to back of hand. (Common chair and table of suitable height may be substituted for armchair.)

Movement: Count (1) fist moved upward and backward in an arc as far as possible, dial locked; (2) fist moved downward and backward as far as possible, pointer locked; (3) subject relaxes, reading taken.

Caution: Forearm may not be raised from chair arm during movement. Fist may not be turned inward or outward during measurement.

HIP

EXTENSION AND FLEXION. *Starting position:* Standing position, feet together, knees stiff, arms extended above head, hands clasped with palms up. Instrument fastened to either side of hip at height of umbilicus.

Movement: Count (1) bend backward as far as possible, dial locked; (2) bend forward as far as possible, pointer locked; (3) subject relaxes, reading taken.

Caution: Knees may not be bent but must remain straight throughout the movement. Feet may not be shifted. Toes and heels may not be raised.

ADDUCTION AND ABDUCTION. *Starting position:* Standing position, feet together, knees straight, arms at sides. Instrument fastened to back of either leg.

Movement: Count (1) starting position, dial locked; (2) leg to which instrument is not attached is moved sideward as far as possible, pointer locked; (3) subject relaxes, reading taken.

Caution: Body must remain in upright position throughout movement. Knees must be kept straight, with the feet assuming a position on line and parallel.

ROTATION. *Starting position:* Sitting position on bench, with left (right) leg resting on and foot projecting over end of bench, knee straight, right (left) leg extending downward, foot resting on floor. Instrument fastened to bottom of left (right) foot.

Movement: Count (1) left (right) foot turned outward as far as possible, dial locked; (2) left (right) foot turned inward as far as possible, pointer locked; (3) subject relaxes, reading taken.

Caution: Knee and ankle joints must remain locked throughout movement. Position of hips may not be changed during measurement.

KNEE

FLEXION AND EXTENSION. *Starting position:* Prone position on box or bench with knees at end of and lower legs extending beyond end of bench, arms at sides of and hands grasping edges of bench. Instrument fastened to outside of either ankle.

Movement: Count (1) foot moved upward and backward in an arc to position as near buttocks as possible, dial locked; (2) foot moved forward and downward until leg is forcibly extended, pointer locked; (3) subject relaxes, reading taken.

Caution: Position of upper leg may be changed during movement.

ANKLE

FLEXION AND EXTENSION. *Starting position:* Sitting position on bench with left (right) leg resting on and foot projecting over end of bench, knee straight, right (left) leg extending downward, foot resting on floor. Instrument fastened to inside of left (right) foot.

Movement: Count (1) left (right) foot turned downward as far as possible, dial locked; (2) left (right) foot turned upward and toward the knee as far as possible, pointer locked; (3) subject relaxes, reading taken.

Caution: Knee of leg being measured must be kept straight throughout movement. No sideward turning of the foot may be allowed.

INVERSION AND EVERSION. *Starting position:* Sitting on end of bench, knees projecting over and lower legs downward with calves resting against end board. Shoes (low cut) should be worn. Instrument fastened to front of foot.

Movement: Count (1) foot turned inward as far as possible, dial locked; (2) foot turned outward as far as possible, pointer locked; (3) subject relaxes, reading taken.

Caution: Position of lower leg may not be changed during measurement.

TRUNK

EXTENSION AND FLEXION. *Starting Position:* Standing position, feet together, knees straight, arms extended above head, hands clasped with palms up. Instrument fastened to either side of chest just below armpit at nipple height.

Movement: Count (1) bend backward as far as possible, dial locked; (2) bend forward as far as possible, pointer locked; (3) subject relaxes, reading taken.

Caution: Knees must be kept straight throughout movement. Feet may not be shifted. Toes and heels may not be raised from floor.

Note: This movement involves trunk and hip extension and flexion. To obtain the measure for trunk extension and flexion alone, the measure for hip extension and flexion must be subtracted from the score obtained above.

LATERAL FLEXION. *Starting Position:* Standing position, feet together, knees straight, arms at sides. Instrument fastened to middle of back at nipple height.

Movement: Count (1) bend sideward to the left as far as possible, dial locked; (2) bend sideward to the right as far as possible, pointer locked; (3) subject relaxes, reading taken.

Caution: Both feet must remain flat on floor, heels may not be raised during measurement. Knees must be kept straight throughout movement. Subject may bend sideward and backward, but must not be allowed to bend forward.

ROTATION. *Starting position:* Supine position on bench, legs together, knees raised above hips, lower legs parallel to bench and body. Assistant holds subject's shoulders. Instrument fastened to middle rear of upper legs, strap going around both legs.

Movement: Count (1) knees lowered to the left as far as possible, dial locked; (2) knees brought back to starting position and lowered to the right as far as possible, pointer locked; (3) subject relaxes, reading taken.

Caution: Subject's shoulders must not be permitted to rise from

TABLE 3. Flexibility Means and Standard Deviations for a Group of fifty 16-Year-Old California Boys[a]

Test	M	σ
1. Neck flexion-extension	123.40	11.82
2. Neck lateral flexion	88.40	10.66
3. Neck rotation	158.40	12.43
4. Right shoulder flexion-extension	257.50	10.60
5. Left shoulder flexion-extension	257.70	10.19
6. Right shoulder adduction-abduction	173.20	8.83
7. Left shoulder adduction-abduction	173.20	9.76
8. Right shoulder rotation	170.40	15.65
9. Left shoulder rotation	170.90	12.82
10. Right elbow flexion-extension	141.10	7.70
11. Left elbow flexion-extension	142.70	6.32
12. Right radial-ulnar supination-pronation	161.90	11.64
13. Left radial-ulnar supination-pronation	161.50	10.53
14. Right wrist flexion-extension	130.10	14.03
15. Left wrist flexion-extension	131.70	13.69
16. Right wrist ulnar-radial flexion	75.50	9.59
17. Left wrist ulnar-radial flexion	75.90	10.31
18. Hip extension-flexion	55.50	13.37
19. Hip adduction-abduction	63.30	14.00
20. Right hip rotation	68.60	12.73
21. Left hip rotation	70.00	13.50
22. Right knee flexion-extension	136.00	13.17
23. Left knee flexion-extension	135.90	11.25
24. Right ankle flexion-extension	62.70	10.67
25. Left ankle flexion-extension	62.80	9.87
26. Right ankle inversion-eversion	43.12	7.97
27. Left ankle inversion-eversion	43.60	8.57
28. Trunk extension-flexion	78.50	21.38
29. Trunk lateral flexion	95.80	15.43
30. Trunk rotation	128.60	9.60

[a] NOTE: All means and standard deviations are computed in degrees and fractions of degrees. The symbol for degree is omitted since no other unit of measure is used. (Courtesy of Professor Jack Leighton, Eastern Washington College, Cheney, Washington, 1957.)

the bench during movement. Knees must be moved directly sideward at the height of the hips, not above or below.

Table 3 contains means and standard deviations for the 30 flexibility measures recorded from a group of fifty 16-year-old California boys.

WELLS SIT AND REACH TEST

The Wells sit-and-reach Test (39) was devised to take the place of the flexibility test which required the subject to stand on a gymnasium bench. In this "bench test," the arms and trunk are relaxed forward, with hands in front of a vertical scale attached to the front of the bench. The subject bobs downward four times, keeping the knees straight, and on the fourth reach holds still in the position of maximum forward-downward flexibility. Because many students had feelings of insecurity and apprehension while performing this test, Wells and Dillon decided that it would be much wiser to perform the tests, if at all possible, from a sitting position.

The equipment consists of a $24'' \times 8''$ piece of plywood, with lines drawn horizontally at half-inch intervals. The center line is marked 0, the inch lines on one side are marked 1, 2, 3 . . . , and those on the opposite side -1, -2, -3. . . . The support for the scale is in the form of an elongated plus sign made of 11-inch boards resting on their edges. These are referred to as the cross board and the stem board. Footprints are outlined on one surface of the cross board, one on either side of the stem board. The scale is attached to the upper edges of the support in such a way that when the subject is seated on the floor with the feet against the footprints, the zero line coincides with the near surface of the cross board and the minus values are toward the subject (Fig. 35). Another method of constructing the number scale is to countersink a portion of a yardstick into the plywood surface.

With the feet placed in the footprints on the cross board, the subject reaches forward, with palms down, along the scale. The maximum distance reached is recorded as the measure of flexibility. The authors report the reliability of this test, when the subjects are permitted three preliminary bobs, as .98.

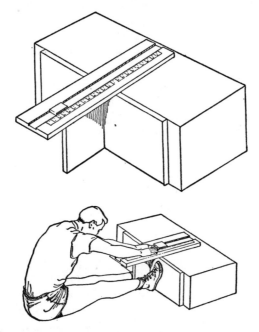

Fig. 35. The Wells sit-and-reach test. The Camaione modification of the instrument permits both sitting and standing flexibility measures. Administration of the standing test can be observed by rotating the picture 90 degrees clockwise.

SUMMARY

Body mechanics should be taught, and hence evaluated, particularly in the elementary and junior high school. Here youngsters are in the formative stages of development, and much can be done to diminish the number requiring remedial or adapted classes as they grow older.

There is no objective evidence of specific relationships between posture and physiological function; thus, the reasons for teaching body mechanics are functional and esthetic, and are a preventive measure for the chronic orthopedic difficulties encountered in later years.

The basic criterion for evaluating body mechanics is expert opinion, and the experts do agree in general as to what constitutes good posture.

The posture screening and functional evaluation tests, as well as the refined posture appraisal, are the most practical. Once skill is acquired through experience, objective and valid results of postural appraisal can be obtained. The screening test aids in selecting those most seriously deficient for further attention in the remedial class.

From the information gained through the screening, an individualized program may be initiated—provided the physical educator clearly understands the underlying causes of the postural deficiency. If the cause of the deficiency is not clearly understood, referral should be made. All subjects with serious lateral imbalances are examples of students who should be referred. The physical educator should follow up on the referral to find out how he can help. When therapeutic services are nonexistent or limited, it is quite possible that the physician may prescribe an exercise program to be conducted by the physical educator. In such situations, refined postural measurements such as those in the Kraus-Weber test will prove valuable in determining progress as well as for motivating the child. This is another important phase of developmental and remedial work in which cooperation of physician and physical educator can make marked contributions to the normal growth and development of our youngsters.

Hence, the evaluation of body mechanics applies to three phases of the physical education program: (1) The screening phase, the primary purpose of which is to locate the seriously deficient students requiring individual attention. (2) The general instructional phase, the primary purpose of which is twofold: to allow practice of such specific skills as standing, walking, and sitting; and, at the same time, to assign a mark of proficiency in each of the events. (3) The more definitive measurement, which is used with those pupils who have a serious deficiency—the ones who have been placed in an individualized program on the basis of the screening test.

REFERENCES

1. Bancroft, Jesse H., *The Posture of School Children*, Macmillan, New York, 1913.
2. Beal, Elizabeth, Chairman, Department Physical Education, Wellesley College, personal correspondence, March, 1956.
3. Boynton, Bernice, "Individual Differences in the Structure of Pelvis and Lumbar Spine as a Factor in Body Mechanics," Master's Thesis, State University of Iowa, 1933.
4. Brownell, C. L., "A Scale for Measuring Anterior-Posterior Posture of Ninth Grade Boys," Bureau of Publications, Teachers College, Columbia University, New York, 1928.
5. Carnett, J. B., Extracts from discussion, *White House Conference on Child Health and Protection, Body Mechanics: Education and Practice*, Century, New York, 1932.
6. Christenson, Cornell Hjalmar, "An Improvement in Technique for Measuring Antero-posterior Posture," *Research Quarterly*, December, 1933, 4 (4).
7. Clarke, H. Harrison, "An Objective Method of Measuring the Height of the Longitudinal Arch in Foot Examinations," *Research Quarterly*, October, 1933, 4 (3).
8. Crampton, C. W., "Work-a-Day Tests of Good Posture," *American Physical Education Review*, November, 1925, 30.
9. Crook, Billie Louise, "A Scale for Measuring the Antero-posterior Posture of the Preschool Child," *Research Quarterly*, December, 1936, 7 (4).
10. Cureton, Thomas K., "The Validity of Footprints as a Measure of Vertical Height of the Arch and Functional Efficiency of the Foot," *Research Quarterly*, May, 1935, 6 (2).
11. Cureton, Thomas Kirk, and Wickens, J. Stuart, "The Center of Gravity of the Human Body in the Antero-posterior Plane and Its Relation to Posture, Physical Fitness, and Athletic Ability," supplement to *Research Quarterly*, May, 1935, 6 (2).
12. Cureton, Thomas Kirk, Wickens, J. Stuart, and Elder, Haskel P., "Reliability and Objectivity of Springfield Postural Measurement," supplement to *Research Quarterly*, May, 1935, 6 (2).
13. Danford, Harold R., "A Comparative Study of Three Methods of Measuring Flat and Weak Feet," supplement to *Research Quarterly*, March, 1935, 6 (1).
14. Fox, M. A., and Young, O. S., "Placement of Gravital Line in Antero-

posterior Standing Posture," *Research Quarterly*, October, 1954, **25** (3).

15. Glassow, Ruth, *Fundamentals in Physical Education*, Lea & Febiger, Philadelphia, 1932.

16. Goldthwait, J. E., *et al*, *Body Mechanics in the Study and Treatment of Disease*, Lea & Febiger, Philadelphia, 1930.

17. Howland, Ivalclare Sprow, *Body Alignment in Fundamental Motor Skills*, Exposition Press, New York, 1953.

18. Howland, Ivalclare Sprow, "A Study of the Position of the Sacrum in the Adult Female Pelvis and Its Relationship to Body Mechanics," Master's thesis, State University of Iowa, 1933.

19. Hubbard, C. H., "Advantages of a New Shadow-Silhouettograph Over the Original," supplement to *Research Quarterly*, March, 1935, **6** (1).

20. Karpovich, Peter V., *Physiology of Muscular Activity*, 4th ed., Saunders, Philadelphia, 1953.

21. Klein, A., and Thomas, L. C., "Posture and Physical Fitness," Children's Bureau Publication No. 205, Government Printing Office, Washington, D.C., 1931.

22. Korb, Edward Martin, "A Method to Increase Validity of Measuring Posture," *Research Quarterly*, March, 1939, **10** (1).

23. Kraus, Hans, and Weber, S., "Evaluation of Posture Based on Structural and Functional Measurements," *Physiotherapy Review*, 1945, **26** (6).

24. Leighton, Jack, "An Instrument and Technic for the Measurement of Range of Joint Motion," *Arch. Phys. Med.*, September, 1955.

25. Lowman, Charles L., Colestock, Claire, and Cooper, Hazel, *Corrective Physical Education for Groups*, Barnes, New York, 1928.

26. MacEwan, Charlotte G., and Howe, Eugene C., "An Objective Method of Grading Posture," *Research Quarterly*, October, 1932, **3** (3).

27. Massey, W. Wayne, "A Critical Study of Objective Methods for Measuring Anterior-Posterior Posture with a Simplified Technique," *Research Quarterly*, March, 1943, **14** (1).

28. Mathews, Donald K., Shaw, Virginia, and Woods, John B., "Hip Flexibility of Elementary School Boys as Related to Body Segments," *Research Quarterly*, October, 1959, **30** (3), 297-302.

29. Mathews, Donald K., Shaw, Virginia, and Bohnen, Melra, "Hip Flexibility of College Women as Related to Length of Body Segments," *Research Quarterly*, December, 1957, **28**, 352-356.

30. McCloy, Charles H., "X-ray Studies of Innate Differences in Straight and Curved Spines," *Research Quarterly*, May, 1948, **9** (2).

31. Rathbone, Josephine L., "Good Postures, the Expression of Good Development," Symposium on Posture, Phi Delta Pi, March, 1938.

32. Report of the Baruch Committee on Physical Medicine (Ray L. Wilbur,

Chairman), 597 Madison Avenue, New York, April 1, 1945.

33. Reynolds, E., and Lovett, R. W., "Method of Determining the Position of the Center of Gravity in Its Relation to Certain Body Landmarks in the Erect Position," *American Journal of Physiology,* May, 1909.

34. Schwartz, L., Britten, R. H., and Thompson, L. R., "Studies in Physical Development and Posture," U.S. Public Health Bulletin, No. 179, 1928.

35. Shaw, Virginia, unpublished data, Washington State University, Pullman, Washington, 1957.

36. Stafford, George T., *Preventive and Corrective Physical Education,* rev. ed., Barnes, New York, 1950.

37. Steindler, Arthur, *Kinesiology of the Human Body under Normal and Pathological Conditions,* Thomas, Springfield, Ill., 1955.

38. Truslow, W., *Body Poise,* Williams & Wilkins, Baltimore, 1943.

39. Wells, Katharine F., and Dillon, Evelyn K., "The Sit and Reach—A Test of Back and Leg Flexibility," *Research Quarterly,* March, 1952, 23 (1).

40. Wickens, J. Stuart, and Kiphuth, Oscar, "Body Mechanics Analysis of Yale University Freshmen," *Research Quarterly,* December, 1937, 3 (4).

Chapter 11

POLIOMYELITIS

Acute anterior poliomyelitis, sometimes referred to as "polio" or "infantile paralysis," is an acute viral infection in which only a small percentage of those infected develop clinical signs and symptoms. The causative agent is a virus which has been isolated and categorized into three distinctive types: Type I (Brunhilde), Type II (Lansing), and Type III (Leon). Exposure to one type usually provides a specific immunity to any further attack of that particular strain of virus; however, subsequent exposure to any of the other types can produce a reinfection. This is the probable basis for a second attack of poliomyelitis in the same individual, which has been occasionally reported.

During epidemics, the virus has been isolated from sewage, flies, and fly-contaminated food. It has been found that infection with all three types of the virus is acquired primarily during infancy and early childhood, from which stems the common term "infantile paralysis."

THE SALK VACCINE

Recent advances in the form of active immunization (the Salk vaccine) for the prevention of acute anterior poliomyelitis will greatly alter the role of this disease as a public health problem. After extensive field trials in 1954, the Salk vaccine appears to be 68 percent effective in preventing paralytic poliomyelitis due to

Type I, and 85 to 90 percent effective against Types II and III. More evidence as to the effectiveness of this vaccine was provided by the 1958 poliomyelitis outbreak in Detroit, Michigan. Ninety-five percent of Detroit's paralytic cases occurred among persons who were unvaccinated or incompletely vaccinated: infants and children under 5 years of age accounted for 61 percent of the paralytic total. A complete analysis of the role the Salk vaccine played in the Detroit epidemic may be observed in Table 4.

TABLE 4.   Reported Poliomyelitis Cases by Vaccination Shots, Detroit—1958

| Type of Cases | Number of Vaccinations | | | | | |
	0	1	2	3	4	Total
Paralytic	251	40	25	16	0	332
Nonparalytic	95	37	57	113	11	312
Total	346	77	82	129	11	645
% Paralytic	73	52	30	12	0	51

SOURCE: Reprinted by permission of the National Science Foundation.

LIVE VIRUS VACCINE

Sabin, Cox, and Koprowski have each developed a live attenuated vaccine (2). They consist of nonvirulent representatives capable of inducing protective antibodies against the three types of polio virus. Even though all three vaccines have been proved to be effective, the one developed by Sabin has been approved by the Public Health Service because of its more extensive testing. Some of the important results of the Sabin vaccine include: (1) In 1960, not a single case of polio was reported in Cincinnati, where the mass vaccine program was initiated. (2) One month following the pre-school immunization program, virtually no polio viruses were found among a random sampling of 1300 children. (3) Immunity spread from vaccinated to unvaccinated youngsters in their families. (4) No harmful side effects were noted. The live virus can be taken orally, making injection of the killed-virus vaccine (Salk) unnecessary. The results of the Cincinnati study were supported by successful immunization programs in Russia, Hungary, Czechoslovakia, Yugoslavia, Mexico, and other localities, totaling over a million dosages.

The Committee on Live Polio Virus Vaccine has expressed concern over the manner in which the new vaccine may be used (1,3). This is because of the unique nature of live polio virus vaccine in spreading virus in a limited manner to nonvaccinated people. The weakened live virus potentially may revert to virulence, which is an important aspect in the community if the vaccine is improperly used.

Even though much progress has been made in ridding America of a crippling disease, 40 percent of the population has not been vaccinated against poliomyelitis. The Public Health Service (4) says that the majority of the unvaccinated are among the less privileged, but another large percentage is waiting for the oral vaccine.

PATHOLOGY

The poliomyelitis virus probably enters the body through the upper respiratory tract or the alimentary canal. For some unknown reason, it has a special affinity for the motor cells of the anterior horn of the spinal cord, although lesions produced by the virus are not restricted to this area; they are also found in the cerebral cortex, the basal ganglion, the thalamic and hypothalamic nuclei, in the midbrain, the pons, the cerebellum, and the medulla oblongata. There is also evidence that the poliomyelitis virus may cause damage in muscles and peripheral nerves, which may account for some of the clinical features of the disease such as spasm, tenderness, and tightness in the muscles.

Today, as a result of propaganda used in collecting money, many people are under the impression that an attack of poliomyelitis will always end in some degree of muscular paralysis; but this is not true. In approximately 80 to 90 percent of those infected, the disease may be so mild as to go unnoticed; and if any clinical signs do appear, they generally consist of slight fever, malaise, headache, sore throat, and some vomiting, which may last anywhere from 24 to 72 hours. Most laboratory findings are negative, and there is no indication of central nervous system involvement. Clinical diagnosis of the disease is most difficult, if not impossible. This type of infection is referred to as *abortive poliomyelitis.*

Invasion of the central nervous system occurs in approximately 10 percent of those infected with the disease. In such cases, the virus may cause damage to or destruction of the motor cells in greater or smaller numbers. Destruction of all the motor cells to a muscle will result in paralysis, whereas destruction of only a portion of the nerve cells supplying a muscle will result in paresis (weakness). Associated with this muscular involvement is a loss of superficial and deep reflexes, but the sensory mechanism usually remains intact. The degree of muscular involvement (paralysis or paresis) depends entirely on the number of motor cells damaged or destroyed by the virus. The site of paralysis or paresis depends on the location of the lesions in the central nervous system. If destruction has taken place mainly in the spinal cord, the patient is said to have suffered an attack of *spinal type poliomyelitis.* If the virus attacks cells at higher levels in the central nervous system—motor nuclei of cranial nerves or cells of the respiratory center in the medulla— the disease assumes the *bulbar form,* in which paralysis of the pharyngeal, laryngeal, facial, and other muscles innervated by the cranial nerves may occur. Difficulty in breathing and swallowing, nasal regurgitation, and a nasal voice are early signs of bulbar poliomyelitis.

CLINICAL FEATURES

The clinical picture of a patient with poliomyelitis is extremely varied and individualistic. However, the course of the disease has been divided by Horstman into two basic patterns: the *minor illness,* or abortive type, and the *major illness.* The minor illness is usually associated with the symptoms of slight fever, general malaise, sore throat, and occasional vomiting or diarrhea, lasting 24 to 72 hours. In the majority of cases, the disease does not progress to the stage of paralysis. The temperature returns to normal after a few days, the signs and symptoms subside, and the patient appears symptom-free. If these patients are put through a muscle test for tightness, certain of them will be found to have definite limitations of movement due to tightness of soft structure tissues including muscles, fascia, ligaments, and tendons. If this tightness is not corrected, so that a full range of motion is possible, it may result in deformity at a later date. Thus, a person may have an attack of acute anterior poliomyelitis that has passed unnoticed, undiagnosed, or attributed to some other illness, and which may leave a residual tightness or limitation of motion. It may be that some of the cases of postural deformity we see in the physical education class are the result of undiagnosed abortive poliomyelitis (minor illness).

In a few cases of minor illness, the symptoms of the disease may occur after several days of well-being, resulting in a major illness pattern. More commonly, however, particularly in older children and adults, the major illness begins without a previous minor illness. Associated with the onset of the major illness is a temperature rise, severe headache, and a hypersensitivity to touch or movement of the extremities of the body. Intense pain and muscle spasm may appear in almost any muscle in the body, but it is most frequently found in the posterior neck, back, and hamstring muscle groups. The spinal fluid during the major illness may show an increased lymphocyte cell count and increased protein, but this is not always true.

TREATMENT

Our present knowledge of poliomyelitis is so limited that once the infection process begins, the whole course of the disease is beyond the control of the physician. He can neither prevent its attack on the spinal cord, nor, as far as we know, control the recovery process of the infected motor cells. It is well established that if these motor neurons are destroyed, they are permanently lost; for regeneration does not occur within the central nervous system. The muscle fibers innervated by these destroyed motor cells atrophy, and eventually are replaced by fibrous tissue. No therapy directed toward the denervated muscle or destroyed motor cells will have any effect in returning voluntary muscle function. However, in a great many instances, not all the motor cells are destroyed; but rather, they may be only damaged, and recovery of motor function occurs spontaneously with recovery from the disease.

Why, then, is treatment so important for the poliomyelitis patient if restoration of motor function occurs spontaneously without treatment, and if there is no known method of controlling the course of the disease? Basically, the reason for treatment is twofold: to save life and to minimize disability. If the poliomyelitis attack is of the bulbar, bulbospinal, or respiratory type, it is necessary to have expert medical care. Effective treatment will not only save the patient's life, but will also greatly accelerate motor recovery and do a better job of restoring motor function.

SAVING LIFE

During the acute stages of poliomyelitis, careful observation of the patient for respiratory difficulty is most important. In the virus attack, if one or more of the medullary centers controlling respiration or swallowing are affected, emergency measures—such as aspiration, administration of oxygen, tracheotomy, and use of the respirator (iron lung)—are sometimes necessary to save the patient's life. It may be necessary to suspend temporarily all other forms of treatment to concentrate on lifesaving procedures. However, once the critical stage is past, it is possible to effectively carry on treatment for the muscular condition even while the patient is in a respirator. The rehabilitation of patients with respiratory involvement is complex and requires the services of a team of physicians and surgeons, as well as nurses and physical therapists.

MINIMIZING THE DISABILITY

Treatment to minimize disability is essential in poliomyelitis even though spontaneous return of motor function may occur with recovery of the spinal cord from the virus invasion. In general, four methods of treatment are used to lessen the disabilities that may occur as an aftereffect of poliomyelitis: (1) supportive measures, (2) heat, (3) therapeutic exercise, and (4) surgery.

SUPPORTIVE MEASURES

Supportive measures to offset the possible development of contractures and bone deformities are usually initiated as soon as the diagnosis of poliomyelitis is made. The use of boards under the mattress helps to maintain proper body alignment, and foot boards aid in the prevention of drop foot. Sandbags, rolled towels, and, at times, bivalved plaster casts and splints are used to position the extremities. The patient is usually turned at frequent intervals during the day and night. Care is taken that malpositioning is not assumed for any extended period of time, for faulty body positioning may result in the development of deformities by stretching weak or paralyzed muscles and by overactivity of the opposing stronger muscles. As pointed out before, it may be necessary to suspend temporarily all supportive measures to concentrate on saving the patient's life; but once the critical phase is over, it is possible to carry on most treatments. Therapeutic measures are possible even while the patient is in a respirator, although the effectiveness of treatment may be somewhat diminished. In the latter stages of recovery, it may be necessary for the patient to be fitted with special corsets, braces, crutches, and other forms of supportive devices. Occasionally, a patient may be required to utilize these supportive devices for the rest of his life in order to remain functional and to prevent further development of deformities.

HEAT

Although we do not know why hot packs relieve pain and cause muscle relaxation, they are one of the most effective methods of treating muscle pain and spasm. Actually, it is not known whether the moist heat of the hot pack is any more effective than other forms of heat. Infrared radiation has been considered effective in relieving pain, and two observers consider hot baths to be even more effective in the relief of pain and stiffness. Probably the reason for the common use of hot packs in the treatment of poliomyelitis is their great adaptability, for they can be used even while the patient is in the narrow confines of a respirator.

The use of hot packs is usually started as soon as muscle pain and spasm appear, even in the acute stages of the disease when the patient has fever. The frequency with which they are changed, and the time at which they are applied each day, varies with the condition of the patient. If pain, spasm, and muscular tightness are not severe, the intensity and duration of hot-pack applications are reduced.

THERAPEUTIC EXERCISE

MUSCLE TESTING

The muscular aftereffects of poliomyelitis may be extensive or limited to a few muscles of one or more extremities—often to only a few fibers of a muscle. It may result in complete paralysis, various degrees of weakness, pain, spasm, and tightness, or in muscular incoordination. With this variance of muscular involvement, a detailed examination of the muscles is necessary in order to design an intelligent and comprehensive exercise program. In medicine, the manual muscle test is generally used in making this evaluation. Although the physical educator should not be concerned with the direct treatment of muscle disability, he is ultimately concerned with the optimum development of the body and the prevention of disability. Therefore, he should be familiar with the details of muscle function and manual muscle testing. (Chapter 7 offers further details on the method of manual muscle testing.)

STRETCHING

Perhaps the most important measure for the prevention of deformities is the restoration and maintenance of normal muscle length. Although the use of hot packs is primarily responsible for the relief of pain and muscle spasm, in many instances heat alone will not eradicate muscular tightness. Once the muscle tests reveal which muscles are tight, passive stretching methods are employed to restore the proper muscle length. As the painful stages of the disease subside, the muscle apparently can be carefully but rather strenuously stretched without danger of injury until the muscle tends to remain supple and at full length.

PATTERNS OF MOTION

The action performed by any muscle or group of muscles is represented in the brain as motion, and not as the specific muscle which produces it. Therefore, when the nerve which supplies a group of muscles is wholly or partially disrupted, the brain still attempts to initiate motion by sending impulses to the region along the intact nerves. If the desired motion is similar to that produced by the weak or paralyzed muscles, it is accomplished readily, although inadequately, by a neighboring group of muscles. For example, an individual with very weak or paralyzed hip flexors will elevate his hip by contracting the *quadratus lumborum* during ambulation. It is not uncommon to see the action of the anterior tibial muscle disappear entirely as the stronger muscles in the area take over its function. If the patient continues to be active, the stronger muscles are used more and more to produce the motion. Eventually, the weaker muscles become suppressed and finally cease to act at all, and a new pattern of motion is developed. If these incoordinated and substitutionary patterns of movement are allowed to persist and become habitual, they ultimately lead to muscular imbalance and progressive deformity.

In the early stages of poliomyelitis, passive range of motion and neuromuscular re-education methods are employed in such a manner that all groups of muscles function to the best advantage. As recovery from the disease progresses, active-assistive, active, and resistive exercises are used to elicit a maximum return of the involved musculature. A detailed description of one method of neuromuscular re-education is presented on page 113; other methods may be found in the bibliography at the end of this chapter.

MUSCULAR STRENGTH

When re-education has been successful, as evidenced by coordinated patterns of motion, progressive resistance exercises may be added to develop maximal strength of the involved muscles. In general, the sequence of progression may be from movement with assistance to movement with the force of gravity eliminated, and then to movement against the force of gravity and increasing resistance. The increments of resistance must be small and gradual, and careful attention must be given at all times to see that motion is coordinated. Since muscles do not recover at the same rate, incoordinated and substitutionary patterns of motion can appear at any stage in recovery of the various groups of muscles.

REHABILITATION

As muscular strength returns and coordinated motion is established, functional activities are incorporated into the treatment program. The goal of this phase of treatment is to teach the patient to master the common obstacles encountered in daily living in a normal environment. Training is given in the basic skills of standing, walking, stair-climbing, and self-care activities, striving always for maximum independence. In many instances, however, the patient may be involved to such an extent that some type of supportive or assistive apparatus will be necessary for him to accomplish these activities with any degree of independence. It may be necessary to permit, and actually encourage and teach, these patients to adopt substitutionary patterns of motion or trick movements to accomplish their goals. Later on, tendon transplant or reconstructive or other forms of orthopedic surgery may be necessary for the successful rehabilitation of the severely disabled poliomyelitis patient to enable him to live within the limits of his disability and to the maximum of his capacity.

It must be remembered that rehabilitation for the poliomyelitis patient, as well as any other patient with a physical disability, is more than total medical care. Rehabilitation also encompasses social adjustment in the home and community. Actually, many professions are included on the rehabilitation team. Physicians, both generalists and specialists, nurses, physical and occupational therapists, clinical psychologists, social workers, vocational counselors, and teachers who are educated to work with the handicapped person must coordinate their services if the rehabilitation program is to be comprehensive and effective. However, we must constantly be reminded that adequate rehabilitation-oriented medical care and guidance is the foundation upon which an effective rehabilitation program is built.

EDUCATION AND THE POSTPOLIO CHILD

Achievement of maximum rehabilitation by the physically handicapped child permits him to work, play, and assume an active role in family and community life. The responsibility of education in this rehabilitation program is greater than mere education of the mind; it must concern itself with the total life of the pupil. Many of these children possess aptitudes and abilities which, when developed by proper academic, social, and vocational training, can assist them in becoming socially and economically independent. It is the obligation of education to provide each child, whether he is typical or atypical, with the opportunity to develop to the maximum of his capacity.

PHYSICAL EDUCATION

The physical educator may do much to help the returning polio pupil meet the physical demands of daily living and increase his ability to live a normal life within the limits imposed by his disability. A carefully designed and guided activity program will aid in developing coordination, strength, and endurance, whereby the student may realize an ever-increasing range of physical function. At the same time, the child may be learning the skills, acquiring knowledge, and developing attitudes toward participation in recreational activities. There is no question that the role played by the physical educator in the aftercare of the pupil with poliomyelitis is as important as any other phase of the rehabilitation program.

In a great many instances, the physical educator will be confronted with a variety of problems when postpolio children return to school. The majority of these youngsters will have no observable aftereffects; others will exhibit only mild weakness and possibly some paralysis; and a few will be severely handicapped as a result of muscle weakness and paralysis. It is quite impossible to discuss each type of situation, for the extent and degree of involvement of each of these children is an individual problem and must be handled as such. However, certain factors are common to all polio children who participate in physical education classes, and these will be presented in the following pages.

MEDICAL CLEARANCE

As with any pupil who has recently returned to school following a serious illness, the physical educator should receive specific medical approval of the proposed program. This can best be accomplished through a consultation with physician, parent, and child. In addition to the usual case history, diagnosis, treatment, and prognosis, the physician's report should include a description of the pupil's physical limitations and needs and, at the same time, recommendations regarding the type and amount of activities to be used in the physical education program. Also, it is most desirable for the physical educator to obtain a copy of the various muscle tests that have been performed on the youngster. These muscle evaluation data will give invaluable information regarding the extent and degree of muscle involvement, as well as the rate and amount of recovery of the various affected muscles. This information is necessary in order to understand the pupil and his individual problems.

The construction of a sound physical education program depends on many factors concerning the youngster and his disability. One factor which is commonly overlooked by the physical educator is that of *overwork*. Although the normal pupil is rarely in danger of overwork, the pupil who has had poliomyelitis is abnormally sensitive to excessive physical effort. Irreversible muscle weakness following overwork can develop many years after the acute stages of the disease, and years after a formal medical treatment program has been discontinued. There is no question that activity, in the form of specific exercise, is the therapeutic device of greatest value in the present-day management of the postpolio youngster. However, we must remember that it does not necessarily follow that if a little exercise is good, more exercise is better. Even though it may be several years after the acute stage of the disease, the physical educator must always be aware of, and on the lookout for, progressive weakness in the postpolio child. The therapeutically dangerous doctrine of "work harder to get in shape" should always be avoided with these youngsters.

ACTIVITIES

In general, the postpolio child should be encouraged to participate in the widest possible range of activities appropriate to his age group. All activities should be considered for their contribution to the development of the student's general physical, mental, social, and recreational needs. The following classification offers the physical educator an opportunity to construct an activity program that will fit each pupil's individual needs and, at the same time, will have sufficient range of activities to be interesting and challenging to him.

BODY MECHANICS AND FUNCTIONAL ACTIVITIES

These are common to all individuals in most daily living activities, and they should receive special emphasis in the physical education program. It is well established that many musculoskeletal deformities may occur or progress as a result of faulty body mechanics; and this is especially true with the young postpolio pupil. The fact that poliomyelitis leaves its victims with varying degrees of muscle tightness, weakness, and paralysis, accounts for the fact that these children may develop abnormal patterns of motion resulting in faulty body mechanics. The restoration and maintenance of correct movement patterns is paramount to the prevention of deformities.

The overall objectives of the physical education program for the postpolio child are the improvement in body mechanics and the coordination of movement so that he can function as efficiently as possible. These objectives may be accomplished in the following manner: (1) by arousing the pupil's desire to improve his body mechanics; (2) by developing in him the proper kinesthetic sense so that he can realize when he is walking, standing, or sitting correctly; (3) by increasing the range of motion in areas that are restricted by contractures and tightness of soft tissue; (4) by obtaining proper balance (strength and endurance) between the various groups of muscles; (5) by obtaining the proper amount of relaxation of the unused muscles; and (6) by improving the muscle function (coordination, strength, and endurance) in maintaining the corrected positions. To attempt to attain these objectives by simply trying to strengthen weak muscles is not only foolhardy but also it can lead to failure. The value of good body mechanics must first be thoroughly understood and accepted by the child. Training must be given in correct muscle habits and in the development of conscious control of good positions of standing, sitting, and walking. Exercises are employed to strengthen the muscles that can maintain the correct positions, as well as to strengthen the habit of correct body mechanics.

RECREATION

The old adage "all work and no play make Jack a dull boy" is of even greater importance to the postpolio youngster than to the so-called "normal" pupil. Many of these children have had prolonged periods of hospitalization, with total emphasis on treatment and very little, if any, opportunity to participate in recreational activities. Frequently, parents of postpolio children feel so burdened by social, physical, and financial demands that little thought or effort is given to the need for active play. Most community recreational centers do not have programs for the physically handicapped. As a consequence, many of these youngsters have missed a lot of play in the past; and, what is so very important, they are in danger of missing more in the future. It is through play activities that the child, for the most part, develops his musculature, rhythm, coordination and timing, and socialization. The natural activities of running, jumping, climbing, throwing, and batting have a great interest for these pupils, both as spectators and as players. The recreational games and sports of physical education constitute one of education's best laboratories for democratic living. It is here that the child is provided with the opportunity of experiencing such fundamental laws of social conduct as: Follow the rules of the game! Wait your turn! Play fair! Be a good sport! Cooperate with your teammates! If we really believe that one of the main aims of the schools is to develop well integrated and socially adjusted citizens, then each youngster must receive the opportunity for development and participation, to the limit of his capacity, in all phases of the physical education program.

Recreation for the postpolio pupil should be any activity from which he obtains enjoyment and pleasure or diversion from work. Although recreation may be therapeutic in nature, this should not be its main emphasis. Usually a child, handicapped or not, likes to play the game the way it should be played. All too frequently, when recreational activities are designed or adapted to accomplish a specific therapeutic purpose, they are not acceptable to the youngster as play. For example, a pupil with weak arms may take great delight in playing basketball; but he prefers underhand shooting because he is more accurate and has better control of the ball. However, he may lose interest in basketball if you insist that he use the one-hand push shot to increase the endurance and coordination of his weakened triceps. For him, basketball should be a game played with other children for fun, not merely an extension of his therapy. The purpose of recreation is not to provide specific therapy for a child's physical disability, but rather to provide the means for bringing fun, skills, and socialization into his life.

Realizing that recreation is a necessity for these children, the teacher of physical education should make every effort to select activities that will emphasize what the handicapped child *can* do rather than what he cannot do. A broad experience in individual, dual, and team games will prove most enjoyable and beneficial to any pupil, no matter how severe his disability. Archery, darts, quoits, bowling, golf, bait and fly casting, shuffleboard, table tennis, selected track events, tumbling, gymnastics, and stunts are good examples of individual and dual activities that may be modified to meet the physical needs of any age group. Team games and sports may be adapted into such activities as wheel-chair basketball; volleyball on mats; baseball with students designated as batters, runners, umpires, or scorekeepers; tennis; and badminton.

In addition to the sports and games area of physical education, aquatics and rhythmic activities are especially useful and adaptable for the postpolio pupil. Many physically handicapped children can be taught to swim and float, since the buoyancy of water helps to counteract any muscular weakness. Some of these youngsters have found that they have been able to play and compete with the physically "normal" children in these water activities. Besides being an outlet that is most enjoyable, swimming may lead to other recreational activities such as boating, sailing, and fishing.

Postpolio patients frequently are in need of rhythm training. The simple alternating movements performed to music and interpretive responses to simple rhythms and folk dances are of great value in developing rhythm, timing, and coordination, as well as being a source of great pleasure for the younger groups. Social and square dancing should receive emphasis with the older groups for their contribution to social poise and grace as well as for being a desirable form of adult recreation.

The teacher should encourage participation in camping and outdoor activities for the postpolio pupil. During the past decade, the number of camps for the physically handicapped has greatly increased. Opportunity for participation in such activities as swimming, boating, sailing, fishing, cookouts, and hiking may best be presented in the camping situation. The camp should be an experience in group living which is frequently lacking in the life of the physically handicapped.

SPECIAL DEVELOPMENTAL AND RE-EDUCATION ACTIVITIES

Mention should be made of the role of special developmental and re-education exercises for the postpolio pupil in school. Training him in coordinated movements, in such a manner that all groups of muscles function to the best advantage and so that weak muscles are used and developed properly, requires special skills and knowledges in neurophysiology, neuroanatomy, functional anatomy, and pathology. Weeks, months, or even years may be required to decide whether maximal benefits have been achieved. In most instances, the physical educator is not adequately trained or prepared, nor does he have the time or facilities, to administer these special developmental and re-education exercises. Actually, this phase of treatment rightfully belongs in the hands of the physical therapist.

SUMMARY

Physical education has a vital role in the total rehabilitation process for the postpolio student. The activities in which he engages can help with his physical, social, educational, and recreational needs. The problems involved are broad and varied, and no one person has all the answers. Each child must be handled in respect to his own particular needs. The integration of the physical education program with the pupil's medical, educational, and vocational programs is essential if maximum rehabilitation is to be realized.

REFERENCES

1. Burney, Leroy E., "Oral Poliovirus Vaccine Statement," *Public Health Reports*, October, 1960, **75** (10), 869-871.
2. "Live Poliovirus Vaccine Approved; Worldwide Trials Reported," *Science*, September 2, 1960, **132** (3427).
3. Melnick, Joseph L., "Problems Associated with the Use of Live Poliovirus Vaccine," *American Journal of Public Health*, July, 1960, **50** (7), 1013-1031.
4. "Polio Immunization Lags," *Science*, February, 1961, **133** (3450), 371.

Chapter 12

CEREBRAL PALSY

Cerebral *palsy* is a term applied to the disability of a person who is suffering from neuromuscular dysfunction as a result of brain impairment. It is a medicosocioeconomic problem that sooner or later confronts nearly every community in the nation, and occurs with about equal regularity among all classes of people. Pupils afflicted with cerebral palsy present a series of problems to the teacher that are far more complicated than is typical of any other group of physically handicapped children. This is true not only in terms of the variability and severity of the physical impairment, but also in terms of the numerous pathological, psychological, and emotional abnormalities that may be associated with the disease.

There is much confusion and misunderstanding of the term *cerebral palsy* in the minds of many lay persons. Terms including *Little's disease, congenital diplegia, congenital spastic paralysis,* and *spastic,* to mention a few, are mistakenly used when speaking of cerebral palsy. These terms are applied not only to people who may exhibit these characteristics, but also to people who demonstrate athetoid and ataxic movements. Because of the confusion that exists in regard to cerebral palsy, it seems worthwhile to discuss its meaning rather thoroughly.

Definition of Cerebral Palsy

Perlstein (8) defines cerebral palsy as a "condition characterized by a paralysis, weakness, incoordination, or any other aberration of motor function due to a pathology of the motor control centers of the brain." Similarly, the American Academy of Cerebral Palsy defines it as "Any abnormal alteration in movement or motor function arising from defect, injury, or disease of the nervous tissues contained in the cranial cavity." However, it must be pointed out that these definitions emphasize only the physical components of cerebral palsy and hence do not do justice to the complexity of the disease. It is well known that cerebral palsy may frequently be complicated by many factors other than merely motor or physical problems, such as psychological, convulsive, visual, hearing, speech, and behavior disorders of organic origin. To be sure, in a few individuals only the neuromuscular factor may be present, while in others any combination of these factors may occur. To define cerebral palsy in any one aspect without consideration of the others is to lose sight of the entire problem.

Going to the other extreme, some authors believe that cerebral palsy should be considered as a broad group of cases under the general title of *brain-damaged syndrome*. Closely related to this theory is that of Schwartz and associate (12), who believe that cerebral palsy should be defined as an aggregate of handicaps, i.e., emotional, neuromuscular, special sensory, and peripheral sensory, caused by damaged or absent brain structures. However, such an expanded definition would include all cerebral lesions causing mental deficiency, personality disorders, and epilepsy, whether or not there is an accompanying neuromuscular aberration. It must be kept in mind that neuromuscular dysfunction is the main characteristic of cerebral palsy, and differentiates it from other forms of brain-damaged syndrome in children. Therefore, it would seem reasonable to encompass the more acceptable aspects of the two extremes and arrive at a specific yet comprehensive definition. Cerebral palsy, then, is characterized by muscle paralysis, weakness, and incoordination as a result of malformed brain structure or damaged tissue occurring before birth, at birth, or immediately following birth.

Magnitude of the Problem

There is still a wide variation in estimates of the number of people with cerebral palsy in the United States. While its prevalence has been subject to numerous studies and investigations, the results have varied; and a truly accurate picture is nonexistent. The most commonly used method of estimating its incidence is the Phelps' formula. Phelps (9) hypothesizes that seven cerebral palsied children are born per every 100,000 births each year. Of these, one child dies in early infancy. Hence, six children remain a clinical problem in terms of diagnosis and treatment. The United Cerebral Palsy Association estimates there are some 550,000 cerebral palsied individuals in the United States, 200,000 of whom are under 21 years of age. Deavers (4) claims approximately one infant in every 200 live births will be born with a brain injury, or one every 53 minutes.

CAUSE OF CEREBRAL PALSY

The cause of cerebral palsy is subject to much speculation. Usually the disease is attributed to developmental defects or interuterine cerebral degeneration. It is also believed that the cause may include abnormal labor, with brain trauma to the motor cortex, anoxia in the immediate postnatal period, cerebral vascular lesions in infancy, and encephalitis or meningitis in infancy. More research is needed to specifically locate the underlying cause or causes.

SIGNS AND SYMPTOMS

Severe brain damage or defect may be evident at birth or shortly thereafter, by such signs and symptoms as: (1) a small or abnormally shaped head, (2) difficulty in feedings, (3) vomiting, (4) apathy, and (5) restlessness or irritability. There may also be convulsions and muscle spasms, and the tendon reflexes may be grossly exaggerated. The most severely affected have extremely low resistance to infection, and usually do not survive. However, in the milder cases, brain damage may not appear until the age of 6 months to 2 years, when it becomes apparent that the child is unable to perform the physical and intellectual feats of his contemporaries. Abnormal movements of the extremities usually do not appear until the second and third year of life.

As a rule, the clinical signs and symptoms reach their maximum degree of severity at the age of 2 to 4 years. After this, there may be some improvement as the youngster learns to adjust and compensate for his disabilities. The child with a mild degree of cerebral damage may develop into adulthood with only slight physical impairment. However, it must be kept in mind that a disability which is of minor importance to a child may be a severe handicap to an adult. Usually the physical handicap is greatest with those who have moderately severe cerebral damage; and as a result, the youngster will requre special care throughout childhood.

Associated Handicaps

While the main characteristic of cerebral palsy is the motor involvement, associated symptoms which reflect brain damage may also be present. These could include mental retardation; convulsions (epilepsy); visual, hearing, and speech disturbance; perceptual dysfunctions; and behavior disorders. Any combination of these associated handicaps may be present, and pose difficult problems in the management and adjustment of the cerebral palsied.

MENTAL RETARDATION

Outside the purely motor dysfunction, mental retardation is perhaps the greatest limiting factor in the habilitation of the cerebral palsy child. In a group of 354 individuals with cerebral palsy, Asher and Schonell (1) found that 65.9 percent had IQ's below 90, with 49 percent of the total falling below 70. Similar results have been reported by Miller and Rosenfeld (5) and Burgemeister and Blum (2). Numerous similar studies have shown some degree of variation in the prevalence of mental retardation in the cerebral palsied, but there is general agreement that the trend is evident.

CONVULSIVE SEIZURES

As compared to about 5 percent of the general population, between 24 and 46 percent of the cerebral palsied have some form of convulsive seizures. The New Jersey Study, (3) which included 1215 individuals, noted that 29.2 percent had a history of seizures. Perlstein and Barnett (7) reported that convulsions occur in approximately 40 percent of children with cerebral palsy. However, in a later study, based on 1217 consecutive patients with infantile cerebral palsy, Perlstein observed that seizures occurred in nearly one-half of all patients with cerebral palsy. Furthermore, the seizures were most common in spastics (63 percent) and least common in athetoid (22 percent) and ataxics (20 percent). The most common types of clinical seizures in cerebral palsy were *grand mal* (53 percent) and the focal or jacksonian (24 percent), while the least common types were *petit mal* (1.6 percent) and psychomotor (0.4 percent).

Control of convulsive seizures by drug therapy is an important phase of treatment with the cerebral palsied, although seizures per se do not hinder or limit an active habilitation program. It will, of course, modify one's decision about training for an occupation in which a seizure may involve the hazard of physical injury.

VISUAL, AUDITORY, AND SPEECH IMPAIRMENTS

Associated disabilities, other than mental retardation and convulsive seizures, take the form of visual, auditory, and speech impairments. Wishik (13) reports the approximate percentage of patients with these secondary handicaps as follows: speech disorders, 50 to 75 percent; visual defects, 50 percent; and auditory defects, 25 percent. The New Jersey study reveals that 68 percent of the subjects had speech defects, 24 percent had visual impairments, and 5.3 percent suffered auditory abnormalities. While there is considerable variation between these two reports concerning the percentage of auditory and visual conditions, there is complete agreement as to the high incidence of speech impairment. When one considers the multiplicity of disorder variables possible in cerebral palsy, the complexity of the problem becomes staggering insofar as habilitation and education are concerned.

CLASSIFICATION

Cerebral palsy may be classified according to various criteria, depending on the point of view and emphasis desired. Perlstein (6) has summarized the most common of these classifications as follows: (1) according to clinical symptoms, (2) according to the anatomic site of brain lesion, (3) according to topographical involvement of the extremities, (4) according to the degree of muscle tone, and (5) according to etiology. Each of these classifications has advantages and certain disadvantages; however, it is in the overlap of these various classifications that we are able to include all of the information pertinent to the cerebral palsy child's handicaps. The classification which is commonly employed, and the one most familiar to the teacher, is that which differentiates the various clinical symptoms of cerebral palsy. This classification includes: (1) spastic, (2) athetoid, (3) ataxic, (4) rigidity, and (5) tremor.

SPASTICITY

In general, the spastic type of cerebral palsy accounts for approximately 40 percent of all cases. It is characterized by increased muscle tone and a greatly exaggerated stretch reflex. Voluntary movement of affected muscles results in motion that may be explosive, jerky, or poorly coordinated. The stretch reflex is characterized by an increased tendency of the muscle to contract when actively or passively moved. This excessive contraction of the affected muscle will resist the motion, and is maximal with rapid movement and minimal with slow movements. This phenomenon is not limited to the stretched muscle alone, but tends to spread to synergistic muscles as well, with the result that mass motion of the whole extremity may occur. It is more commonly found in the antigravity muscles, such as the biceps brachii, gastroc-soleus, and quadricep muscle groups, than in the agonists or gravity muscles.

In the spastic type, contractures are more common than in any other types of cerebral palsy. Over a period of time, prolonged contraction of the spastic muscles against weak opposing muscles will cause the development of permanent contractures. This muscular imbalance also causes the child to assume certain characteristic posture patterns, which are peculiar to each individual case. When the spastic condition involves the lower extremities, the adductor muscles are usually contracted and the opposing abductor weakened, the knees are flexed, and the contracted gastroc-soleus calf group draw the heel up so that the child walks on the outer portion of the ball of the foot and toes. The muscle contractures draw the legs together and internally rotate them at the hip joint, resulting in the typical scissor gait. If the upper extremities are involved, the arms are drawn in toward the body with the elbows flexed, forearms are pronated, and wrists and fingers are flexed. Any combination of arm and leg involvement may be present. Convulsive seizures and mental retardation are more common in the spastic cerebral palsied, especially in children with marked hand involvement.

ATHETOID

The percentage of athetoid type of cerebral palsy varies considerably. Pohl (11) reports that it is the second most common type of cerebral palsy and makes up 19 percent of all cases. Hopkins, Rice, and Colton (3) state that 23.6 percent of all cases are athetoid. Phelps (9) reports as high as 45 percent. Although there is a marked difference between these reported figures, it is generally agreed that the athetoid is one of the two most prevalent types of cerebral palsy.

The athetoid is marked by irregular, unrhythmic, uncontrollable, and unpredictable writhing or wormlike movements. The atheoid, unlike the spastic, has no difficulty in moving; however, he moves when he does not wish to and not necessarily in the desired direction. He tends to start moving before he is ready, and any effort to move an arm or leg is generally followed by nonessential movements in other parts of the body. Posture is unpredictable and inconsistent, but tends to be repetitive in the same individual. Frequently, the head is drawn back, the mouth is open, the tongue protrudes, and there is a tendency to grimace in such a manner as to erroneously suggest mental retardation. (Actually, there may be mental retardation present, although it is somewhat less likely than with the spastic.) Involuntary and unpredictable movements of the face, tongue, and throat muscles seriously interfere with speech and swallowing. The handicap is least noticeable at rest, absent in sleep, and increases with voluntary motion and emotional or environmental stimulus.

ATAXIC

Children with this type of disorder make up 2 to 5 percent of the total. Severe cases are the exception rather than the rule; and frequently the milder cases go unrecognized. The outstanding symptom is disturbance in the sense of balance and equilibrium. It is not usually noted until the child attempts to walk or maintain posture. The ataxic child may appear awkward and clumsy during play or in attempting to perform motor skills. Frequently, the child will appear quite normal in the school environment; and the disorder may not become apparent until he participates in the physical education program.

RIGIDITY

Rigidity is the result of widespread brain damage, and usually affects a large part of the body. It is also closely associated with severe mental retardation. The outstanding clinical feature in rigidity is the hypertonicity of the muscles. Both contracting muscles and their antagonists are affected, but the antagonists to a greater extent. Thus, total motion is at a minimum. In rigidity, unlike spasticity, there is greater resistance to slow passive motion than there is to rapid passive motion. At times, this resistance to passive motion is continuous, resulting in the sensation of bending a lead pipe. This is sometimes referred to as lead pipe rigidity or stiffness. In some cases, rigidity is constant; in others, it is intermittent.

TREMOR

The tremor type of cerebral palsy is characterized by uncontrollable and involuntary movements with a regular pattern. The tremors are due to the rhythmic contractions of agonist and antagonist muscles. In some people, tremors are continually present, at rest as well as in activity (nonintentional tremor). In others, it is absent at rest, and appears only with attempted movement (intention tremor). The musculature generally is good, and the individual usually performs heavy feats of muscular activity more effectively than lighter and more refined types of work. The person with tremor type of cerebral palsy appears to be somewhat noisy when speaking, for the muscles of speech seem to work best when he talks loudly.

TREATMENT

As yet, there is no treatment for cerebral palsy which will mend the original lesion in the brain or effect a cure. Experience has demonstrated, however, that the function of that portion of the brain not affected by the lesion can be improved by a well-managed training program. The youngster with cerebral palsy does not know what is wrong with his muscles, or does he know how he can use them effectively. If he is allowed to grow and develop on his own, he will emphasize his disability by developing abnormal and faulty patterns of motion. It is imperative to initiate a training program as early as possible to prevent this from happening.

The program must be based on the type of cerebral palsy, the extent and degree of involvement, the muscles affected, and the child's mental capacity and secondary handicaps. Knowing the mental capacities and associated handicaps is obviously essential, since these factors influence the cooperation and amount of improvement that can be expected from the program. Therefore, accurate diagnosis by experienced physicians and others qualified to contribute to the total evaluation of the *physical, mental,* and *emotional* status of the youngster should preceed the developmental programs.

Periodic medical examinations and check-ups are an important phase of the total treatment program. Children with cerebral palsy are subject to all the health problems found in other children; in addition, they may have special health problems which are of particular importance to their handicaps. For instance, most of those working with cerebral palsy agree that many of these youngsters have poor nutritional status. The constant involuntary motions of the athetoid cause him to burn tremendous quantities of energy. As a consequence, the athetoid is often smaller and thinner than the average child of the same age. Children with spasticity, ataxia, and rigidity are relatively inactive and tend to be overweight. As an illustration, Phelps (10) cites one athetoid boy who required 6000 calories a day to maintain his correct weight, whereas a spastic boy of the same age was found to require only 1500 calories. Other health problems of paramount importance to the cerebral palsied are sleep disturbances, convulsions, fluid or electrolyte balance, diarrhea, dental health, and home safety. If the child is examined and followed continuously, the physician not only can treat these special medical and health problems that arise, but also he is often able to offer special health advice to the parents which may be preventive in nature. Furthermore, re-evaluation at periodic intervals shows the child's rate of development and progress, and is invaluable in the continuous habilitation program.

DRUG THERAPY

Because of the ever-mounting and favorable publicity given to drug therapy, everyone is looking for a wonder drug for cerebral palsy. Actually, drug therapy plays a small role in the treatment program. Relaxants may be useful in diagnosis, since they make it possible to estimate muscle length, degree of joint range of motion, and the presence of contractures. Sometimes these drugs are used as an adjunct to physical therapy when the therapist is attempting to teach relaxation or give neuromuscular education. However, to date, none of the drugs have proved useful for spastic muscle conditions or control of involuntary motions; and most of them produce undesirable side-affects. Under the sponsorship of various health organizations, such as the United Cerebral Palsy Association and the Society for Crippled Children and Adults, research is being intensified in the area of drug therapy; and it is hoped that these studies may lead to new drugs of greater value than those presently available.

As stated earlier, convulsive seizures have a high prevalence in cerebral palsy; and their control is a prerequisite to a successful habilitation program. Anticonvulsive drugs have proved 80 to 85 percent effective in either controlling these seizures or improving the condition. However, as with the relaxant drugs, any of the anticonvulsive drugs may have toxic effects; and they should be used with caution.

PHYSICAL HABILITATION

Treatment for cerebral palsy presently consists primarily of physical habilitation. Physical, occupational, and speech therapies form the major components of physical habilitation; and other measures, such as music and recreational therapy, make valuable adjunctive therapeutic contributions. Physical therapy includes such basic procedures as: (1) evaluation, consisting of muscle testing, functional evaluation, balance and gait analysis, and re-evaluation to determine progress; (2) relaxation training; (3) neuromuscular education and the development of correct patterns of movement training in such activities as balance, coordination, muscle control, and gait; and (4) training in the use of braces and other mechanical aids that may be necessary. Occupational therapy is used quite extensively to emphasize training in daily living activities and for education in diversional and recreation activities. Evaluation of the speech and hearing mechanism and language development is a necessary part of the habilitation program. Speech therapy is carried on in conjunction with other therapeutic and educational services.

SURGERY

Operative procedures involving the muscles, tendons, bones, and nerves are performed to correct deformities and enhance the habilitation process. Most orthopedic surgery is reparitive rather than curative. The use of orthopedic surgery is usually confined to the spastic type of cerebral palsy, and results are generally better in the lower extremities than in the upper extremities. Neurosurgical procedures have been utilized, but with little success. Recent development of the chemopallidectomy operation, which has been successful in controlling involuntary movements in Parkinson's disease, has met with some rather dramatic success in selected patients with cerebral palsy; however, it is still too early to ascertain the permanent value derived from this type of surgery.

EDUCATION AND CEREBRAL PALSY

The aim of education is to provide the amount and kind of educational experiences most profitable to each child. The realization of this ideal is as important to the cerebral palsied youngster as it is for the more fortunate disability-free children. At best, numerous and complex problems in education are created by the multiplicity of handicaps associated with cerebral palsy. Ordinarily, education is accomplished through the senses of sight, hearing, and touch; and it is not uncommon in the cerebral palsied to find one or more of these senses impaired. In addition, physical disabilities, mental retardation, and other manifestations of brain damage impose limitations on the inherent exploration activities which are necessary for continual growth and development of all children.

The educational program should be part of the total program planned for the child. Methods of instruction should be highly specialized, requiring teachers who are well trained in understanding children with cerebral palsy, and who are ready to adjust, adapt, experiment, and explore the endless ways and means of making the school experience really valuable and productive for each child. The teacher must recognize that the majority of these pupils are educationally retarded and that educational achievement is likely to be less than that expected from normal children of similar age. The school must have equipment and facilities, and see that physical, occupational, and speech therapists are available to all students who may benefit from their services. A curriculum fitted to the needs of each child must necessarily be flexible and nonconfining. Best results are attainable only when the physical and educational programs are correlated and integrated.

Educational Placement of the Cerebral Palsied

A detailed evaluation of each youngster should precede placement in any school program. Better teaching may be realized if each child is placed according to his stage of development rather than according to the traditional chronological age and grade levels. Such a classification may be based on one of many criteria; however, the following system appears to be the most realistic and functional for educational purposes:

1. *Cerebral Palsied Children Needing Custodial Care:* These children fall into three groups: (1) those for whom education might mean only achievement of varying degrees of self-help and self-function; (2) those who can achieve minimal, if any, success in self-help because of severe mental deficiency and physical handicaps; and (3) those children who have very severe physical disabilities, such as

blindness and hearing loss, but with little or no mental impairment. These children, because of their disabilities, cannot be accomodated in regular or special programs in a public school system.

2. *Cerebral Palsied Children with Mental Retardation:* This is the group of children who are mentally handicapped in specific or all areas, but who profit from an appropriate curriculum. Special classes are based on the physical and mental levels of development.

3. *The Intelligent Cerebral Palsied with Severe Physical Handicaps:* This group includes the child with an alert mind but whose physical handicaps are such that education is possible only in a special school or class. They are apt to be nonambulatory, often nonself-feeders, and frequently cannot accomplish the more basic activities of daily living, i.e., bathing, dressing, and toilet care. Progress is exceptionally slow, and it is not uncommon to find teen-agers in the third or fourth grade levels even though they may be highly intelligent.

4. *The Cerebral Palsied Child with Mild Physical Handicaps and Normal Intelligence:* These are the children whose handicaps are so slight that they have little or no need of special schools or classes. However, they are usually slow, awkward, and clumsy in the physical education class and require special help and guidance.

It must be recognized that the above classifications are very generalized, and may encompass a wide range of varying conditions within each group. Any classification for educational purposes must be general and flexible, and placement is not necessarily a permanent one. Later observation and tests may change the placement level for any student. At all times, each youngster's activities must be kept within the range of his developmental level. Proper classification and placement of the cerebral palsied pupil will minimize wasted time, for the children as well as the teachers and therapists, reduce frustration, and facilitate better emotional and social adjustment.

PHYSICAL EDUCATION FOR THE CEREBRAL PALSIED

Without exception, every cerebral palsied child attending school can benefit from a well planned and supervised physical education program. As a result of their condition, these youngsters have been deprived, or retarded at least, in the normal process of physical, mental, and social development. Their need for opportunities to experience the disciplines of life, such as success and failure, self-confidence, self-realization, self-expression, and a feeling of worth-whileness, is paramount, and can best be met through a physical education program. Through carefully selected games and recreational activities, the child is given the opportunity to develop interpersonal relationships and social adaptability, neuromuscular skills, coordination, and relaxation, balance, and muscular strength and endurance. We recognize all of these factors as being essential for a purposeful and happy life.

Contrary to the beliefs and teachings of some physical educators, the primary objectives of physical education for the cerebral palsied pupil are not to restore neuromuscular function or overcome contractures. These require the special skills, training, knowledge, and experience of the physical and occupational therapists. Admittedly, such concomitant outcomes may occur (and it is most desirable if they do) as a result of an intelligently planned physical education program; but it must be recognized that these values and outcomes are not the primary concern of the physical educator. The real value of physical education in the habilitation program of the cerebral palsied is in its psychosocial effect rather than as a supplement to physical or occupational therapy.

As with all handicapped pupils, evaluation of the complete case history for each child should be the first step in the planning of an individualized physical education program. It is important that the specific conditions and extent of involvement are understood. Such a report should include not only a physician's evaluation, but also findings by the physical, occupational, and speech therapists, psychologist, social worker, and preschool teacher. Usually, these children have been under medical care and guidance for many years prior to their entrance into the school system, and have received a considerable amount of speech, physical, and occupational therapy as well as some preschool training. Careful analysis of all reports contained in the case history will give the physical educator greater insight into and understanding of the child and his problems. Close attention should be given to such factors as the physician's diagnosis, treatment, prognosis, and recommendations; the aims and goals of the habilitation program; levels of motor, emotional, and social development; communication problems; adaptive behavior; and the amount and rate of progress made in the past with the various therapies.

Once the preliminary report has been thoroughly studied and understood, perhaps requiring special conferences with the child's parents, physician, therapists, or psychologist, a tentative physical education program should be established. Such a program must be designed not only to fit the individual needs of each pupil, but it must also harmoniously integrate with the rest of each youngster's habilitation program. It must be extremely flexible and cover the broadest range of activities. These children have had very limited play experiences in the past, and it is essential to see that they are exposed to as great a variety of games as possible. At the same time, caution must be used to insure that all activities are interesting and challenging to him, as well as remaining within his motor development level. Modification of sports and games must not be so severe that the activities loose their identity. These children come to class for physical education activities, not physical therapy. Close observation of the pupil in this tentative physical education program for a short period of time will determine any changes that may have to be made. At all times, the activities must be within the ability range of the child.

ON THE ELEMENTARY LEVEL

The physical education program in the elementary grades should give the pupil a sense of pleasure and accomplishment, and thus motivate him to further activity. His endeavors should be directed in performing even the basic simple movements. Activities in walking, running, skipping, hopping, kicking, and throwing should be encouraged as the basis for proficency in more advanced sport skills. Do not modify the activities to emphasize movement in the affected part; for example, in attempting to kick a ball, the pupil will automatically use the leg least affected. Do not insist that he use the more involved leg to kick the ball just because you think it may increase the youngster's coordination and strength. It is more important for that pupil to experience success in kicking the ball than it is for him to develop better coordination, or whatever qualities a teacher may think are necessary. Remember, the student is in class for fun, enjoyment, accomplishment, and sociability—not for therapy. Many adapted physical education programs have failed because this cardinal rule was ignored by the physical educator.

Music and rhythmic activities with a slow tempo are excellent for increasing interest and pleasure in the physical education program, as well as for facilitating motor function, release from tension to enhance relaxation, and self-expression. Action songs and singing games are particularly good. Games of low organization, such as duckpins, shuffleboard, croquet, circle tag (walking), and kickball will not only contribute to the teaching-learning goals, but also present opportunities for much-needed social development.

ON THE SECONDARY LEVEL

All activities should approximate those used in the normal physical education class, with only such modifications as are necessitated by the youngster's physical handicap. The activities are selected with an emphasis not only on recreation values and interests of the pupil, but also on their general effects, such as development of skills, poise, initiative, imagination, self-expression, and creativeness. Rhythms—particularly folk, social, square, and simple waltz clog dances with a slow tempo—and individual and dual recreational activities such as archery, badminton, shuffleboard, bait and fly casting, bowling, and swimming (if possible) are basic to the program. Camping experiences, and all the activities associated with camping, are excellent for the adolescent child with cerebral palsy. Team games, such as volleyball, soccer, football, and softball, may be worked in occasionally; but intense competition and its resulting tensions should be kept to a minimum. Extensive posture work and developmental exercises may be used only under the supervision of a physician. These activities are, for the most part, the responsibility of the physical therapist and are classified as medical treatment. The physical educator should plan his program to emphasize the development of recreational skills and social competencies.

SUMMARY

Physical education for the cerebral palsied child presents one of the greatest challenges to the physical educator. The significance of individual differences is never so meaningful as with the cerebral palsied. The multiplicity of handicaps create problems that are not common to any other group of atypical children. Because of the peculiar needs of these children, the services of specialized medical (including physical, occupational, and speech therapists), psychological, and educational personnel are essential. Integration of a sound physical education program into the total habilitation schedule can be most beneficial to these pupils. The primary aim of physical education is to contribute to the social, emotional, and recreative competence of the cerebral palsied through an adapted sports program. Such an opportunity will greatly aid the cerebral palsied child to take his place in society as a respected citizen, capable of living effectively and happily with his fellow man.

REFERENCES

1. Asher, P., and Schonell, F. E., "A Survey of 400 Cases of Cerebral Palsy in Childhood," *Archives of Disease in Childhood,* December, 1956, **25** 360-379.
2. Burgemeister, B. B., and Blum, L. H., "Intellectual Evaluation of a Group of Cerebral Palsied Children," *Nervous Child,* April, 1949, **8** (2), 177-180.
3. Deaver, G. G., "Cerebral Palsy: Methods of Evaluation and Treatment," Rehabilitation Monograph IX, Institute of Physical Medicine and Rehabilitation, New York University–Bellevue Medical Center, 1955.
4. Hopkins, T. W., Rice, H. W., and Coton, K. G., "Evaluation and Education of the Cerebral Palsied Child: New Jersey Study," International Council for Exceptional Children, Washington, D.C., 1954, pp. 46-48.
5. Miller, E., and Rosenfeld, B. G., "The Psychologic Evaluation of Children with Cerebral Palsy and Its Implications in Treatment," *Journal of Pediatrics,* November, 1952, **41** (11), 613-621.

248   PHYSICAL EDUCATION FOR HANDICAPPED CHILDREN

6. Perlstein, M. A., "Infantile Cerebral Palsy: Classification and Clinical Correlations," *Journal of the American Medical Association,* May 3, 1952, **149** (1), 30-34.
7. Perlstein, M. A., Barnett, H. E., "Nature and Recognition of Cerebral Palsy in Infancy," *Journal of the American Medical Association,* April 19, 1952, **148** (16), 1389-1397.
8. Perlstein, M. A., "Medical Aspects of Cerebral Palsy," *Nervous Child,* April, 1949, **8** (2), 128-151.
9. Phelps, W. M., "The Cerebral Palsies," in Nelson, Waldo E. (Editor), *Mitchell-Nelson Textbook of Pediatrics,* 5th ed., *Saunders,* Philadelphia, 1950, pp. 1361-1366.
10. Phelps, W. M., "Dietary Requirements in Cerebral Palsy," *Journal of the American Dietetic Association,* October, 1951, **27** (10), 869-870.
11. Pohl, J. F., *Cerebral Palsy,* Bruce, St. Paul., 1950, p. 224.
12. Schwartz, R. P., *et al,* "Motivation of Children with Multiple Functional Disabilities," *Journal of the American Medical Association,* March 31, 1951, **145** (13), 951-955.
13. Wishik, S. M., "An Outline of Administrative Guides for the Community Cerebral Palsy Program," *American Journal Public Health,* February, 1954, **44** (2), 158-165.

Chapter 13

OTHER NEUROLOGICAL
CONDITIONS

IN ADDITION to poliomyelitis and cerebral palsy, discussed in the previous chapters, there are many other neurological conditions commonly seen in children attending school. Since the distinctive feature of the nervous system is its specialization of structure and function, the signs and symptoms of dysfunction and disability are dependent more on the site or location of the pathology than on its nature. Each group of cells in the nervous system has its own task to perform, and a small lesion may cause a total loss of some important function. For example, a hemorrhage the size of a 25-cent coin, located in the brain, may cause total hemiplegia. A tumor no larger than the tip of your finger, situated in the spinal canal, may cause a complete paralysis of the lower extremities. In relation to the size of area damaged, the person with a lesion in the nervous system loses a great deal more than from a comparable lesion elsewhere in the body, and the loss is more apt to be permanent. Compounding the problem of rehabilitation is the limited and even questionable physiological potential for cellular regeneration within the central nervous system.

A comprehensive survey of the neurological conditions is beyond the scope of this presentation; nevertheless, a brief review of the general principles of some common conditions encountered in children attending school is necessary if we are to adequately understand how these pathologies may be considered in the physical education program.

EPILEPSY

As a teacher of physical education, you may occasionally be called on to take care of a youngster who is having an epileptic seizure or convulsion. Unfortunately, it is a rather common affliction, and carries with it a stigma which dates to pre-Hippocratic times. In ancient days, a person with seizures was thought to be possessed of demons; and only a couple of hundred years ago, epilepsy was considered the work of witches. Even today, many people regard epilepsy as an incurable horror, and associate it with feeblemindedness or mental illness. These attitudes spring from a fear of the unknown, for it was the only way people could explain this occasional strange behavior. The truth is, however, that the great majority of persons subject to seizures are in every other way perfectly norman human beings. Some epileptics have IQ's at the genius level; and history recounts that such famous individuals as St. Paul, Dante, Byron, Julius Caesar, Napoleon, Guy de Maupassant, and Van Gogh were among those suffering from epilepsy. Actually, we now know that a person with epilepsy may have an excellent chance of recovering and living a normal life providing he has good medical care and the opportunity to develop physically, mentally, socially, and emotionally.

What Is Epilepsy?

Epilepsy is a Greek word meaning "to seize." It is understood to be a sudden, brief or prolonged loss of consciousness, usually accompanied by convulsions or convulsive phenomenon which may range anywhere from a slight twitching of the eyelids to a violent shaking of the entire body. It is one of the more common forms of convulsive attacks, although it is well to bear in mind that not every convulsive attack means epilepsy and that seizures of unconsciousness may have many causes. Although a number of manifestations frequently precede, accompany, or follow the seizures, it is essentially characterized by some disturbance of consciousness with more or less complete amnesia and the convulsive state. In general, patients with seizures are divided into four groups according to the clinical signs and symptoms manifested during the time of an episode: (1) *grand mal* or generalized attacks, (2) *petit mal* or minor attacks, (3) jacksonian attacks, and (4) psychomotor attacks and epileptic equivalents.

GRAND MAL ATTACK

A *grand mal*, sometimes referred to as "great illness" or "generalized attack," affects more people than any other type of epileptic seizure. During an attack, the patient collapses with a sudden shriek or yell, the so-called epileptic cry. This is the tonic phase of the episode, which lasts for seconds or several minutes. During this time, the head and eyes are turned to one side, the hands clenched, elbows flexed, and legs rigid. The pupils are dilated and fixed, and there is a faulty respiration. The clonic stage, which follows the tonic phase, exhibits general convulsive movements; the tongue may be bitten, the patient foams at the mouth, the face is congested, and the pulse is irregular. The convulsive movements may be mild or severe; there may be incontinence. Finally, the convulsions diminish and breathing becomes regular. The clonic stage lasts from 1 to 10 minutes (it seems much longer to the bystander) to an hour, after which time the patient wakes up exhausted and stiff. He may then sleep heavily for hours, or he may get up but feel dull and drowsy for a while. Such an attack may be followed immediately by another, in which event the condition is known as *status epilepticus.*

Grand mal seizures may occur at any time of the day or night. In some patients, these attacks occur at regular intervals; or they may disappear entirely for months or even years. In others, there may be transient periods when the attacks are much more frequent than usual.

Approximately 50 percent of the patients who have *grand mal* seizures will experience an aura prior to their attack. The aura is an ill-defined sensation described as a feeling of dizziness, weakness, fear, numbness, tingling, or just a "peculiar feeling." The duration of the aura may be long enough to allow the person to lie down, but more commonly it is only a few seconds before the seizure develops.

PETIT MAL SEIZURES

Petit mal seizures—"small illness" or "minor epileptic attack"—are characteristic of childhood, and rarely, if ever, occur after the age of 20. In the majority of cases, the onset of a *petit mal* seizure is in the first decade of life, although it may be delayed to the time of puberty. The seizures may become less frequent as the child grows older, and in many cases they disappear before the age of 20. *Petit mal* attacks may be associated with *grand mal* seizures, either preceding, alternating, or entirely replacing them. At times an individual may have a series of minor attacks, and at other times he may have the major seizures.

Petit mal seizures are characterized by a sudden momentary loss of consciousness that may last from a few seconds to half a minute. The patient ceases his activity (he is momentarily "absent") and then resumes where he broke off. Occasionally he goes through automatic and purposeful acts, such as walking, dressing or undressing, and so forth. He may drop his head for a second or two, stagger a few steps, or lose control of the urinary sphincter; but even in the most severe attacks, it is rare for him to fall. For a moment, his eyes are fixed and there is a blank expression that may go unnoticed except by the most careful observer. The *petit mal* attack may take the form of yawning, staring, or twitching of the eyelids, lips, tongue, face, or limb. Unlike *grand mal* seizures, *petit mal* attacks occur with greater frequency. Some individuals may have only a few attacks daily; but in others there may be as many as 20 or 30 in a single hour. In general, the attacks occur most frequently during the first few hours after rising, or when the person is sitting quietly as when eating, reading, or studying. These seizures are relatively infrequent during exercise.

JACKSONIAN SEIZURE

This type of seizure, named after the neurologist who first described it, occurs almost exclusively in patients with an organic lesion in the cortex. The attack starts with convulsive twitching in one portion of the body, usually the distal part of an extremity. As the attacks recur, the convulsive movements spread to adjacent muscles and may even pass to the other side of the body, in which event the seizure becomes similar to the *grand mal* attack. For example, if the attack starts in the fingers, the spread is to the wrist, the arm, the face, and then to the ipsilateral leg. If the spread is to the opposite side of the body, consciousness is lost. A jacksonian seizure indicates that the attack arises in a certain part of the brain, opposite to the side of the body in which the attack begins.

PSYCHOMOTOR ATTACKS AND EPILEPTIC EQUIVALENTS

Psychomotor attacks are minor seizures that may appear to be similar to *petit mal* epilepsy. They are characterized by a loss of contact with the environment lasting from 30 seconds to several minutes. The patient may stumble or stagger a few steps but, as in *petit mal* attacks, he rarely falls. There may be twitching or writhing movements of the extremities and incoherent speech. The person does not understand what is said at the time of the attack, and may resist aid. There is complete amnesia for the entire episode, and there is mental confusion for a half minute to several minutes after the attack has apparently ended.

Epileptic equivalent is a term used to describe prolonged periods of mental cloudiness, with complete amnesia for the entire time. These seizures may last for hours to days or even weeks. They may take the form of temper tantrums or "strange behavior," or the patient may become an exhibitionist and destructive to the extent that he may commit a misdemeanor or serious crime. In many cases, it is hard for parents and friends to believe that the individual's behavior is caused by anything but a "mean streak."

EXTENT OF THE PROBLEM

Epilepsy constitutes a major health problem in the United States. Estimates of the number of people suffering from this condition vary from 550,000 to 1.7 million. The actual incidence is not known, however, for the epileptic person hesitates to reveal his affliction because of social attitudes toward the condition. At least one in 200 have this disease in a mild or severe form; and about six in 100, or more than 10 million people, have some sort of convulsive episode at one time or another during their lives. The number of epileptic persons under 21 years of age is said to be 200,000 to 300,000; and one child in 15 has had at least one epileptic seizure. The disorder occurs twice as frequently in boys as in girls. It is as common as diabetes or active tuberculosis and occurs four times more often than poliomyelitis.

TREATMENT

Management of the person with epilepsy should be approached from several aspects. General principles of treatment include: (1) removal of organic and psychological factors that may be responsible for the occurance of seizures, (2) institution of measures to promote physical and mental hygiene, and (3) administration of anticonvulsant drugs.

REMOVAL OF ORGANIC AND PSYCHOLOGICAL FACTORS

The first step in such a program is the elimination of all factors that may be important in the causation of seizures. In the event of brain tumors, abscesses, scar tissue, a depressed fracture of the skull, and so forth, operations are usually indicated. If the attacks are of endocrine dysfunction or inflamatory origin, appropriate medical measures must be instituted. Sometimes the convulsions continue despite the removal of the organic cause; they may recur after an interval of time; or removal may aggravate the condition. Psychotherapy may be of value, in some cases, in aiding the child to adjust to his difficulties; but it cannot be expected to have any significant affect on the frequency of attacks.

INSTITUTION OF MEASURES TO PROMOTE PHYSICAL AND MENTAL HYGIENE

Even though we have no evidence that poor physical and mental hygiene are specific causes of convulsions, common sense dictates their elimination in every case. The individual with epilepsy must be encouraged to use all his resources to overcome feelings of inferiority and self-consciousness resulting from his condition as well as from the social and environmental attitudes of the public.

The teen-ager should be assisted in training for productive work which will occupy his time and still be renumerative. Commitment of the youngster to a farm, a colony for epileptics, or an institution may be necessary when mental deterioration occurs, or when frequent and violent attacks are not controllable with drugs.

Good personal hygiene and regular meals with a balanced diet may be of help, although they do not constitute a cure. Stimulants, such as alcohol and coffee, are to be avoided. Medical authorities agree that lots of physical activity is beneficial, and actually may make the difference between success and failure of the drug therapy program. All children with epilepsy should be encouraged to participate in the school's physical education program. Activities which endanger the lives of others, such as driving an automobile or working around machinery, should be prohibited.

DRUGS

Without question, the greatest hope for the patient with epilepsy is drug therapy. At present there are many effective drugs for the prevention and control of epileptic seizures. With the anticonvulsants and other forms of medication, 80 to 90 percent of the patients can enjoy complete or partial freedom from seizures. The right medicine, used under expert medical guidance, will in most instances greatly reduce the frequency and severity of seizures, and, in many cases, stop them completely. Decisions about which drug should be used in a given case depends primarily on the nature of the attacks, and is, of course, something to be determined by the physician.

The most effective medication in the control of seizures is the use of anticonvulsive drugs—phenobarbital, dilantin sodium, and tridione. There are many other drugs that may be as effective, or more so, in certain cases; however, the above-mentioned are perhaps the most commonly used and consequently the most familiar to the layman.

Bromides have been employed in the past, but they have been replaced by the more effective anticonvulsants. Phenobarbital has proven to be the most effective drug controlling seizures. Although it may cause a skin rash or a drowsy feeling at first, it is largely free from the disadvantages associated with the bromides, and it may be continued indefinitely. Dilantin sodium is particularly valuable in the treatment of *grand mal* and psychomotor attacks and, as a result, is the drug chosen by many physicians. Regulation of dosage is more difficult than with phenobarbital, and minor toxic symptoms may be frequent. These may include nervousness and sleeplessness, gastric disorders, nausea and vomiting, unsteadiness of gait, and hyperplasia of the gums. The latter, hyperplasia of the gums, is most common in children; it may range from a light swelling of the gums to complete covering of the teeth. At times, dilantin is administered in combination with phenobarbital for greater effectiveness. Tridione is one of the more effective drugs for *petti mal* attacks. It may cause skin rash, photophobia (abnormal sensitivity to light), and severe anemia, although rarely with fatal results. Complete blood counts should be made at regular intervals in patients receiving tridione.

School and the Epileptic

A child who is generally healthy except for his seizures should have the same opportunities to participate in a school program as the so-called "normal" youngster. However, fear, ignorance, traditional prejudice, and public misconceptions regarding epilepsy still prevail in many communities, and the educational opportunities for many of the children are still lacking. Even when seizures are well controlled, some school authorities object to accepting these youngsters; they feel they cannot subject other pupils to the traumatic ordeal of witnessing a seizure.

In the light of modern thinking and medical treatment, there is no reason why the majority of noninstitutionalized children with epilepsy cannot attend school. Epileptics as a group are educable. Lennox (3), after studying nearly 2000 noninstitutionalized epileptic patients, found 67 percent with average or above-average IQ's, 23 percent with slightly below-average; and only 10 percent grossly deficient. Himler and Raphael (2, 1) have shown that epileptics in college make creditable records and adequate postgraduate adjustments. Naturally, when seizures continue to be frequent and severe even after medical treatment, there must be some changes in the school program. Special schools and classes or home-visiting teachers are examples of the way some of the more enlightened school systems are making it possible for children with epilepsy to have the advantages of an education.

WHAT THE TEACHER CAN DO DURING A SEIZURE

A teacher with an epileptic child in the classroom can do a great deal for him during a seizure. Obviously, the course of action taken by the teacher will depend on the situation and the type of seizure the child may experience. During any type of attack, however, it is essential for the teacher to remain calm. Usually, witnessing a seizure will arouse a child's curiosity; but it does not frighten him unless, of course, an adult shows alarm. Once the situation has been fully explained to the class by the teacher, subsequent attacks should provoke little excitement.

Although a child having a *petit mal* seizure requires no attention, the following procedures may be of great help to the pupil during a *grand mal* or jacksonian attack:

1. If there is an aura, or warning signal, the student may be moved from the classroom to a place of safety and seclusion.
2. He should be lowered to the floor, away from all furniture and other objects that might prove dangerous.
3. Keep all bystanders away from him. Do not try to restrain him during the convulsive stage of the seizure, or try to revive him with stimulants such as throwing water on him or forcing liquids down his throat. There is no sense trying to rush the child to the hospital or doctor's office; once an attack has begun, nothing will stop it.
4. When the convulsive movements have ceased, the pupil should be left in a quiet place and allowed to regain consciousness naturally. He may or may not sleep heavily for a while after the seizure. When he so desires, he should be allowed to rejoin his class.

PHYSICAL EDUCATION

The success of modern drug therapy in controlling the frequency and severity of seizures has changed the disability of epilepsy to one that is more social than physical. As such, physical education can and should play a prominent role in the school life of every young-ster with this affliction. The coeducational program allows for teaching and practice of social skills. In the games and sports area we find one of education's best laboratories for democratic experi-ences. The pupil with epilepsy, as any other pupil, must learn to respect rules, cooperate with teammates, and treat opponents fairly and with courtesy. At the same time, he will enjoy the experiences of group participation and group acceptance. The development of competence in recreational skills can lead to expanded participation in other social activities, such as dances, parties, and club activities, as well as motivate the youngster in continued physical education activities.

Contrary to the opinion of some physical educators, there is no reason why a pupil with controlled epilepsy cannot fully participate in the same physical education program as his classmates. Epilepsy is not a contraindication for competitive or contact sports, such as football, soccer, ice hockey, or wrestling. Use of gymnastic apparatus, such as parallel bars, horizontal bars, and rings, and tumbling are permissible when adequate spotting and ordinary safety precautions are employed. The student can participate in swimming activities, although he should be cautioned always to remain close to a com-panion who knows his condition while he is in the water. To be sure, there is always the possibility that a pupil with epilepsy will have a seizure and suffer some kind of accident while participating in the physical education class. However, we cannot condemn physi-cal activity per se, or say that it caused or precipitated the seizure. Medical authorities are in agreement that attention, concentration, and vigorous physical activity seem usually to ward off seizures. Whatever risk is associated with these activities is justifiable, in most instances, to prevent the development of chronic invalidism and social withdrawal.

VERTIGO

Vertigo is a disturbance in which the individual has a subjective impression of movement in space or of objects moving about him. It is accompanied by a tendency to fall, occasionally by nausea or vomiting. At times the terms *vertigo, dizziness,* and *giddiness* are used interchangeably. Actually, true vertigo, as distinguished from faintness, lightheadedness, and other terms of dizziness, occurs invariably as a result of direct disturbances of the equilibratory apparatus, i.e., semicircular canals, eighth cranial nerve, vestibular nuclei and connections, eye, and sensory nerves of the muscles, joints, and tendons. Indirect or reflex causes will also produce vertigo. We are all aware of the vertigo, or sense of dizziness, which may occur when we are looking down from a great height. Seasickness, airsickness, and carsickness, are some of the more distressing types of reflex vertigo.

A pupil may say that he is dizzy when in reality he is describing a mild headache, fullness in the head, or nervousness. Anxiety, constipation, acute infectious diseases, infection of the sinuses of the head, hunger, aftereffects of alcohol and tobacco, excessive heat, and so forth, may produce varying degrees of vertigo. As a rule, however, vertigo is a transitory and not too serious affliction.

The well-informed physical educator should be aware of vertigo and the dangers associated with it. Rope climbing, high-bar and parallel-bar activities, even running on an upstair indoor track may precipitate vertigo and result in a serious accident. When a student has a previous history of vertigo, this factor must be taken into consideration in planning his physical education program. If persistent or recurring attacks of vertigo are experienced by a student, he should be referred immediately for proper medical care and treatment.

HEADACHE

Headache, one of the most common symptoms to which man is subject, is usually so transitory and harmless that it receives little attention. The vast majority of discomforts and pain in the head stem from readily reversible bodily changes. Headaches may be equally intense whether they occur in the absence of organic pathology or as a manifestation of serious disease. A person who suffers from this condition will soon appreciate its importance and realize that at times it is most annoying and incapacitating, although not necessarily a serious condition. Although there are a few instances in which pain may mean little in terms of tissue injury or damage, failure to differentiate the serious from the trivial may even cost a life. Headaches which occur infrequently may usually be related to fatigue, eyestrain, acute infection, or indiscreet dietary habits. Other causes are intercranial tumors, head injuries, cerebral anoxia, and diseases of the eye, ear, nose, or throat. In the majority of cases of headache with unknown etiology, symptoms are usually due to migraine or related to psychological tensions.

MIGRAINE

Migraine, or sick headache, is common, but its cause is not known. It is presently thought to be more common in women and to have a distinct tendency to run in families. The onset of symptoms may occur at any time in life; however, the vast majority begin in the early teens, and for several years thereafter are likely to increase in frequency and severity. Migraine headaches have a tendency to subside gradually after the age of 40.

At times, the physical educator may be a little annoyed or skeptical whenever a student requests permission to leave a gym class because of a headache. It is important to remember that pain always means that something is wrong, and headaches are no exception. This common symptom should not be passed over too lightly. The teacher should realize that at times a student may annoy him by what may be a very minor complaint, but this common symptom may be the forerunner of serious trouble. Rest and a reduction of physical and emotional strain may be sufficient to alleviate the headache. The student should always be referred to competent medical consultation if the headaches recur or are of chronic nature.

UNCONSCIOUSNESS

It is not uncommon for the physical educator to be called on to attend a student who has fainted or is unconscious. Although it is not essential for him to make a diagnosis of the student's condition, the better he understands the problem, the more intelligently he can meet the emergency. The physical educator may well be in a position to save a life, to say nothing of assisting the physician and having the satisfaction of knowing how to handle the situation. Unconsciousness is a general term used to describe a state of unawareness. Usually the individual is in a state of insensibility, and there is an abolishment of reflexes. Unconsciousness may be transitory, as in *syncope* (fainting), or it may be prolonged. It may vary in depth from semiconsciousness, or stupor, in which the individual can be aroused only with difficulty, to the profound state, to coma, in which the individual does not respond to ordinary stimuli.

The loss of consciousness is a manifestation of some underlying disease or injury; and its mode of onset, duration, intensity, and other characteristics will depend on the etiological conditions. The possible causes are many and varied, but the most common are poisons, cranial trauma, cerebrovascular causes, metabolic or toxic causes, epilepsy, acute infectious diseases, cardiac conditions, and mental states. Since the cause of the unconscious state is seldom immediately known, it is important that someone should be instructed to call a physician and make arrangements for the removal of the patient to a hospital. Any of the following emergency procedures may be necessary pending arrival of the physician: control of hemorrhage, maintenance of a clear airway, artificial respiration, or treatment of shock. Stimulants, food, fluids, or any other medication by mouth are to be avoided while the patient is unconscious. All possible facts relating to the immediate problem should be obtained from family, friends, and bystanders. Information as to whether it was a sudden or gradual onset, injury or convulsions, headaches, diabetes, and so forth, may be of great aid to the physician. Caution should always be observed in moving the individual; it is wise to remove bystanders who may have gathered around the stricken youngster.

SUMMARY

Neurological diseases form a rather large and heterogenous group, extending from the simple headache to the complex and varied forms of cerebral palsy. Whatever the cause of the disorder, there is one common denominator—a disturbance of the neuromuscular apparatus which controls normal movement. In many of these disorders, complete restoration of function is impossible; in some, deterioration is inevitable; and when recovery does take place, the disability is a changing one and there may or may not be a permanent residual disability.

Essentially the principles of care for the neurological patient, whether in the hospital, in the home, or in the school, are the same; but the emphasis will vary, depending on the disease, the extent of disability, and the facilities available. A child with a neurological disorder suffers not only from the destructive process of the disease proper, but also from the impact of the social and psychological problems associated with it.

Physical education embraces two distinct but united phases of the total treatment program for these youngsters: the physical and the sociopsychological. While the main responsibility for the physical restoration of these youngsters rests largely with the physical therapist, there is no question that an intelligently planned physical education program will reap many concomitant physical rewards. It should be stressed, however, that the main emphasis of the program should be directed toward the social and recreational objectives while keeping in mind the need for maintaining a high state of fitness.

REFERENCES

1. Himler, L. E., and Raphael, T., "A Follow-up Study on 93 College Students with Epilepsy," *American Journal of Psychiatry*, May, 1945, **101**, 760-763.
2. Himler, L. E., and Raphael, T., "Epilepsy Among College Students," *Mental Hygiene,* 1940, **24,** 459.
3. Lennox, W. G., "Brain Injury, Drugs and Environment as Cause of Mental Decay in Epilepsy," *American Journal of Psychiatry*, September, 1942, **99** (2), 174-180.

Chapter 14

HEART DISEASE AND PHYSICAL EDUCATION

THIS chapter is concerned with the fundamental principles of establishing a physical education program for the youngster with a heart disease. It is not intended to be a complete medical picture of the cardiovascular system and its associated abnormalities, but rather to show how clinical medicine, basic science, and physical education must be integrated to establish a solid foundation for an activity program for the child with a cardiac condition. Emphasis is placed on those cardiac problems that are likely to be of greatest concern to the physical educator.

THE PROBLEM

Of all the chronic diseases that beset our population, those of the cardiovascular system are by far the most frequent cause of death and disability in the world today. They affect all segments of the population from infancy to old age, and all too frequently threaten disability, partial or total, in the prime of life. A measure of the magnitude of the cardiovascular problem may be seen in the number of deaths attributable to the disease. In 1950, approximately 745 thousand people in the United States died of this problem—51 percent of the total deaths. In 1955 this percentage rose to 53.3. However, in comparing death rates for different years we must realize that the proportion of older people has increased, and that an adjustment has to be made. The age-adjusted rate actually shows

263

that the cardiovascular death rate (per 100 thousand people) has been decreasing. People now live longer because of decreased infant mortality from infectious diseases and improved medical care, and it is in the older age groups that cardiovascular diseases take their greatest toll.

No one will question the fact that cardiovascular disease is one of our more pressing medical problems today. However, having a heart condition does not necessarily mean that a person is relegated to the role of an invalid for the rest of his life. There is evidence that the "cardiac" can and does participate in physical work. As early as 1935, Stroud (14) stated that work (employment) and physical rehabilitation are the best form of therapy for the cardiac patient with slight to moderate limitations. Simonson and Enzer (12) cite numerous cases where the patient with compensated valvular heart disease performed athletic feats far exceeding those of average healthy subjects. More recently, Rasch (11) pointed out that several members of our 1956 Olympic wrestling team showed abnormal electrocardiographic readings. Contrary to popular belief, severe heart disease does not necessarily manifest itself in clinical signs or symptoms, nor does it always impair maximum physical performance. In some cases, pathological lesions of the heart may be fully compensated not only for resting conditions, but also for maximum physical exertion.

ANATOMY AND PHYSIOLOGY OF THE HEART

In order to properly appreciate and understand the function of the cardiovascular system, it is necessary to know certain anatomic facts. Some of the more general and essential features of the heart are reviewed here and may be observed by referring to the schematic diagram in Figure 36.

The heart is a hollow muscular organ forming four chambers: the right and left *auricles* (or atria) and the right and left *ventricles*. The thin-walled auricles have little contractile force, and serve primarily to receive and store the blood brought to them by the veins from all parts of the body. On the other hand, the ventricles have relatively thick muscular walls and exert considerable force

YOUR HEART AND HOW IT WORKS

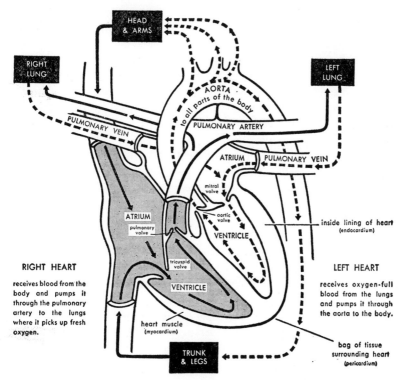

Fig. 36. Your heart weighs well under a pound and is only a little larger than your fist, but it is a powerful, long-working, hard-working organ. Its job is to pump blood to the lungs and to all the body tissues.

The heart is a hollow organ. Its tough, muscular wall (myocardium) is surrounded by a fiberlike bag (pericardium) and is lined by a thin, strong membrane (endocardium). A wall (septum) divides the heart cavity down the middle into a "right heart" and a "left heart." Each side of the heart is divided again into an upper chamber (called an atrium or auricle) and a lower chamber (ventricle). Valves regulate the flow of blood through the heart and to the pulmonary artery and the aorta.

The heart is really a double pump. One pump (the right heart) receives blood which has just come from the body after delivering nutrients and oxygen to the body tissues. It pumps this dark, bluish-red blood to the lungs, where the blood gets rid of a waste gas (carbon dioxide) and picks up a fresh supply of oxygen which turns it a bright red again. The second pump (the left heart) receives this "reconditioned" blood from the lungs and pumps it out through the great trunk-artery (aorta) to be distributed by smaller arteries to all parts of the body. (Courtesy American Heart Association.)

during contraction. It is the contractile force of the ventricles and the elasticity of the arteries and veins which enable the blood to circulate throughout the whole body.

All the systemic veins of the body eventually merge into the superior and inferior *vena cava,* which empty into the right auricle. Upon contraction of the heart walls (which normally occurs simultaneously on both sides) blood is pumped through the tricuspid valve into the right ventricle, and hence through the pulmonary valve into the pulmonary artery which divides into two branches, one to each lung. There carbon dioxide is eliminated and oxygen is absorbed by the blood. The oxygenated blood is then brought back to the left auricle of the heart via the pulmonary veins. When the left auricle has been filled, contraction of the heart muscle pumps the blood through the mitral valve to the left ventricle, which in turn propels it through the aortic valve to the aorta artery. Through the many subdivisions of the aorta, oxygenated blood is delivered to all portions of the body.

The nutrition of the heart muscle is furnished by the right and left coronary arteries, which arise from the aorta just beyond the aortic valve. These arteries send penetrating branches into the heart muscle to provide the all-important blood supply of the heart. Interruption in the function of these coronary arteries is commonly referred to as coronary heart disease, and is a major cause of cardiovascular pathology.

The rate of heartbeat is some 60 to 90 times a minute, in regular fashion, propelling blood throughout the entire body. Each contraction of the heart (systole) sets up a pressure of blood in the aorta and its arterial branches, which is known as systolic blood pressure— normally some 100 to 150 mm. Hg. After each contraction of the heart there is a period of relaxation (diastole) when the heart chambers fill with blood and the pressure is lowered (diastolic blood pressure) to some 70 to 90 mm. Hg. The valves which lie between the auricles and their respective ventricles and the openings into the pulmonary arteries and aorta, allow a free flow of blood through the heart chambers and into the great vessels in only one direction. During relaxation, or diastole, of the heart, these valves close to prevent backflow, or regurgitation. Interference with the proper function of certain of these valves is characteristic of valvular heart disease.

The entire heart is surrounded by a fibrous sac known as the pericardium: which is analagous to the pleura of the lungs. The wall between the right and left side of the heart is called the septa: the interauricular septum and the interventricular septum. These septa are frequently involved in congenital heart disease.

HEART DISEASE

HEART MURMURS

It is beyond the scope and purpose of this presentation to include a discussion of all the murmurs or disturbances in heart sounds that may occur in heart disease. Actually, there is little need for the physical educator to understand the fundamental mechanisms of murmur production and their relation to heart disease, for the medical doctor is the one who is directly concerned if there is any abnormality in heart sounds. However, since the term *heart murmur* is so freely and improperly interpreted by many laymen, it is imperative that mutual agreement be reached as to its meaning.

Basically, any abnormal sound heard over the region of the heart may be considered a heart murmur. The sounds are produced by vibration of the valves and walls of the heart and great vessels as a result of the flow of blood from a passage of relatively narrow caliber to one of greater caliber. It is important to realize that it is the relationship between the caliber of the two adjoining sounds (murmurs). Usually the sound is designated as a mitral, aortic, tricuspid, or pulmonary murmur, depending on the site of origin in the heart. These abnormal sounds are further described according to the period of the heart's cycle (during contraction and relaxation) into: systolic murmurs—those occurring during systole; diastolic murmurs—those occurring during diastole; and presytolic murmurs —those occurring just before systole. Thus, we may see a specific heart murmur listed as a systolic mitral murmur, indicating that the abnormal heart sound was heard during systole (contraction phase of heart's cycle) over the mitral valve area of the heart.

Perhaps most of us are more familiar with the old nomenclature of heart murmurs, that of functional and organic murmurs. Under this method of classification, the functional murmur is believed to result from a physiological disturbance in the heart; whereas the organic murmur is limited to structural defects in the heart, usually the valves. Some are of the opinion that there is no sign of heart disease with a functional murmur and that there is little danger associated with it, but that the organic murmur usually denotes a cardiac disease which may or may not be serious. However, White (17) states, "The old time-worn phrases 'functional' and 'organic,' as applied to murmurs, are highly unsatisfactory, for important reasons in each case." This statement is based on the fact that often it is impossible for a physician to decide at first whether valvular deformity or heart dilatation without valvular disease is responsible for a murmur even though it is obviously a pathological condition. Also, many heart murmurs have been labled "functional" even though there may be present a much more serious disease than the physiological cause that produced the murmur. Therefore, White and associates recommend that the terms *functional* and *organic* be dropped and the designations *physiological* and *pathological* be used instead, with proper subdivisions of *pathological* into extra-cardiac causation and intracardiac causation.

It is of great importance for the physical educator to realize that serious heart disease may be present in the absence of all heart murmurs or even with normal heart sounds. A mild cardiac involvement may give rise to a pronounced murmur; and then when the disease progresses to a greater degree, the murmur disappears. For instance, a systolic mitral regurgitation (functional or organic) may be slight in degree but with forceful heart action (as a result of exercise), and there is likely to be a pronounced systolic murmur. If this mitral regurgitation becomes extensive, with a large opening between the auricle and ventricle, no murmur at all will be found, even though the condition is much worse.

RHEUMATIC HEART DISEASE

Perhaps the most frequent and important variety of cardiac disease to confront the present-day school teacher is rheumatic fever

and its associated form of heart disease. It is important chiefly because hundreds of thousands of children in the United States are
actual or potential rheumatic cardiac cripples. The incidence of
rheumatic fever has not been accurately determined in the past
because the disease was not always reported. However, useful and
reasonably accurate estimates are to be found.

During the 15-year period from age 5 to 20, rheumatic fever with
heart disease is the leading cause of death in the United States;
and at age 20 to 25, it is second only to tuberculosis. In New York
City in 1938 there were 1105 deaths reported from rheumatic fever
and rheumatic heart disease, as compared with a combined total
of 247 from whooping cough, meningitis, measles, diphtheria, scarlet
fever, and poliomyelitis. Martin stated that 1 million people in the
United States had rheumatic carditis, which caused 40 thousand
deaths yearly at the average age of 30. The incidence of rheumatic
heart disease in school children ranged between 0.7 and 1.0 percent.
The Children's Bureau estimated that in this country 500 thousand
children are handicapped by rheumatic fever and rheumatic heart
disease.

Despite the rather gloomy picture of the above statistics, there
is an encouraging trend in the overall mortality rates. In the United
States the death rate from rheumatic fever and rheumatic heart
disease in persons aged 5 to 24 fell from 32.3 per 100,000 in 1917
and 1918 to 9.7 in 1943. Each 5-year period since 1932 has shown a
lowered mortality rate and a decrease in the percentage and severity
of cardiac damage. Present-day studies show that rheumatic fever
and rheumatic heart disease account for approximately 2.4 percent
of all cardiovascular deaths, further illustrating the decline in incidence of this disease. However, it still accounts for approximately
98 percent of all heart disease in patients under 20 years of age,
and constitutes a problem of major consequence to the public
school teacher.

NATURE OF THE DISEASE

Generally speaking, rheumatic heart disease refers to damage of
the heart valves as a result of rheumatic fever. Although the real
cause of rheumatic fever is still unknown, it is agreed that it stems

from an acute infectious disease related to the group A streptococcus. Uncertainty still exists as to whether the streptococcus bacteria is directly responsible for rheumatic fever or whether it is a precursor of the disease. In general, rheumatic fever is a child's disease, although occasionally the first attack may come in adult life. After the first few years of life and through adolescence, a child may be taken with an acute infection manifested by migratory joint pain (usually in the ankle, hip, knee, and wrist), with localized heat, redness, and swelling. There is moderate fever. The attack is usually preceded by a history of tonsillitis, sore throat, cold, or general malaise. The acute infection may subside with medical treatment and remain in a low-grade subacute form, with lingering signs and symptoms of the infection, for months or even years. During this period, evidence of heart involvement may or may not appear.

About two-thirds of all cases show variable degrees of heart involvement following an episode of rheumatic fever; involvement generally is confined to the mitral or aortic valve. An examination often reveals a leak or regurgitation of the mitral or aortic valve, or a blocking (stenosis) of these valves. Occasionally, the tricuspid valve is also involved. There may be varying degrees of enlargement of the heart resulting from overwork of the heart muscle to propel blood through these defective valves. With a mild mitral regurgitation (systolic murmur), the youngster may have essentially no incapacity and an excellent outlook barring further infection and heart damage. The same may be true of mild aortic valve regurgitation. However, stenosis of either valve may prove to be more serious, often leading to congestive heart failure and death.

Unfortunately, the initial attack of rheumatic fever does not result in the development of an immunity to the disease: on the contrary, it seems to increase the individual's susceptibility to recurring attacks. It is unfortunate that repeated attacks of active rheumatic infections usually result in further scarring and contractures in the already damaged valves. All too often these recurring attacks go unrecognized as simple "growing pains" or general poor health. Thus, the student with a history of rheumatic fever is of unusual interest to the physical educator and warrants closer observation and follow-up than most. The avoidance of undue exposure to temperature extremes, coldness and dampness, etc., a satisfactory balance between rest and activity, and adequate food and clothing are factors that may prevent recurrence of the disease; and many of these factors are controllable while the student is in the school environment. The teacher should not only be aware of these factors, but should also utilize this knowledge when establishing a physical education program for the youngster with a rheumatic heart.

TREATMENT

Naturally, the medical doctor controls and directs the treatment program for the youngster with a rheumatic condition. If supportive therapies (social workers, vocational guidance counselors, special teachers, occupational or physical therapists, etc.) are required, they will enter into the treatment program only on the request and under the direction of the attending physician. Generally, in acute rheumatic fever, the primary treatment is bed rest, lasting for periods of weeks or even months. For years, aspirin has been the usual medication. Recently, cortisone and its related products have produced rather dramatic effects in suppressing symptoms of acute rheumatic fever, but little is known of their relative value in shortening the disease process or preventing late complications. It is during the acute phase of the disease that heart damage occurs as a result of an inflammatory reaction of the heart valves, muscles, or surrounding pericardium. After a period of weeks to months, the acute infection begins to subside, as evidenced by lowered temperature, blood sedimentation rate, white cell count, and electrocardiographic findings. Usually, the youngster will be left with some degree of heart involvement, primarily in the mitral or aortic valve. In some instances, the child may be fortunate enough to have no residual heart condition. During this phase of recovery, he is extremely susceptible to recurring attacks of rheumatic fever as a result of fatigue, inadequate nutrition, prolonged exposure to cold and dampness, or contact with individuals with streptococcal infections, i.e., scarlet fever, "strep" throat, colds, etc. For this reason, constant medication in the form of penicillin or sulfa is usually recommended. Recurrent infections will often lead to further damage to the heart valves, and they must be avoided.

CONGENITAL HEART DISEASE

Congenital heart disease is the result of defective fetal development of the heart and great vessels; it occurs in many combinations and varieties. It may be found at any age level; but it is most common, of course, in the infant and very young child. Many victims live but a few years at most, and often only for weeks or months, after birth. In the past, there was little hope that the youngster with a congenital heart defect would ever live to reach school age; but today that attitude is being changed, and the outlook is much brighter for many of these youngsters.

Although adequate statistical information about the incidence of congenital heart disease in various parts of the world is lacking, it is generally believed to be found everywhere and in about the same total incidence. Available data indicate a rather low total incidence, averaging well under 1 percent of all deaths. An analysis of 34,023 unselected autopsies in Boston showed congenital cardiovascular diseases in 1.33 percent, but this figure dropped to 0.5 percent after the age of two. A clinical series of 31,771 outpatients in Copenhagen contained 85 cases of congenital heart disease among 4,746 individuals with cardiovascular abnormalities—a relative incidence of 1 to 8 percent.

Specific causes of congenital malformation of the cardiovascular system has not been definitely established, but it seems to be closely associated with the presence of infectious virus, vitamin deficiency, and metabolic and endocrine disturbances during the first 3 months of pregnancy. For example, if German measles, a virus disease, attacks the mother during the first two or three months of pregnancy, it appears to result in a combination of congenital defects in a considerable number of instances. More recently, other viruses have been suspected of causing congenital defects of the heart and aorta in the fetus during early pregnancy, but accurate information about this is still lacking.

While the overall picture of congenital heart disease does not play a numerically large part in the cardiovascular problem, it nevertheless will play an ever-increasing role in the schools. In White's (16) opinion, "more progress has been made in our understanding and recognition of congenital heart disease during the last two decades than in any other type of heart disease." Recent advances in understanding causative factors, more accurate diagnosis, and spectacular progress in surgical procedures for the correction and amelioration of several of these defects have resulted in the saving of many lives that previously would have been considered lost. These advancements will have increasing significance to the educator as more and more youngsters with congenital heart conditions are returned to the school program.

ARTERIOSCLEROSIS AND HYPERTENSION

While arteriosclerosis and hypertension comprise the most important categories of cardiac disability, and pose the greatest problem in rehabilitation, they are of little concern to the public school teacher. Kessler, quoting the Metropolitan Life Insurance Company, states, "every other person past the age of fifty dies of cardiovascular disease, half of which are probably due to essential hypertension." Arteriosclerosis and hypertension together account for over 90 percent of all deaths due to cardiovascular disease. As these two heart conditions appear in middle age and after, there is little possibility that the physical educator will encounter them in his school program.

GENERAL CONSIDERATIONS

As stated previously, our basic assumption is that any child who is well enough to attend school is well enough to participate in some form of physical education program. As with any atypical youngster, this statement holds true for the cardiac child. For next to the medical diagnosis and prognosis, the individual with heart disease and his family are most vitally concerned with the amount of physical activity he may be able to undertake in day-to-day living. Obviously, this is a medical decision; and under no circumstances should the teacher assume this responsibility. It is imperative that the physical educator work in close harmony with the recommendations of the physician regarding the child's activity program.

Suppose that you, as the physical educator in a school, are confronted with the situation of having a pupil with a heart disease placed in your program. What are you going to do with him? How will he fit into your program? What should you watch for? What is he capable of doing and, conversely, what phase of your program is contraindicated by his cardiac condition? These and many other questions come to mind. If you are fortunate enough to be in a large school system where there are established classes for the atypical youngster, many of these questions will be answered for you. Unfortunately, this situation does not exist to any great extent, and most of the time you will be faced with the prospect of integrating the cardiac pupil into your program. To be sure, it is easy to send him to his homeroom or study hall during his scheduled physical education hour, but then you are not fulfilling the ethical or moral obligations of your chosen profession: physical education. The following procedures are presented to help you plan an intelligent activity program for the student with a heart condition.

PUPIL HISTORY

Before admitting any student with a history of heart disease to your classes, it is essential to have as complete a picture of his physical condition as possible. In order to do this, you will have to get, not only a medical history of the student, but also his medical diagnosis, treatment, and prognosis. This information should be obtained from the physician rather than from well-meaning but often misinformed parents, relatives, and friends. To avoid the possibility of costly mistakes, get this information directly from the attending physician. At times it may be rather difficult to interpret the technical medical terminology, but clarification of the doctor's report may be had from the school's medical advisor or from the physician himself. It may even be necessary for you to study on your own or consult with other authorities; but above all, be sure you understand the student's condition and the related problems.

INTERVIEW

Once you are fully informed of the medical condition of the student with a heart disease, make a point of becoming familiar with the student. During the interview, try to find out: (1) how well the student really understands his medical condition and its influences on his participation in physical activity; (2) what kind of psychological adjustment he has made; (3) what his interests—likes and dislikes—regarding physical education are; (4) whether he realizes to what extent he may physically extend himself; and (5) whether he knows the signs and symptoms of cardiac distress. It may take only one or perhaps several of these interviews to obtain the desired information; but whatever the time required, it is well worth the effort. And the interview may afford a dividend value in that student-teacher rapport can be established which may be of inestimable value for the success of the program.

This first series of "get acquainted" interviews does not signify the end of the physical educator's counseling activities with the cardiac pupil. To be sure, the family physician, school medical authorities, or professional counselor will advise the youngster and his family about healthful living habits and other matters pertinent to the situation; but the teacher, because of frequent and regular association, is in a position to augment and reinforce such counsel. At the same time, individual counseling periods are of value for observing the physical condition of the pupil; such factors as failure to gain weight, skin pallor, undue fatigue, colds or sore throats, unexplained fever or pain, and unusual restlessness or irritability may be indicative of recurring attacks or rheumatic fever and should be reported to proper medical authorities immediately.

VOCATIONAL COUNSELING

The cardiac pupil must be educated as to his potentialities—physical, recreational, and vocational. Vocational guidance and counseling are important phases of the rehabilitation program of the young person afflicted with a heart disease, and it is imperative that well trained instructors with insight into the problem be brought in for consultation. The physical educator is not trained to do this type of work and should never assume that he is. However, the physical educator should see that the cardiac pupil is not only well advised to choose his life's work carefully, but also that it is within his exercise (physical) tolerance. Should the character of the selected vocational objective be more strenuous than the cardiac reserve will tolerate, long-lasting and possibly permanent disability may ensue. A person with cardiac involvement should be encouraged to prepare for his future employment in the light of the restrictions imposed by his own particular condition. It is now generally accepted that no one can set up arbitrary standards for employment, and that a cardiac patient may do almost any type of work as long as it lies within his functional capacity. The youngster with a cardiac disease can learn to live a long, full life within a prescribed range, but he requires more than the ordinary amount of professional help.

MEDICAL AIDS

It is absolutely essential that the kind and amount of physical activity for each pupil with a heart disease be approved by a medical doctor. In many instances, medical approval is obtained by submitting an itemized activity check list to the pupil's physician for selection of the proper activities. Admittedly, this procedure is the most convenient for the physical educator to follow, but the values derived from such a procedure are questionable. Few physicians have a true knowledge or understanding of the activities contained on such a list, nor do they realize what they entail. Moreover, using a check list is the first step toward standardization of an activity program—perhaps the greatest weakness of those who work with the atypical youngster. It must be remembered that each pupil with a heart condition is an individual; each heart condition is just a little different from the next; and each pupil with a heart condition will respond to a given activity in a slightly different manner, depending on numerous environmental, social, psychological, and physical factors. Therefore, it is essential that an individualized physical education program be established for each pupil with a heart condition.

The most desirable procedure to follow in establishing such a regimen would be for the pupil's physician and the physical educator to sit down together and construct a program. Unfortunately, many times this is not feasible; and the physical educator must then turn to the school's medical advisor for assistance. Only after these first two procedures fail to produce the desired information should the teacher resort to the activity check-off list—for despite its weaknesses, the information it affords will be more valuable than no guidance at all.

CLASSIFICATION

As stated above, it is the physician's role not only to explain the mechanisms of the heart condition, but also to ascertain as well as possible the limit of activity in which the youngster may participate. A classification developed by the New York Heart Association has been adopted by a large number of physicians as a standard for the amount of physical activity to be undertaken by the person with a heart condition. This classification may serve as a guide to all teachers in controlling the activities of students with heart disease:

Class A. Patients with cardiac disease whose physical activities need not be restricted.

Class B. Patients with cardiac disease whose ordinary physical activity need not be restricted, but who should be advised against unusually severe or combative efforts.

Class C. Patients with cardiac diseases whose ordinary physical activity should be moderately restricted, and whose more strenuous habitual effort should be discontinued.

Class D. Patients with cardiac disease whose ordinary physical activity should be markedly restricted.

Class E. Patients with cardiac disease who should be at complete rest, confined to chair or bed.

This classification is only a rough estimate of the capabilities of the cardiac youngster, but at least it is a starting point for the program. Close observation and follow-up of the student's responses to the physical education program should always be maintained. As his exercise tolerance increases it may be possible to elevate the pupil into a higher classification, with more varied and interesting activities. Naturally, any elevation in his classification must come from medical authority.

SIGNS AND SYMPTOMS OF CARDIAC DISTRESS

The physician may describe to the patient the warning signs of cardiac distress and urge him to find his own level of activity participation. But it is also important for the physical educator to be aware of these signs and symptoms. If, at any time while participating in physical activity, the student shows any of these signs or symptoms of cardiac distress, he should be encouraged to stop immediately and rest. If they persist over a period of time, or if they appear with increasing frequency and magnitude, the pupil should immediately be referred to the proper medical authorities. These signs and symptoms do not necessarily mean that the individual is having a "heart attack"; they indicate only that there is a temporary disturbance of function. They may or may not be caused by trouble to the heart or great vessels. However, only a medical doctor is competent or qualified to make this decision, and the physical educator should avoid the responsibility of making such a diagnosis. Listed below are some of the more classical signs and symptoms that accompany cardiac distress or recurring attacks of rheumatic fever. Learn them well and always look out for them whenever you have a pupil in your class with a history of rheumatic fever or any heart condition.

1. Pain—chest pain, abdominal pain, pain in the extremities, headache, or pain in the joints (ankle, knee, hip, or wrist).
2. Breathing difficulties—dyspnea (labored breathing), rapid breathing, exceptionally slow breathing, arhythmical breathing.
3. Palpitation—an unpleasant sensation of heart action, whether slow, fast, regular, or irregular; sometimes accompanied by throbbing sensation of pulse in head or extremities.
4. Undue fatigue and dizziness.
5. Skin pallor.
6. Unusual restlessness or irritability.
7. Unexplained nosebleeds and fever.
8. Complaint of sore throat or cold.

THE SCHOOL

There are still differences of opinion among the authorities as to whether the cardiac pupil should be integrated into regular classes or placed in special classes. Although authorities debate among themselves on this topic, perhaps we should stop a moment and consider the advice of one of the most experienced and outstanding cardiologists of our day, Dr. Paul Dudley White (16): ". . . most children with heart disease at any age can safely and profitably attend school and need not, in fact should not, be separated off in special categories or classes, except for rare individuals who are unusually crippled by early and marked valvular deformity, cardiac arhythmias, or congenital defects of noncyanotic type." Experience has shown that a cooperative plan can be arranged among school authorities, parents, and the family doctor whereby the pupil may be watched and guided without making him feel overanxious, resentful, or set apart. In many communities, home-visiting teachers are utilized when the youngster is unable to attend school as a result of a recurring attack of rheumatic fever, thus keeping up instruction and morale. The school may help the child with a heart disease in many other ways; a few of the more important of these are as follows:

1. Conduct regular and periodic medical examinations.
2. Modify class periods to fit the tolerance of each pupil with a heart disease; schedule rest periods throughout the school day.
3. Provide transportation to and from school, if needed.
4. Develop an attitude of tolerance for absenteeism; indeed, encourage the cardiac pupil to stay home during adverse and extreme weather conditions.
5. Restrict classes to one floor to avoid climbing stairs.
6. Avoid exposure of the youngster with a heart condition to other students with upper-respiratory infections.
7. Provide adequate instruction in health education.
8. Provide adequate vocational counseling and training.

Naturally, all these services should be in addition to the regular educational experiences which the school must provide for any youngster.

PHYSICAL EDUCATION AND THE CARDIAC

It is essential for the physical educator to know certain fundamental rules that underlie and regulate all activity programs for the youngster with a heart condition. Close adherence to these rules are necessary for the safety and well-being of the pupil, as well as for the success of your physical education program. These rules may be listed as follows:

1. All activities should be mild in nature and short in duration. Activities requiring an all-out effort are to be avoided, as should participation in prolonged and extended activities.
2. Isometric (static) muscular contractions are more demanding on the cardiovascular system than isotonic (dynamic) contractions, and are therefore to be avoided.
3. Frequent rest periods should be incorporated into all activities. The student should be encouraged to take frequent rest periods—perhaps as long as, if not longer than, the movement itself. Decreasing the length and frequency of these rest periods will depend entirely on the pupil's reaction to the activity. A good rule to follow in this respect is: as long as he can exercise with his mouth closed, he is within his exercise tolerance.
4. All movements should be done slowly and progressively. The pupil should start out with the simpler movements and slowly progress to those of a more demanding nature. Usually, any change in body position will have an immediate effect on the cardiovascular system. Progression would be from lying to sitting to standing position. Whether the movement involves a change in body position or just in moving one extremity, care should always be taken to accomplish the movement in a slow cadence.
5. Participation in any activity, physical or mental, that creates an atmosphere of tension and emotional stress is to be avoided. White and associates emphasize this by pointing out that pressure and emotional stresses associated with present-day competitiveness is not only contraindicated for the cardiac patient, but in many cases may be a precursor to recurring attacks.
6. If, during the course of any activity program, signs and symptoms of cardiac distress appear, the youngster should be encouraged to stop immediately.

The Activity Program

Constructing an activity program for the cardiac student is one of the most challenging tasks to confront the physical educator. The whole range of physical education activities should be explored for the kind of material that is best suited to the limitations imposed by the individual's heart condition, and yet will provide desired educational experiences. Proper selection and modification of these activities can give the child with a heart disease a nearly normal physical education experience. On the elementary level, such activities may be selected from the great number of line, circle, tag, and goal games, as well as from the following:

1. Rhythms—slow tempo and light movements.
2. Story games, singing games, and simple folk dances.
3. Mimetic activities—mild movements.
4. Fundamentals of team games of low organization—foul shooting, baseball throw (distance or accuracy), football kicking, etc.

Remember that all-out effort is to be avoided, and for this reason, participation in most individual athletic events and self-testing activities is to be discouraged. To keep up his interest and avoid a left-out feeling, the cardiac child may be given a chance to help—perhaps as scorekeeper—in some less-demanding occupation.

In general, every student with a heart condition, whether he is on the elementary or secondary school level, should begin with the simplest type, dosage, and frequency of exercises, and progress at a rate commensurate with his exercise tolerance. Especially on the secondary level, exercises should be designed specifically to: (1) increase cardiorespiratory efficiency; (2) develop neuromuscular coordination, strength, and endurance; and (3) to increase the overall physical work capacity of the student. Progressive movements (as from lying to sitting to standing position) should be followed as the pupil's exercise tolerance improves. As a guide to the physical educator, the following are examples of progressive activities that may be used (with medical approval) either as a means of determining the level of exercise tolerance, or as a form of general exercise for the student with heart condition:

LYING POSITION

1. Supine position, arms at side, knees bent, and heels flat on floor close to buttocks.
   a. Inhale deeply (concentrate on chest rather than abdominal movement) and hold for count of 3. Exhale slowly. Repeat 10 times.

    b. Slide arms away from body along floor until they are overhead (abduction). Inhale during this movement. Exhale slowly while returning arms to original position. Repeat 10 times.

    c. Raise arms straight up from floor over the head (forward flexion), inhaling deeply during the movement. Return arms to starting position while exhaling slowly. Repeat 10 times.

    d. Force small of back against floor (by contracting abdominal muscles) and hold for count of 3. Relax. Repeat 5 times.

2. Supine position, arms at side, legs straight.

    a. Lift head off floor, rolling chin downward to chest (keep mouth closed). Return to starting position. Repeat 5 times.

    b. Slide right heel along floor toward right buttock, flexing right knee and hip. Rest. Return right leg to starting position in reverse manner. Rest. Draw left leg up in the same manner, and then return it to the starting position. (Alternate right and left legs.) Repeat 3 times.

    c. Draw right knee to chest (use hands to assist if necessary). Hold for count of 3; return leg to starting position. Rest. Repeat same for left leg. (Alternate right and left legs.) Repeat 3 times.

    d. Draw both knees to chest. Hold for count of 3. Return legs to original position. Repeat 3 times.

    e. Lift heels 4 to 6 inches off floor and hold for 3 count. Slowly return legs to floor. Repeat 3 times. (Caution: Be sure the small of the back is tight against floor during entire movement.)

    f. Lift head and shoulders off floor, rolling into a ball as you come up into a sitting position. Return to supine position slowly. Repeat 3 times. Note: Exercise becomes increasingly difficult if the pupil first holds arms at side, then folded across chest, and finally hands behind head while attempting to do the sit-up. Also, exercise is more difficult if the subject flexes hips and knees, feet flat on ground close to buttocks, before attempting the sit-up.

SITTING POSITION

1. Sit on floor, legs straight and spread apart, fingers laced behind the neck.

    a. Inhale deeply and stretch upward (extending spinal column and lifting thoracic cage high) and retract shoulders (scapular retraction). Relax while exhaling. Repeat 5 times.

    b. Trunk twisting alternate sides. Repeat 5 times.

    c. Alternate touching right hand to left toe, then left hand to right toe. Repeat each movement 5 times.

2. Sitting on floor with legs straight in front, lean backward resting on hands.

a. Draw right knee to chest; return right leg to starting position; then draw left knee to chest, and return to original position. Alternate right and left legs in this manner. Repeat each movement 3 times.

b. Bring both knees to chest simultaneously. Return to starting position. Repeat 3 times.

c. Lift heels 4 to 6 inches off floor and hold for count of 3. Slowly return legs to starting position. Repeat 3 times.

STANDING POSITION

1. Perform breathing exercises from standing position.
2. Stand with feet apart and hands on hips.

   a. Trunk rotation (twisting) alternate sides. Repeat 5 times.

   b. Touch right hand to left toe; return to erect position; and then touch left hand to right toe. Repeat each 3 times.

3. Feet apart about 6 to 10 inches, hands on hips. Perform $1/4$ or $1/2$ squats (knee bends). Repeat 5 times.

4. Feet together and arms at side.

   a. Bend elbows (elbow flexion); bring palms of hands toward shoulder. Slowly return hands to side. Repeat 5 times. Note: Exercise becomes more difficult by adding weight to the hands, i.e., sandbags, dumbbells, books, etc.

   b. Slowly raise arms sideward (abduction) to shoulder level, palms of hands facing downward. Return arms to starting position slowly. Repeat 5 times.

   c. Bring arms forward and upward (forward flexion) to shoulder level, (thumbs of hands pointing straight up). Return arms slowly to sides. Repeat 5 times.

   d. Raise arms to 90-degree abducted position (shoulder level), and open and close fist forcibly 5 times. Slowly return arms to sides. Then bring arms forward and upward (forward flexion) to shoulder level, and repeat forced fist squeezing 5 times. Slowly return arms to starting position. Repeat 3 times for each movement.

5. Standing position with feet together. Raise up on toes (toe raising). Repeat 10 times.

6. Practice proper walking (heel-ball-toe) with head up, abdomen in, and chest held high.

7. Slow stationary running (knees high). Do 10 steps and rest. Repeat 3 times.

It must be clearly understood that the above activities are not presented as a "model" exercise program for all pupils with a heart condition. Rather, they are offered as a simple illustration of the order and progression one may follow in establishing a suitable exercise program. Start with the most elementary form of exercise whenever a new cardiac pupil comes into the program. Close observation while he is performing these exercises will give you a good indication of his exercise tolerance. As the youngster's exercise tolerance improves, the dosage of the activity program may be increased by: (1) progressing up the ladder of severity from lying to sitting to standing position; (2) increasing the number of repetitions; (3) increasing the duration of activity or reducing the rest periods between movements; and (4) imposing an external resistance in the form of weights (barbells, sandbags, etc.), changing the body position so that gravity may be a more or less important factor, spring resistance, etc. The magnitude and range of physical activity in which a pupil may participate is limited only by the imagination, ingenuity, knowledge, and understanding of the physical educator.

SUMMARY

If a cardiac pupil has been told frequently that he cannot do this and he cannot do that, he becomes afraid that something is going to happen to his heart if he exerts himself in the slightest manner. In such cases, he will look upon himself as an invalid and lack self-confidence. Actually, there is no reason why a youngster with a heart condition should be classified as an invalid (except in rare instances). Many of these youngsters will respond favorably to a carefully prescribed and medically guided exercise program. The joy of participation and accomplishment has great meaning to these youngsters, and there is no reason why they should be deprived of the opportunity of being in a physical education program.

REFERENCES

1. American Heart Association, Council on Rheumatic Fever and Congenital Heart Disease, "Prevention of Rheumatic Fever and Bacterial Endocarditis Through Control of Streptococal Infection," *Circulation*, January, 1957, 15 (1), 154-158.

2. Armstrong and Wheatley, "Studies on Rheumatic Fever," Metropolitan Life Insurance Company, November, 1944.
3. "Cardiovascular Diseases in the United States," Bulletin published by the American Heart Association, March, 1958.
4. Duman, L. J., and Gibbons, J. H., "Role of Bed Rest in Treatment of Rheumatic Fever," *Journal of the American Medical Association*, July 27, 1957, **164** (13), 1435-1438.
5. Gelfman, R., and Levine, S. A., "Incidenece of Acute and Subacute Bacterial Endocarditis in Congenital Heart Disease," *American Journal of the Medical Sciences*, September, 1942, **204** (3), 324-333.
6. Krugman, Saul, and Ward, R., "The Rubella Problem," *Journal of Pediatrics*, May, 1954, **44**, 480-498.
7. Lenroot, K. F., "Statement of Physically Handicapped Children," U.S. Department of Labor, Children's Bureau, December 15, 1944.
8. Martin, A. T., "Twenty Years Observation of 1438 Children with Rheumatic Heart Disease: Analytic Study Following Convalescent Care from 1921 to 1941," *Journal of the American Medical Association*, November 15, 1941, **117** (20), 1663-1669.
9. "Mortality Among Children with Rheumatic Fever," Metropolitan Life Insurance Co., Statistical Bulletin No. 34, 1943.
10. National Office of Vital Statistics, U.S. Public Health Service, Washington, D.C., *Monthly Vital Statistics Report*, May 10, 1957, **5** (13).
11. Rasch, P., *et al.*, "An Electrocardiographic Study of the United States Olympic Free Style Wrestlers," *The Research Quarterly*, **29** (1), 46-53.
12. Simonson, Ernst, and Enzer, N., "Physiology of Muscular Exercise and Fatigue in Disease," *Medicine*, **21** (4), 348-349.
13. Smyth, C. J. *et al.*, "Rheumatism and Arthritis: Review of American English Literature of Recent Years," *Annals of Internal Medicine*, February, 1959, **50** (2), 382-394.
14. Stroud, W. D., "The Rehabilitation and Placement in Industry of the Handicapped with Cardiovascular Disease," *Journal of the American Medical Association*, **105** (18), 1401-1405.
15. Thordarson, O., "Clinical Studies on Relative Incidence of Congenital Heart Disease," *Acata Med. Scandinav*, 1947, **127** (233).
16. White, Paul D., *Heart Disease*, Macmillan, New York, 1951, p. 1015.
17. White, Paul D., Adams, F. D., and Craib, D., "A Note on Cardiac Murmurs: Recommendations for a Revised Terminology," *American Journal of the Medical Sciences*, January, 1942, **203** (1), 52-54.

Appendix A

A BASIC WEIGHT-LIFTING PROGRAM FOR JUNIOR HIGH SCHOOL THROUGH ADULTHOOD

LIFTING weights is the most effective means of hypertrophying a muscle. Selecting weights which cause the muscle to work in the overload zone and then progressively adding resistance as the muscle becomes stronger is the fundamental principle of the progressive resistance exercise program. Exactly what should be the intensity and frequency of the exercise regimen is not known. However, studies show that the heavier the resistance with fewer repetitions, the more significant are the results.

A practical exercise load can be determined by the amount of resistance that will permit the person to raise the weights 10 times. He works with this load until he reaches 15 repetitions; then weight is added to reduce the number of repetitions to 10. Exercise should take place at least 3 times a week, with each period averaging 30 minutes to an hour depending, of course, on the person's condition and the speed at which he exercises.

Weight training is dynamic in that significant changes take place rapidly. As a result, there are certain precautions that should be taken. Make sure each exercise is performed through complete range of motion; if not, the muscle group will gradually become shortened. The lifts should be executed with as near-perfect body mechanics as possible. Because of the dynamic nature of weight-lifting, muscular imbalances can be developed. Also, cases of poor body mechanics can be easily aggravated through the use of weights.

By employing a minimum of 10 repetitions, injury as a result of lifting too much weight will be avoided.

Weight-lifting is an excellent way to develop strength and a better looking physique. Contrary to the teachings of some coaches, it has been scientifically demonstrated that weight-lifting, performed in the proper manner, significantly contributes to better performance in athletics.

Following is a general body-building program devised to suit the needs of junior high age through adulthood. It is simple and extremely effective; exercising 3 times each week, it will cause noticeable strength gains within a 4-week period. The program can be mimeographed and handed out to the pupils. One school had the art department make large silhouettes of the lifts to be hung in the weight-lifting room as illustrations of good lifting form.

The proper weight to use when you first start is one with which you can do the exercise *correctly* for 15 repetitions. This weight will differ for each exercise, depending on the strength of the muscles. Each day strive to increase the number of repetitions for the exercise, being careful to use correct form. When you are able to do 20 repetitions, increase the weight 5 pounds. Do this for the first 2 weeks of training. It is perfectly normal for some muscle soreness and tightness to occur during the first few weeks of training, but this will soon disappear. The weights used will not be heavy enough to cause any injury. After 2 weeks, use a weight which you can properly handle for 10 repetitions, and do not increase the weight until you can do 15 repetitions.

In most exercises you should inhale as you lift the weight and exhale as you lower it. Never hold your breath as you lift, for this increases the blood pressure by compressing the vessels in the chest and neck and may cause you to black-out. All exercises should be done with a regular rhythm. Do not jerk the weight or use momentum to help lift it. When lowering the weight, do not drop it rapidly, but lower slowly.

Before every workout, you should spend 5 or 10 minutes on calisthenics to increase the circulation to the muscles. Cold muscles and stiff joints are more easily injured. The warm-up should consist of calisthenics which will exercise the arms, shoulders, back, and legs.

A BASIC BODY BUILDING PROGRAM

1. *Warm-up Calisthenics:*
   A. Arm-swinging
   B. Arm-flexing and extending
   C. Side-bending
   D. Toe-touching
   E. Knee-bending

2. *Barbell curl (biceps exercise)* (Fig. 37)
   Hold the barbell in front of your thighs with palms forward and hands about shoulder width apart. Raise the weight by flexing arms at the elbows until arms are fully bent and the bar is touching the chest.

Fig. 37. Barbell curl.

Elbows should be kept at the sides, but should not be braced against the body or moved backward or forward. The bar should be lifted in a continuous motion without jerking or using a backbend. The weight should be lowered slowly in the same manner until arms are *fully extended.*

3. *Barbell press (triceps and shoulder exercise)* (Fig. 38)
   Hold the barbell just in front of your chest, with palms forward and hands shoulder width apart. With a pushing motion, the weight is raised overhead, passing just in front of your face until the arms are fully extended overhead. There should be no backbend or assistance by bending the knees. Knees should be locked, hips forward, and muscles of the buttocks and lower back tensed. Lower the weight slowly to the original position.

Fig. 38. Barbell press.

4. *Sit-up (abdominal exercise)* (Fig. 39)
Lie on a mat on your back with feet flat on the floor and knees flexed.
Sit up as far as you can, with a curling motion of the trunk, contracting the abdominal muscles as much as possible. Reach forward with
the arms as you sit up. Slowly lower to the starting position. To increase the resistance, clasp hands behind the head; and for still more
resistance hold a barbell plate behind the head. Do not sit up with a
jerking motion. Exhale as you sit up.

Fig. 39. Sit-up.

5. *Knee bend (leg exercise)* (Fig. 40)
Place a barbell on your shoulders behind your back. A towel may be
used to pad the bar. Have feet spread slightly. Lower to a squatting
position until upper leg is parallel to the floor and then immediately
rise to the starting position. Look straight ahead as you go down and

up as you rise. Do not round your back; keep it as flat as possible. Keep as erect as possible throughout the exercise. Correct form is essential in this exercise to avoid back injury.

Fig. 40. Knee bend.

6. *Pullover (chest and shoulder exercise)* (Fig. 41)

Lie on your back on a bench about 9 to 12 inches wide. Hold a barbell above your chest with palms of hands forward and arms locked. Keeping arms locked, lower the weight to a position over your head, at the same time inhaling as deeply as possible. Then raise the weight to the starting position in an arc and lower it slowly to the thighs. Raise the weight overhead again, inhaling, etc.

7. *Stiff-legged dead lift (lower back and back of legs)* (Fig. 42)

Hold the weight in front of your thighs with palms to the rear. Keeping knees locked, lower the weight by bending forward at hips until it just touches the floor. Raise the weight by straightening up. Never use weight exceeding body weight in this exercise. Do not attempt to progress too rapidly.

8. *Press on bench (chest, arms, shoulders)* (Fig. 43)

Lying on your back on a bench, hold a barbell over your chest with arms extended and palms forward toward your feet. Arms should be slightly further than shoulder width apart. Lower the weight until it touches your chest by bending your arms, elbows outward to sides. Push the weight up to the starting position.

9. *Bent rowing motion (upper back)* (Fig. 44)

Grasp the bar with palms back and hands slightly further than shoulder

Fig. 41. Pullover.

Fig. 42. Stiff-legged dead lift.

Fig. 43. Press on bench.

width apart. The body is bent at the hips to form a right angle, and knees are bent slightly. Keep the back flat. Pull the weight up until it touches the chest just below the nipple line. Do not jerk the weight up or lower the trunk to meet it. Now lower the weight until it is just above the floor and arms are extended.

Fig. 44. Bent rowing motion.

10. *Rise on toes (calf)* (Fig. 45)

Place a barbell across your shoulders behind neck. Place toes and balls of feet on the edge of a board 2 to 3 inches high, with heels off the board. Rise up on toes as high as possible. Lower until heels touch the floor. Vary each workout by turning toes in one time, out the next, then straight ahead.

Fig. 45. Rise on toes.

11. *Lateral arm raise (shoulders)* (Fig. 46)

Hold a dumbbell in each hand with palms facing each other and arms hanging at sides. Raise arms sidewards and outwards until they are above the level of the shoulders. Lower to sides. Keep arms extended and locked at elbows.

The above regimen is a complete general workout. The exercises are basic ones, of which there are many variations. Many of the

Fig. 46. Lateral arm raise.

barbell exercises can also be done with dumbbells. The beginner should stick to this program for at least 6 months before varying it. He should not become confused by seeing other men using different exercises. This program will produce results as rapidly as any other program for the beginner. There are hundreds of different exercises that may be performed with barbells and dumbbells, but you must limit yourself to a well-balanced program suited to your needs and available time. Some advanced men repeat each exercise 3 or 4 times in a workout. This is referred to as doing *sets* of an exercise.

Appendix B

LIST OF EXERCISES

NORMAL MOVEMENT OF JOINTS

NECK EXERCISES *(These exercises should be done slowly with eyes closed)*
1. Bend head forward and touch chin to chest, keeping mouth closed.
2. Bend head backward.
3. Bend head toward left shoulder and try to touch ear to shoulder (do not raise shoulder). Straighten.
4. Bend head toward right shoulder and try to touch ear to shoulder (do not raise shoulder). Straighten.
5. Turn face to left side. Straighten.
6. Turn face to right side. Straighten.
7. Move head in circles.

TRUNK
1. Bend body forward. Straighten.
2. Bend body backward. Straighten.
3. With hands on hips bend body to left and then to the right.
4. With hands on hips twist body to face first left and then right, without moving the feet.

SHOULDER
1. Raise arm forward and straight above the head.
2. Raise arm sideways and straight above head.
3. Place palm of hand on back of neck; then bring hand forward, down, under the arm, and back, touching back of hand to shoulder blades (do not allow elbows to drop).

ELBOW
1. Bend arm until fingertips touch shoulder, then straighten it out completely.
2. Bend elbow to right angle. Turn palm up, then down.

WRIST

1. Rest forearm on table with palm down. Move hand first to left and then to right without moving forearm.
2. Rest forearm on table with palm down. Lift hand up off table as far as possible without moving forearm.
3. Rest forearm on table with palm up. Lift hand up off table as far as possible without moving forearm.

FINGERS AND THUMB

1. Make a tight fist, then straighten fingers completely.
2. With fingers straight, spread wide apart, then bring together.
3. Bend thumb and make it lie in center of palm.
4. Rest forearm on table with palm up. Place thumb over base of index finger, then lift it straight up.
5. Touch tip of thumb to fingerprint of little finger, then open hand wide and do this with each of the other fingers.

HIP

1. Lying on back, bend hips and touch knees to chest.
2. Lying on back, move legs sideways as far as possible keeping knees straight and toes pointed straight ahead. Return to starting position.
3. Lying on abdomen, move leg up and back as far as possible, keeping knee straight. Do first with right and then with left leg.
4. Sitting on edge of bed, move lower leg and foot from left to right, like a pendulum.

KNEE

1. Bend knee so that calf touches thigh. Then straighten knee completely.

ANKLE *(Sitting on edge of bed with lower leg hanging free)*

1. Bend foot up.
2. Bend foot down.
3. Turn foot out.
4. Turn foot in.
5. Make circles with foot.

TOES

1. Curl toes down.
2. Curl toes up.

EXERCISES FOR SHOULDER

1. Sit as straight as possible on a chair for count of 5 to 10, with palms of hands at back of neck, elbows at shoulder level and pulled back.

2. Sit with hands at back of neck, elbows at shoulder level and drawn back.
   a. Stretch back, chest, and head up toward ceiling.
   b. Relax.

3. Sit with arms folded loosely across chest.
   a. Unfold arms while swinging extended arms out and back at shoulder level.
   b. Return to original position.

4. Stand erect with arms at sides.
   a. Shrug shoulders forward and up.
   b. Relax.
   c. Repeat.

5. Stand erect with arms straight out from sides at shoulder level.
   a. Raise arms sideways and up until backs of hands meet above head (keep elbows straight).
   b. Relax and repeat.

6. Stand facing a corner of room with one hand on each wall, arms at shoulder level, palms forward, elbows bent, and abdominal muscles contracted.
   a. Slowly let upper part of trunk lean forward and press chest into corner, inhaling as body leans forward.
   b. Return to original position by pushing out with hands. Exhale with this movement.

7. Stand erect with arms at sides.
   a. Bend neck to left, attempting to touch left ear to left shoulder without shrugging shoulder.
   b. Bend neck to right, attempting to touch right ear to right shoulder without shrugging shoulder.
   c. Relax and repeat.

8. Lie face down with hands clasped behind back.
   a. Raise head and chest from floor as high as possible while pulling shoulders back and chin in. Hold this position for a count of 3. Inhale as chest is raised.
   b. Exhale and return to original position.
   c. Repeat.

9. Lie on back and place rolled towel or small pillow under upper part of back between shoulder blades (no pillow under head).
   a. Inhale slowly and raise arms up and back over head.

b. Exhale and lower arms to sides.
c. Repeat 5 to 20 times.

10. a. Grasp overhanging bar. Keep hands the width of shoulders apart.
b. Suspend body 1 to 2 minutes without bending elbows and, except for hands, remain as relaxed as possible.

ABDOMINAL EXERCISES

1. Lie on back with knees bent, feet flat on the floor.
   a. Inhale, raising ribs. Exhale slowly.
   b. Inhale, allowing abdomen to expand. Exhale slowly and force lower part of back to the floor.

2. Lie on back with legs straight, arms alongside the body.
   a. Raise head, bringing chin to chest. Relax.
   b. Raise head and shoulders off floor and hold. Relax.
   c. Raise head and shoulders off floor, pull in abdomen, and roll body into a sitting position.
   d. Raise right leg (knee straight) so that heel is about 15–20 inches off floor. Hold for count of 3. Relax. *Be sure to keep lower part of back to the floor.*
   e. Repeat with left leg.
   f. Repeat, using both legs at same time.
   NOTE: When 15 to 20 of the above exercises can be performed with ease, discontinue and proceed to exercises 3 and 4.

3. Lie on back with knees bent, feet flat on floor, arms folded across chest.
   a. Repeat exercise 2, a, b, and c.

4. Lie on back with knees bent, feet flat on floor, hands behind neck.
   a. Repeat exercise 2, a, b, and c.
   b. Do sit-up exercise (2, c), twisting trunk to left so that right elbow touches left knee.
   c. Return to starting position. Relax, then repeat sit-up, twisting trunk to right so that left elbow touches right knee.
   d. Return to starting position. Relax, then repeat entire series.

EXERCISES FOR THE BACK

1. Lie face down on bed or floor with arms alongside the body.
   a. Raise head and shoulders and hold for a count of 5.
   b. Return slowly to starting position. Relax and then repeat.

2. Lie in same position as in the preceding exercise.
   a. Raise arms, as well as head and shoulders, up and back, arching the back.
   b. Return to starting position. Relax and then repeat.

3. Lie face down on bed or floor with hands clasped behind head.
   a. Raise head, shoulders, and trunk, arching the back, and hold for a count of 5.
   b. Return to starting position. Relax and repeat.

4. Lie face down on bed or floor with knees bent.
   a. Raise right thigh, keeping knee bent, and hold for a count of 5.
   b. Return slowly to resting position.
   c. Raise left thigh in the same manner. Relax.
   d. Repeat, raising thighs alternately.

5. Lie face down on bed or floor with knees straight.
   a. Raise right leg, keeping knee straight, and hold for a count of 5.
   b. Return slowly to resting position.
   c. Raise left leg in the same manner. Relax.
   d. Repeat, raising legs alternately.

6. Lie face down on bed and grasp top of bed with hands.
   a. Raise both legs, keeping knees straight, and hold for a count of 5.
   b. Relax and repeat.

SPECIAL RHYTHM EXERCISES (to rhymes) FOR CHILDREN
Used for spastics or paralytics

Legs

Lying on back:

1. Dorsiflexion of foot—keep toes bent down and pull foot straight up.

2. Eversion foot—turn foot out.

3. Toe flexion—bend toes down. Give support on sole of foot, keeping foot at right angle.

4. Abduction of legs

> *One, two, buckle my shoe,*
> *Three, four, shut the door,*
> *Five, six, pick up sticks,*
> *Seven, eight, lay them straight,*
> *Nine, ten, a big fat hen.*

Push both legs out to side as far as possible. Carry them back in. Watch that foot does not drop down and that leg is held straight.

5. Hip and knee extension

Gallop and trot,
Gallop and trot,
This is the way
To the blacksmith shop.
Shoe the old horse,
And shoe the old mare,
And let the little coltie
Go bare, bare, bare.

Start with hip and knee bent up. Forcefully straighten leg out and carry it back to bent position. Watch that foot is held straight and does not drop down.

6. Outward rotation hip

Roll over, roll over,
So merry and free.
Come playfellows dear,
And join in my glee.

With knee and foot straight, roll whole leg over and out. Carry back.

Lying on face:

1. Hip extension

Jack and Jill went up the hill
To fetch a pail of water.
Jack fell down and broke his
crown,
And Jill came tumbling after.

Lying on face on table with feet off end of table, raise whole leg up off table with straight knee. Give support with hand and arm under thigh and knee. Carry back to table.

Sitting on edge of table:

1. Abdominal contractions—pull abdomen in (may do this lying on back).
2. Back flattening—may do this lying back.
3. Knee extension—swing legs alternately.

Riggity-jig and away we go,
Away we go, away we go,
Riggity-jig and away we go,
Heigh-ho, heigh-ho, heigh-ho

With legs hanging off edge of table, swing right leg up until knee is straight, then swing back down. Repeat with other leg.

Walking:

1. *Cock-a-doodle-do!*
The dame has lost her shoe;
The master's lost his fiddling
stick,
And he doesn't know what to
do.

Walking with feet turned out, toes down, pick leg up with bent knee. Straighten knee and set foot down with heel touching first and then toe. Repeat with other leg.

2. Walk "like Charlie Chaplin" in a straight line, with toes pointing out, heels hitting floor first, toes down last.

ARMS

1. Extension of fingers

This is little Tom Thumb
Round and fat as any plum.
This is little Peter Pointer,
He must be a double jointer.
This is little Toby Tall,
He's the biggest one of all.

Straighten each finger separately.

This is little Ruby Ring,
She's too fine for anything
And the little wee one, maybe
Is the little finger baby

2. Opposition

Peter Thumkin and Pointer
finger
Say, "How do you do."
Peter Thumkin and Tall Man
Say, "How do you do."
Peter Thumkin and Ring Man
Say, "How do you do."
Peter Thumkin and Wee Man
Say, "How do you do."

Bring tip of thumb to tip of first finger, straighten thumb back. Bring tip of thumb to tip of next finger. Repeat for remainder of fingers.

3. Finger extension—all fingers together

Little birdies in their nests
Go hop, hop, hop, hop, hop.
They try to do their very best
And hop, hop, hop, hop, hop.

Straighten all fingers together.

4. Wrist extension

This way, that way, blows the
weather vane,
This way, that way, blows and
blows again.
Turning, pointing, ever show-
ing,
How the merry wind is blow-
ing.

With palms of hand together bend left hand back at wrist and return to straight position. Repeat with right hand.

5. Supination of forearm

Roll over, roll over,
So merry and free,
Come playfellows dear,
And join in my glee.

With palms down and hands and forearm on knees, turn hands over, palms up.

6. Elbow extension

Up and down, up and down,
This is the way we go to town.
What to buy? To buy a fat pig,
Home again, home again,
Rig-a-jig-jig.

Starting with elbow bent and palm of hand facing shoulder, straighten arm carry back up. Watch to keep wrist and fingers straight.

7. Shoulder abduction

Pump the water, pump the
* water,*
Pump, pump, pump, pump.

Raise upper arm, elbow bent, palm turned up, out to shoulder level. Carry back to side.

8. Shoulder outward rotation

Grind the coffee,
Grind the coffee,
Grind, grind, grind,
Grind, grind, grind.

Sitting with upper arm supported at shoulder level and elbow bent, turn forearm and hand up and back.

Pound for the baby,
Pound for the baby,
Pound, pound, pound,
Pound, pound, pound.

Sitting with back against wall, grasp object (like small dumbell) in hand, raise hand up and back and pound on wall.

9. Elevation of arms

Ready rocket, 'Shoot,'
And twinkle like the stars.
Ready rocket, 'Shoot,'
And twinkle like the stars.

Start with arms bent at elbows and hands touching shoulders. Stretch hands straight above head with palms facing each other.

10. General arm exercises

Wind, wind, wind, wind,
The other way around
Pull, and pull, and pull,
And pound, pound, pound.

Rotate hands one around the other. Reverse and go the other way around. Pull hands apart and straighten elbows. Pound with one fist upon the other.

Up, up, up, goes the sun,
Down behind the hills,
And out go the rays.

Raise arms over head with hands touching. Put hands down behind neck. Extend arms to straighten elbows.

EXERCISES FOR FOOT AND ANKLE
These exercises should be done barefooted

A. *Sitting with knees straight:*

1. Bring feet up and bend feet down. Do together at first and then alternate.
2. Turn feet in and try to make soles touch, then turn feet out.
3. Make a circle with each foot. Repeat, using both feet.
4. Placing a folded towel or wide belt under forefoot
   a. Hold ends in hands and bring feet up, curling toes down.
   b. Pull on towel forcing foot up, while relaxing muscles in legs (see drawing).

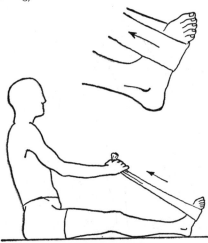

B. *Sitting in straightback chair with arm rests:*

5. Bring toes up, keeping heels on floor. Next bring heels up, keeping toes on floor. Do together at first and then alternate.
6. Place bath towel under feet; gather towel with toes.
7. Roll a rubber ball between soles of feet.
8. Place book under feet. Bend toes down over edge of book.
9. With feet pointing straight ahead and 6 inches apart, roll feet on outer borders keeping toes curled.
10. Place six marbles on towel with a dish alongside.
    a. Grasp marbles with toes and drop in dish.
    b. Pick up marbles with toes and place in hand alongside opposite knee.
11. Cross feet at ankles.

    a. Move feet apart and curl toes down.

    b. Holding most of body weight on hands, rise slowly out of chair, placing some weight on outer borders of feet. After several periods of doing this exercise, gradually allow more weight to be placed on feet.

C. *Standing:*

12. With feet together and toes straight ahead, place weight on outer borders of soles, curling toes under.

13. With toes together and heels apart, rise up on toes.

14. Walk on straight line, placing weight on outer borders of soles.

15. Place book on floor; stand with toes of left foot on book, keeping heel on floor. Grasp chair for support and bend right knee slowly, lowering body. Repeat exercise with right foot. As exercise becomes easier, substitute a thicker volume (see drawing).

SINGING RHYMES AND EXERCISES FOR THE UPPER EXTREMITIES
Start exercises with the dominant arm

FLEXION AND EXTENSION OF THE SHOULDER   POSITION: *Supine*

Directions: Start with the arms at the sides, palms down. Carry the right arm forward and upward, close to the ear, and return to the original position. Start the same motion with the left arm as the right arm starts its return. The total motion is reciprocal.

Rhyme: "Shoot the Rocket."

> *Shoot the rocket*
> *Shoot the rocket*
> *Shoot, shoot, shoot.*

ABDUCTION AND ADDUCTION OF THE SHOULDER   POSITION: *Supine*

Directions: Start with the arms at the sides, palms down. Abduct both arms to shoulder level sliding them along the surface of the table. Adduct to original position.

Rhyme: "Sunbeams."

> *Sunbeams rise and fall*
> *And rise and fall.*

INTERNAL AND EXTERNAL ROTATION OF THE SHOULDER   POSITION: *Supine*

Directions: Start with arms abducted to shoulder level, elbows flexed to right angles. Rotate the shoulders internally and externally.

Rhyme: "Pump the Water."

> *Pump the water,*
> *Pump the water,*
> *Pump, pump, pump.*

FLEXION AND EXTENSION OF THE ELBOW   POSITION: *Supine*

Directions: Start with arms at the sides and forearms in supination. Flex the right elbow and bring the hand to the right shoulder. Return to the original position. Start the same motion with the left arm as the right arm starts its return. The total motion is reciprocal. (Reach and Grasp)

Rhyme: "Up and Down."

> *Up and down, up and down*
> *This is the way we go to town.*
> *What to buy? To buy a pig.*
> *Home again, home again*
> *Rig-a-jig-jig.*

SUPINATION AND PRONATION OF THE FOREARMS   POSITION: *Supine*

Directions: With the elbow flexed supinate and pronate forearm.

Rhyme: "Roll over"

> *Roll over, roll over,*
> *So merry and free,*
> *Come playfellows dear,*
> *And join in my glee.*

FLEXION AND EXTENSION OF THE WRISTS   POSITION: *Supine*

Directions: Flex and extend the wrist.

Rhyme: "Weather Vane."

> *This way, that way,*
> *Blows the weather vane,*
> *This way, that way,*
> *Blows and blows again.*
> *Turning, pointing, ever showing,*
> *How the merry wind is blowing.*

FLEXION AND EXTENSION OF THE FINGERS   POSITION: *Supine*

Directions: Flex and extend the fingers.

Rhyme: "Birdies"

> *Little birdies in their nests*
> *Go hop, hop, hop, hop, hop.*
> *They try to do their very best*
> *And hop, hop, hop, hop, hop.*

THUMB AND FINGER OPPOSITION   POSITION: *Supine*

Directions: Bring the thumb and index finger tip to tip and extend fully.
Repeat with each finger in turn.

Rhyme: "Thumbkin and Pointer"

> *Thumbkin and Pointer say "How do you do,*
> *How do you do, how do you do."*
> *Thumbkin and Tallman say "how do you do,*
> *How do you do, how do you do."*
> *Thumbkin and Ringman say "how do you do,*
> *How do you do, how do you do."*
> *Thumbkin and Weeman say "how do you do,*
> *How do you do, how do you do."*

SINGING RHYMES AND EXERCISES FOR THE LOWER EXTREMITIES
Start with the leg that corresponds with the dominant hand.

FLEXION AND EXTENSION OF THE HIPS   POSITION: *Supine*

Directions: Start with the legs straight on the table. Keeping the knees straight and with no inward or outward rotation, raise the right leg and return to the original position. Start the same motion with the left leg as the right leg starts downward. The total motion is reciprocal.

Rhyme: "Shoot the Rocket"

Shoot the rocket
Shoot the rocket
Shoot, shoot, shoot.

HYPEREXTENSION OF HIPS   POSITION: *Prone*

Directions: Start with legs straight on table. Keeping knees straight and pelvis flat on table, raise right leg and return to original position. Start the same motion with left leg as right starts downward. The total motion is reciprocal.

Rhyme: "Shoot the Rocket"

Shoot the rocket
Shoot the rocket
Shoot, shoot, shoot.

ABDUCTION AND ADDUCTION OF THE LEGS   POSITION: *Supine and prone*

Directions: Start with legs straight and together. Abduct the legs sliding them along the surface of the table. The knees should be kept straight and no inward or outward rotation take place. Return to the origial position.

Rhyme: "One, Two."

One, two, buckle my shoe,
Three, four, shut the door,
Five, six, pick up sticks,
Seven, eight, lay them straight,
Nine, ten, a big fat hen.

INTERNAL AND EXTERNAL ROTATION OF THE LEGS   POSITION: *Supine*

Directions: Start with the legs straight and slightly apart. Rotate the thigh inward and outward.

Rhyme: "Roll Over"

Roll over and over
So merry and free
My playfellows dear
Come join in my glee

COMBINED FLEXION AND EXTENSION OF HIPS AND KNEES   POSITION: *Supine*

Directions: Start with the legs straight. Flex the right hip and knee sliding the sole of the foot along the surface of the table. Return to the original position. Start the same motion with the left leg as the right leg starts downward. The total motion is reciprocal.

Rhyme: "Gallopy Trot."

Gallopy trot to the blacksmith shop
To shoe the horse and shoe the mare
And let the wee baby colt go bare.
Gallopy, gallopy, gallopy trot, trot.

FLEXION AND EXTENSION OF THE KNEES   POSITION: *Prone*

Directions: Start with the legs straight. Flex the right knee carrying the heel toward the buttocks and return to the original position. Start the same motion with the left leg as the right leg starts downward. The total motion is reciprocal.

Rhyme: "Up and Down."

Up and down, up and down,
This is the way we go to town.
What to buy? To buy a fat pig,
Home again, home again,
Rig-a-jig-jig.

PLANTAR AND DORSIFLEXION OF THE ANKLES POSITION: *Supine and Prone*

Directions: Plantar and dorsiflex the ankles starting dorsiflexion of the right and plantar flexion of the left at the same time. The total motion is reciprocal.

Rhyme: "Up and Down."

Up and down, up and down,
This is the way we go to town.

What to buy? To buy a fat pig,
Home again, home again,
Rig-a-jig-jig.

PRONATION AND SUPINATION OF THE ANKLES   POSITION: *Supine*

Directions: Supinate and pronate both ankles at the same time

Rhyme: "This way, that way"

This way, that way,
Blows the weather vane.
This way, that way,
Blows and blows again
Turning, pointing, ever showing,
How the merry wind is blowing, blowing.

FLEXION AND EXTENSION OF THE TOES   POSITION: *Supine*

Directions: Flex and extend the toes, starting flexion of the right and extension of the left at the same time. The total motion is reciprocal.

Rhyme: "Birdies"

Little birdies in their nests
Go hop, hop, hop, hop, hop.
They try to do their very best,
And hop, hop, hop, hop, hop.

WALKING

Directions: Walking practice is done with or without skis using high steppage or normal placement of feet.

Rhyme: "Bobby Shaftoe."

Bobby Shaftoe's gone to sea
With silver buckles on his knee.
When he comes back he'll marry me,
Says pretty Bobby Shaftoe.

EXERCISES FOR COORDINATION

Head should be positioned so that patient can see every movement. Movements should be slow and precise. To avoid fatigue, no exercise should be repeated more than 5 or 6 times at each exercise session.

1. Flex leg at hip and knee joints, sliding heel along bed. Return to original position.

2. Flex as in #1, and from flexed position abduct, return to flexed position and then to original position.

3. Flex leg at hip and knee to half the angle in exercise #1. Return.

4. Repeat exercise #2 to half the angle.

5. Flex one leg at hip and knee joints. Stop at any position in either flexion or extension when "halt" is called by technician or some member of the family.

6. Both legs are flexed simultaneously in hip and knee joints.

7. Both legs are flexed at hip and knee joints and, from the flexed position, are abducted to normal angle (not to maximal range). Return to flexed position and extend.

8. Both legs are flexed to one-half the angle of exercise #2.

9. Flex both legs to one-half angle, abduct from this position, and return to flexed position and extension.

10. Flex both legs, and stop at any angle in flexion or extension when "stop" is called by a member of the family.

11. Flex both legs at hip and knee joints, abduct from this position, return to flexed position and extension. Stop and continue in any angle at command.

12. Flex both legs to one-half angle, abduct from this position, return to flexed position and extension. Stop and continue at command.

13. Flex one leg at hip and knee with heel raised from bed.

14. Flex one leg and bring heel to rest above other kneecap.

15. Flex one leg, bring heel to rest on other kneecap.

16. Flex one leg, bring heel to rest on middle of other shin.

17. Start at original position, flex one leg at hip and knee, bring heel to rest on top of ankle of other leg, and return to original position.

18. Same as above except that heel comes to rest on toes of other foot.

19. Same as #1 except that heel is first put on kneecap of other leg, raised and rested on middle of tibia, raised to ankle joint, lifted again to toes, and returned to original position.

20. Start with both limbs flexed. One remains flexed while other is extended, heels touching bed.

21. Both limbs flexed, and extended, heels raised during extension.

22. Same as #2 except that heels are raised during flexion.

23. Both limbs flexed and extended. Heels should be kept off bed during both movements.

Note: The next series is made more difficult by abduction and adduction.

1. One leg is first flexed, then abducted, while other leg is being flexed. The abducted leg is then adducted, while other is extended. Return to original position.

2. Same as #1 except that when legs are extended, heels are raised from bed.

3. One leg is flexed in the knee and hip joints, then extended without touching the bed, while other is flexed, abducted, then adducted.

4. One leg is flexed in hip and knee joints, while other is flexed, abducted, and adducted. Both legs are brought together in flexed position and extended without touching bed.

5. Start in original position. Heel of one foot is placed on opposite knee then moved down crest of tibia to ankle joint. Leg is extended. Repeat in reverse order.

6. Same as #1 except that heel slides along tibia past ankle and over foot to toes. If heel reaches toes of other foot, leg of this foot must be flexed slightly at knee joint. Repeat in reverse order.

7. Same as #1, except that heel slides along the tibia to middle, stops, continues to ankle joint, and stops and continues to toes as in #1.

8. Same as #1, except that movement is stopped and continued at command of some member of the patient's family.

9. Both lower limbs are flexed at hips and knees, with malleoli and knees in apposition, then extended.

10. Same as #1 except done to half the angle.

11. Same as #1 except that voluntary halts are made.

12. Same as #1 except that exercise is stopped and continued at command of some member of the family.

INDEX